BEYOND THE BOX OF SPACE AND TIME

BEYOND THE BOX OF SPACE AND TIME

≈≈≈≈

Quantum Physics, Buddhism, and Ancient Wisdom

Jim Raschick

FIVE SPACE MEDIA

Third Edition (revised)

For information about permission to reproduce selections from this book,
write to: Permissions, 5 Space Media, Box 1595, Pahoa, Hawaii 96778
Web site: www.fivespacemedia.com
Email: five.x.space@gmail.com

V3.0 [18.08.97PB]

ISBN-10: 0983540527
ISBN-13: 978-0-9835405-2-6

Cover credits, copyright and license notifications in endnotes.[1]

To Jude

'Normal' science... is the activity of the non-revolutionary, or more precisely, the not-too-critical professional: of the science student who accepts the ruling dogma of the day... in my view the 'normal' scientist... is a person one ought to be sorry for... He has been taught in a dogmatic spirit: he is a victim of indoctrination... I can only say that I see a very great danger in it and in the possibility of its becoming normal... a danger to science and, indeed, to our civilization.

~ Sir Karl Raimund Popper, 1970 [2]

Do not go where the path may lead,
Go instead where there is no path, and leave a trail.

~ Ralph Waldo Emerson

PART I
THE ANCIENT COSMOS
Recalling a lost tapestry of reality: The ancients called it a survival strategy, deep wisdom and a connection with the Earth.

PART II
THE MIND AND PHYSICS
Traversing the Shapes of Experience: Perception unfolding as a grand illusion; and thought forms framed as geometry.

PART III
INSTANT PHYSICS
Surveying a timeless universe: A radical new paradigm of physics based on conjoining geometry and ancient wisdom.

CONTENTS

Many of the ideas in this book are statements of parallel thought where a footnote lends clarity. A separate class of notes indicating licensing and attribution information are listed as endnotes. The footnotes are at the bottom of the page and the endnotes are in the end pages of the book.

Alpha indicators point to footnotes, and numeric indicators point to endnotes. Examples:
An alpha superscript indicating a footnote is… text[A].
A numeric superscript indicating an endnote is… text[1].

A medieval monk reaches the horizon where the earth and the heavens meet. The *Flammarion Woodcut*, c. 1888.[3]

INTRODUCTION

Modern science arose out of the rich interplay between it and the philosophies and religions of Western culture. Its offspring is a map of reality that we see as the laws of nature. But, as sometimes happens in families, science (i.e. the parent) is unwittingly being held captive by the child it produced. The captivity is particularly evident if we look deeply at our present definitions of space and time—which strongly reflect Western cultural history.

What is the nature of space? What is the nature of time? The answer to these questions forms the (generally unexamined) basis for what we see as the irreproachable laws of nature, according to the sciences. Those laws define a box out of which we cannot escape, if elements of the box are used as tools in the escape attempt.

A larger vision, beyond this figurative box, can be had if we describe space and time using the terms of modern science within the confines of the historic wisdom traditions of certain indigenous societies—such as the Tibetan, Mongolian, Native American and Hawaiian cultures. This is not to say that these traditions are the same (they are *very* different from each other!) but instead it's a statement that they share an essential taste of an ultimate condition of reality that is more far reaching than what is described by the contemporary sciences.

Out of this viewpoint comes a mapping of the sciences onto a worldview that is indicative of the indigenous societies. In those terms the map identifies a boundary encircling all of recognized reality, and then using analogs, describes what is outside of that boundary—beyond the phenomenal and psychological world normally associated with space and time. In this way the map includes much of what has heretofore been classed as the domain of spirituality, but not the entire domain. For example: the map will not take a spiritual seeker beyond the veil of conceptual reality. However, it can logically provide a view of the physical sciences and of the nature of mind that is beyond all constraints of space and time—as those constraints are now posed by the sciences.

What follows is the result of overlapping infatuations with indigenous worldviews and modern physics. The information comes from personal experiences and, mostly, from the two and one half millennia long archive of documents, artifacts and knowledge associated with various indigenous cultures, with the majority of the information being from the historic documents chronicling the Vedic and Buddhist wisdom.

As you read on you will find a figurative bridge between two main viewpoints; 1) a map of physical reality put forth by classical and quantum relativistic physics, and 2) a holistic worldview best described as typical of central Asia 2500 years ago. To create this bridge both viewpoints have had to flex and bend to allow a juncture in the middle. At the end of the book the reader will find themselves straddling that juncture, while carefully holding a vision of both reality maps.

At first glance this writing may appear to be a polemic in favor of Buddhism. It is not. It is a polemic in favor of the idea that certain wisdoms from long ago indigenous societies may trump modern efforts to deal with the incompleteness of our sciences.

Over the years, whenever I met a traveling Tibetan lama, I would ask the question "what is 4ᵗʰ time?" I knew the concept was an unusual, seldom mentioned feature of esoteric Tibetan Buddhism but the answers I received were always unexpected. For example:
"It's just like regular time, but only different."
Or: "It's the time spent during deep meditation".
Another one was: "It's a nontemporal condition of reality."
The one I liked the best was: "4ᵗʰ time? Well... you have the past, the future, and the present. What's left over is 4ᵗʰ time."
There never was a concise answer, but once, when visiting a Bonpo monastery, I believe I found the key to the puzzle. The Bonpos are adherents of an ancient religion from before there was "a kingdom of Tibet" or "a religion of Buddhism"—historically dating back 4,000 years, or according to them 18,000 years. Nowadays the Bon religion is some ways similar to Tibetan Buddhism.
The Bonpo lama said: "There are five dimensions surrounding this planet." His statement eventually led to my formulation of an *explanation* of 4ᵗʰ time, which is specifically different than the *experience* of 4ᵗʰ time—an important distinction for a person studying Buddhism or Bon.
In brief, 4ᵗʰ time is seen as another layer of time that figuratively rests on top of normal time, virtually positioned in a fifth dimension outside of the four dimensions of spacetime found in Western classical and quantum physics. Philosophically 4ᵗʰ time appears as the ground upon which rests causality. Cause and effect is at the basis of Western science—if we do some specific thing [the cause] we can, accordingly predict a certain outcome [the effect]. Causality is similarly the basis of an "Eastern view of science", which is identified herein with the Buddhist term *vidyä*. Where Western science strives, in spirit, to improve the overall physical state of humanity, *vidyä* conversely has developed as a science of the mind seeking to improve the inner reality of the human condition.[4]
Vidyä is a Sanskrit noun meaning "right knowledge" or "clarity". In Buddhism it generally describes a situation where one is actively working to alter patterns of thought and action that bespeak aggression,

greed, pride and jealousy, along with sometimes physical states of discomfort. It also describes phenomenal and psychological reality as essentially an illusion which spontaneously manifests… representing another [true] condition of reality that is essentially without definition and "beyond all concepts". An example of *vidyā* is the practices performed by yogis who train their mind to conquer all negative emotions (among other endeavors). In this context karma, seen as the cause of all effects, can be controlled or managed with diligent practice and training.

A dedicated practitioner of *vidyā* is credited with having a deep and profound understanding of the true nature of reality, be it the phenomenal world or the realm of mental events (thoughts, feelings and emotions). The goal of a yogi is enlightenment—a state of being that is generally arrived at through long diligent practice using specific mental tools and exercises to transform the mind and empty it of conceptual thought. Developed over millennia, these tools can gradually lead the practitioner to single-pointed concentration and the ultimate control of the mind and body. Generally this is done during long periods of solitary retreat. For example in the Kagyu school of Tibetan Buddhism there is a prescribed tradition of retreat for three years, three months, and three days. Other disciplines may take even longer.

In Tibetan Buddhism the reached-for state being is described as enlightened reality. It is generically described as the state of *Mahamudra*. The Nyingma teachings specifically identify the "state of *Dzogchen*"[5], which is identical to the state of *Mahamudra*. The state of *Dzogchen* describes the nature of all sentient beings. These Tibetan terms generally refer to a unique condition of existence described in some of the oldest of the tantras (a "**tantra**" expounds a system of thought or a set of doctrines or practices.) One of the more ancient tantras is the Kalachakra Tantra (Sanskrit: wheel of time or time-cycles). As with most tantras, there are different traditions and transmissions. The Kalachakra Tantra arrived in Tibet and became part of the culture only a thousand years ago, but there is evidence that a version of it may have been taught by the Buddha[6] c. 2400 years ago in old India at a place called Nylanda. [In later years Nylanda became the site of the world's first university.]

The Kalachakra Tantra refers to an advanced, very complex and difficult to comprehend teaching and practice in Tibetan Buddhism. The Deep Awareness Chapter of the Kalachakra specifically comes within the sphere of *Dzogchen*.[7] Historically, *Dzogchen* dates back to the teacher

Garab Dorje, 360 years after the death of the Buddha, but it may be much older.

Many have tried to map the basic tenets of *vidyā* in terms of Western physics, but none have succeeded. To do this is to lay a virtual map of one system upon the other, effectively identifying communalities between figurative peaks and valleys. In terms of Western physics it appears that the failure to develop a common map for the two systems of thought occurs because of the fashion in which *vidya* describes: 1) the nature of the individuated self; 2) the illusory nature of substantial existence; 3) the nature of free will when karma is portrayed as the cause of all actions; and 4) the essentially subjective nature of the flow of time.

The problem in developing a map appears to have revolved around the secrecy and complexity of the esoteric tantras. It was only in the last twenty years or so that their unusual and difficult to understand logic has gained even a small foothold on the stage of global understanding. In attempting to map *vidya* onto Western science scholars have tended to describe and understand the nature of the goal in terms of the practices (or processes) that lead to the goal. This technique is a strong feature of Western science but not necessarily a feature of *vidya*. For example: when considering *Mahamudra*, it's very easy to confuse the practices which lead to the realization of the state with, the nature of the state. The confusion occurs because the practices are within the flow of time and are accomplished by an individual, while the state *Mahamudra* itself is nontemporal (outside of time flow) and there is functionally "no individual" present, in terms of space and time as we know it. [These ideas and others will be much more understandable by the end of the book.]

Another example is the typical requirement of many years of effort to transform the mind and gain the clarity that is essential to the state of *Mahamudra*. The invested time and effort obviously cannot be a necessary feature of the state of *Mahamudra*, where the flow of time is seen as a single illusory meta-instant within a grand nontemporal state of existence. Also, in a nontemporal state, verbs (for example: "to transform") can't be used to succinctly express concepts—because logically there is no time for the action of a verb to transpire. Therefore, if we grant that the state of *Mahamudra* exists, we must axiomatically define existence as being viable in an instantaneous and timeless condition of reality, and thus define it accordingly.

An effort to map *vidya* (i.e. Buddhism) onto the sciences is difficult because; the impossible-to-define, reached-for goal of Vidya is a state where one is uninterested in the illusion of substantial reality. Whereas the mapping itself describes a goal that is *not* uninterested in the illusion of substantial reality.

As with *Mahamudra* the practice of *Dzogchen* is similarly distinct from the state of *Dzogchen*; however in the *Dzogchen* tradition realization may occur without the years of practice associated with the realization of *Mahamudra*. For me this affords the possibility of a certain, unique relationship with the state of *Dzogchen*, which allows a figurative view of the relative condition of reality to be described by an analog. The analog includes all of the cognitive sciences; quantum and classical physics; and much more that is beyond space and time as we know it, but not beyond the vail of conceptuality—thus pointing at the state of *Dzogchen*, but not specifically identifying it (this statement will become more clear as you read on.)

The book takes into account the above mentioned problems of mapping *vidyä* onto Western physics, often using graphics and geometry. To facilitate this, the analog is used as a framework[A] for a constructed "Theory of Totality" (the "ToT") that includes all things, thoughts, beings, energy, time, space and causality—basically all concepts when these items are described as experiences (nouns).

Within the ToT there are logically coherent, but very unusual, concepts used to map *vidyä* against the probabilistic nature of quantum mechanics. These probabilities describe the uncertainty encountered when determining the position and momentum of particles of mass. In quantum theory this is called the *uncertainty principle*—which is an expression of the complete inability of being able to determine the time and place of the transfer of energy and momentum between the wave-like and particle-like properties of matter—thus forcing a reliance on probability.

In this way the laws of probability are regarded as fundamentally rooted in the very structure of matter. However, if we explain quantum theory in terms of hidden variables that describe where and when each quantum transfer takes place, then the appearance of probability will be seen as merely an expression of our ignorance of these variables.

[A] The *framework* is essentially virtual because, in the depths of philosophical logic, its existence is an oxymoron (remember, "Philosophy" exists in time).

If we assume that such hidden variables exist and that in them we can find underlying causal laws for the quantum transfer, then it would appear that we would first have to disprove existing quantum theory as it now stands—a difficult task because thus far quantum theory has been in complete accord with a very wide range of experiments. However it remains obvious that in the domain of relativistic quantum theory and in the study of the nature of the elementary particles the present theory is incomplete.

Thus we must approach the development of a new interpretation from a viewpoint where the incompleteness of the present theory is subsumed by an overarching meta-interpretation containing unknown variables that are not constrained by the logical bounds of the present theory's incompleteness. For example: Consider the stated velocity of light. According to normal science it is a constant in our universe and a philosophical concept describing a relative velocity which cannot be attained. In the ToT the speed of light describes a value that holds constant within any single universe, but is uniquely different in every other universe comprising a multiverse. The ToT is also a philosophical concept describing a protocol that allows communication between individual entities within any single universe.

The ToT includes a single, quintessential, universal constant that holds across the multiverse. The constant describes the number of beats of consciousness that produces the illusion of one second of time flow. The constant is based on the idea of a "mind moment", a putative phenomenon first described over two millennia ago in old India and recorded in the Pali canon, an ancient Theravada Buddhist text. In the Vajrayana Buddhism of Tibet it has been logically negated, but the negation appears *not* to hold if all universes (i.e. the multiverse) are described as instantaneous in nature. In an instantaneous multiverse the "flow of time" is totally an illusion.

In the ToT *all of conceptual reality* is found to be an illusion, and thus the complete multiverse is essentially instantaneous in nature. For this viewpoint to be logically coherent there can be no substantial reality as we know it—there can be only the *experience* of substantial reality; and the term experience must be understood as a noun, never a verb.

In the book the concept of *vidyä* is generally referred to as a holistic reality map.

The ToT employs a worldview from long ago based on what I call "wisdom traditions". It is a view of reality had by figuratively looking through glasses of a different color that were originally minted millennia in the past. From this viewpoint comes a more deterministic (less uncertain) vision of quantum mechanics that embraces, but does not violate, the tenets of the present theory.

Indigenous societies saw their wisdom traditions as a method of "manipulating the momentum of reality" and hence controlling natural forces. For them such actions were spiritually based, useful skills and survival strategies; but for us they can bring a new way of living in our universe. The hypothesis here is that, in various degrees, we all have the natural ability to manipulate reality as it unfurls, but today's science can't functionally explain it, and thus tells us otherwise.

This book is unlike almost all others, because in terms of what it is proposing; reality [and the book itself] cannot be conceived in terms of normal cognitive or physical sciences. For example, herein the designation of the nature of the true "self", or the "individual" is very special. The *apparent self* that attempts to understand the nature of reality cannot succeed, because that *self* is defined as <u>the totality of all information</u> that describes conceptual reality, which of course includes the *apparent self*. Therefore, in the context of normal science, the observer is part of that which is being observed, indicating a loss of objectivity. What's required is a vision of reality beyond the box of space and time where what is now seen as *super natural* or *magical* conceivably becomes normal science.

What follows is laid out as a story, or a journey that is pointed in the direction of that vision of reality. It's best to start at the beginning because what is said often relies on what comes before. Initially you, the reader, will be figuratively standing back and analyzing what is said and fitting it into your existing scheme and understanding. This is done in the context of who the reader considers himself or herself to be, in terms of their understanding of reality—which is the way we do things according to normal science.

At the end of the journey you will gain a certain conceptualization that the one that is *apparently* doing the understanding is merely <u>the information</u> being presented as the flow of life. The apparent "self" will become an instantaneous, simultaneous, sequential set of packets of information (commonly called "memories") describing what has been viewed. The memories *will not be held* by the individual—the "memories" *will be* the individual; and the observer of reality will be a grand non-personal Awareness not associated with any concept of a "self".

THE BOOK DESCRIBES:

- o How a paradigm of physics is a function of the belief system of the culture in which it is embedded.
- o An overview of existing science as an evolvement of the underpinnings of Western philosophy and religion.
- o The nature of a belief system that is characteristic of holistic, traditional cultures.
- o An alternate measurement for time not based on a change in position; but derived from an interpretation of the number of quantum beats of consciousness needed to produce the *experience* of one second of time flow; as it is historically described c. 500 BCE.
- o How natural time-dependent concepts can be seen as instantaneous; such as:
    - nontemporal velocity,
    - nontemporal sequence [time] dilation,
    - true simultaneity and
    - nontemporal causality.
- o A universal constant that holds across a multiverse whose constituent universes each have a unique value for the speed of light.
- o The description of the universe as essentially non-temporal and unchangeable.
- o A Theory of Totality outlining a new paradigm of physics that incorporates viewpoints and techniques found in the wisdom traditions of ancient societies.

In contemporary classical and quantum physics the reality of space and time is described as being under the umbrella of relativity. This Theory of Totality brings the observer of reality (the individuated SELF) under that same umbrella.

ACKNOWLEDGEMENTS

Special thanks to Chögyal Namkhai Norbu for personally communicating a view regarding the nature of reality, as well as concepts and ideas found in contemporary Buddhism, ancient Tibet and before. In addition, I am indebted to H. H. The Dalai Lama for the clear vision delivered in his writings and talks. Personal interactions with Ram Dass, Sacheen Littlefeather, Grandfather Semu Huaute, Herb Kawainui Kane and Lopon Tenzin Namdak helped in gaining an experience of long ago reality maps. Dr. Carol Aronoff and Dr. Charles Stein were instrumental in the initial stages of creating this book. Kaitlyn Oliver's belief in the essential magic of multiple realities provided a backdrop for the writing. Ted Nelson introduced me to the vision of a massively parallel display of information.

I extend thanks as well to many, many others whose teaching, guidance and assistance has been invaluable. Especially to those friends who were put upon to proofread and reflect upon strange concepts in the initial versions of the text, particularly my many friends in the International *Dzogchen* Community.

I am grateful to Paula Thomas for her persistence and excellence in editing, to Dian Burroughs for her continuing support and to Wikipedia and the NASA Web site with their easy to use references.

The ideas and conclusions found in this book are based on concepts and understandings that I have been exposed to in the writings and teachings of many great philosophers, teachers and scientists who are no longer with us in physical form. They are primarily represented by: Buddha Śākyamuni, Garab Dorje, Nagarjuna, Naropa, Padmasambhava, Longchenpa, Bernard Riemann, Henri Poincaré, Albert Einstein, Niels Bohr, Max Planck, and Jean Klein.

PART I

AN ANCIENT COMOS
Recalling a Lost Tapestry of Reality

The ancients called it a survival strategy, deep wisdom and a
connection with the Earth.

1.1 - BEGINNINGS

I have rich memories of my experiences in the hot, humid, screen door summers of Minnesota where I grew up. They are images that lie in stark contrast to winters with white blankets of deep snow, grey skies and the sometimes bitter cold. Life was close to the earth for me as a child. My mother was raised on a farm in the northern, Swedish area of the state and my father was a carpenter in the city of St. Paul. That's where I picked up the skill. The understanding of how to build houses and assemble things is generally how I have made a living for the last 40 years or so.

Having that background, I find myself searching for some sort of credential that may stand against the advanced degrees held by, it appears, every author of a book addressing a theme similar to the one in this book. This brief biography is intended to serve as a personal reference for the book's creation as well as to offer a bit of insight into the origins of the unusual ideas being propounded.

When I look back at the person I remember myself to be in those growing-up-years, I see someone who would never have written a book such as this; but then all that we do in this life apparently leads to who we are in the moment we are thinking about it.

The whole world around us (as it appears to stream through time) is a continual learning situation – in varying degrees of intensity. Some are hard, some are easy. Some happen through raw experience, some in formal and structured settings—like a university.

In 1969 I earned a BA degree from the University of Minnesota. The school was established in 1851, and I don't believe the administrators have ever called a day off from classes for a snowstorm or sub-zero temperatures. I remember winter days when it was blowing, hard, freezing cold with drifting snow and -20 °F (-29 °C) and we were still expected to attend classes. The administration apparently saw no reason to let weather interfere: after all, the local farmers had been doing it for over 100 years.

I started out in the school of technology, taking the standard undergraduate series of classes in physics and math. I eventually finished with a degree in psychology and a minor in math. Part of my psychology curriculum featured an emphasis on paper and pencil, multiple-choice testing. In order to learn about the tests, we took the tests ourselves and graded them.

Among other things, I discovered that my interests were not at all aligned with those of a policeman, a priest or a baseball player and that I was very good at spatial relations. I also came to think that I was a slow learner and a bit naïve. It seems that it takes me a long time to figure out what it is that is being taught to me.

Nevertheless, those were good years to attend a university, for two reasons: 1. young males were drafted into the Vietnam War if they weren't in school[A]; and 2. it was the 60s, "the greatest decade in the history of mankind."[B] When I finally did graduate, I had many more credits than I needed.

After I got the degree I left Minneapolis with a friend of mine who was AWOL from the Navy (he had issues with the way the Navy operated). We drove Highway 80 across the western half of America in my Chevrolet. It took us 42 hours to make San Francisco, driving straight through. This meant an unbroken, round-the-clock vista of America's western prairies and mountains. The only time the engine was not running was at truck stops (which never closed). It was like a movie punctuated with fast food.

We eventually found a cheap apartment in Berkeley.

I plied different trades—as a bartender, a machinist and then a used car salesman in the industrial South Bay area. After a time, this whole situation began to feel like a dead end. My friend felt the same way; he decided to return to Minnesota and get right with the Navy. I decided to stay. I had no idea what was coming next. At the time it was a wonderful feeling of lightness—like what is expressed in the second

---

[A] That was the nature of those times. It appears that the inequity of college deferments was something that eventually helped bring about a professional American army.

[B] A quote from *Withnail and I* (1986) a cult British comedy film.

half of Bob Dylan's song "Like a Rolling Stone..." but without the resentment. I moved on. New friends showed up at parties in San Francisco and eventually I got a job as a margin clerk at a stock brokerage in the financial district. I stayed with it for about six months and then left out of boredom.

In the early 70s everything changed for me. I moved to the little town of Fairfax in Marin County, just across the Golden Gate Bridge, north of San Francisco. It was night and day different from the South Bay. Marin County was a wonderful place. There was very little industry, a lot of forests, a few lakes and some small towns. Fairfax rests just north of beautiful Mount Tamalpias, the forest-covered mountain occupying most of the central area of Marin. People call the mountain the *Sleeping Lady*. There were (and still are) deer, mountain lions, raccoons, hawks, vultures and many other animals living in the forests there.

At that time, Fairfax was just beginning to be considered a bedroom community for some people who worked in San Francisco; but it was also often described as being "full of hippies." Fairfax is near the town of San Rafael where a little known producer (George Lucas) was shooting a movie using miniature space ship models set up in a parking lot under the mid-day sun. People talked about it because this sort of stuff was usually done in Hollywood.

A NATIVE AMERICAN EXPERIENCE

Marin County was a delightful place to spend summers, especially during the 1970s, which for me was a follow-up to the cultural awakening of the 60s. There were craft fairs, gatherings, concerts and summer festivals. They were "hippy gatherings" and they were great fun.

It was also the time when Native Americans were redefining their place in American culture. Indians across the country would hold *powwows*—dances and social gatherings to celebrate and reinforce their culture. The *powwows* were mainly attended by Indians; but sometimes at the hippy gatherings there would be a medicine man or woman, or an elder from one of the tribes. He or she would speak about the culture and the traditional Indian way of seeing the world.

That was my introduction to the Native American viewpoint. It may appear that this stands outside the main topic of this book (which mainly concerns Buddhism) but it does not.

Sacheen Littlefeather[8]

I've studied Buddhism for many years, and I understand my relationship with it to be cradled in a vision of the natural world portrayed as an Indian might see it. For me this vision serves as an earth-connecting, emotional, and spiritual framework for the strict play of logic I find in Buddhism. I believe that students of Buddhism commonly find a grounding framework in the teachings themselves; however for me it is easier to see it through lenses colored by a Native American vision. This position of relative detachment from Buddhism may be what provides the opportunity to see things the way I do, and put forth my views in this book.

My connection with Indians began at a warm, mid-summer gathering on a ranch in California. The ranch lay in the green, low coastal

5

hills, north of San Francisco. It was there that I met Sacheen Little-feather, a native woman who had acted on Marlon Brando's behalf when he refused the Oscar for Best Actor in the movie *The Godfather* in 1973. The event can be viewed on YouTube. It's very interesting.[C]

The gathering at the ranch had two Native American speakers and mostly hippies for an audience. The first time I saw Sacheen, she was standing on the other side of a large room having a conversation with someone. She was a natural beauty wearing no makeup.

I struck up a conversation with her and we got to know each other. Soon we became friends. She was like a sister to me. With her I attended a few *powwows* and traveled around the state meeting and visiting with some of the native elders and Medicine people.

With Sacheen I met Semu Huaute, who was a Medicine man. In the native community he was respectfully referred to as "Grandfather." He didn't assume the title. It was an honor conferred upon him by others.

The following can be found on his Web site:[9] Grandfather Semu Huaute… was born into the Owl Clan in the mountains of Santa Barbara California. His father was a respected healer of the Road Runner clan. His apprenticeship began with the Elders of the Owl Clan and continued with Medicine people and elders from the Chumash, Yaqui and Aztec Indian peoples. This journey took him almost forty years.

The Chumash Indian tribe is located in the Southern California coastal regions around Santa Barbara, north of Los Angeles. The Yaqui people are in the area of southern Arizona and the Aztecs are in Mexico.

When Grandfather Semu was a young man he was prize fighter. Later he became a decorated US Navy veteran of World War II, wounded while fighting in the Pacific theater. He was in a sense, a true warrior. When I met him he had a ranch in the area of Santa Barbara called *Red Wind* where his family and a number of other Indians lived.

I recall an episode at *Red Wind* where Grandfather Semu, Sacheen and I were talking about the condition of being human, according to an Indian. I remember my emotion at the finish of the talk. It was that for an Indian, all of the stuff of the world is much closer to the spirit realm than the fashion in which modern society portrays it. To be alive

---

[C] The Oscar is the most prestigious award offered by the Academy of Motion Picture Arts and Sciences. In 2010 Sacheen stared in *Reel Injun,* a film from the Native American point of View. Written and directed by Neil Diamond, a Native American film director.

(described in its finest sense) is a matter of seeing all action as an implicit part of nature, and every step on the Earth a prayer.

Grandfather Semu Huaute[10] (1908-2004)
Chumash *Aluh-teh* (medicine man)

I kept asking Grandfather for answers to questions about the nature of the Indian worldview. I had many thoughts on this. He explained that to really understand I would have to become an Indian. The next afternoon, without comment, he took me to a special place on the ranch. He called it an Underground House. It was a round building with an earth berm up the wood sidewalls and over the log-supported roof. Inside, a big log post anchored the center. The area was about the size of a large double garage (but it was round). If memory serves, the door was facing west. The strongest impression was that it was underground; in the Earth.

Standing at the door, before we entered, he showed me that to turn around counter-clockwise was a symbol of respect for the place. In spirit this was the Earth's lodge.

I then followed Grandfather through the door of the lodge and walked counter clock-wise around the room. When we had traveled almost all of the way around we sat down on one of the wall benches that circled the room. He picked up an old red coffee can that contained a tobacco and herb mix, called *knik knik*. He made two cigarettes. We each smoked, not saying much of anything. I remember looking at the light in the doorway. Everything inside of the underground lodge felt connected to the Earth… me as well. It was an unusual feeling, but very real. Then, after a bit, we got up and he led me out of the room to the door, this time traveling clockwise.

A short while later I thought about the episode. I had gone into the Earth's lodge thinking with my intellect and came out feeling with my heart.

Later I asked an Indian fellow I had met on the ranch to explain what had happened. He said with a small smile: "Grandfather Semu probably has something important he wants you to learn."

The next morning, Sacheen and I left *Red Wind*. Grandfather Semu said goodbye as we got into my VW bus.

How strange what ensued. I was driving on a road crossing a desert-like landscape not far from *Red Wind*. The bus had two separate front seats. Sacheen was in the other seat and turned to face me. She was singing using a small hand drum for accompaniment. She intoned: "This is Indian country… this is bear country. The beat of the drum is the sound of your heart, this is different reality . . ." I remember having the distinct thought that the drum sounded like the heartbeat of all living beings simultaneously. As she sang a new and different reality began to make sense to me.

All this occurred while I was slowly driving the VW bus. When we came to a stop sign I halted the vehicle. Her drumming had simultaneously ended with a single, pronounced beat. She appeared to be taking everything in stride; then she looked at me and made the simple statement: "You are a very grounded person."

I replied: "Okay." It was all I could come up with.

. . . .

As we moved further away from *Red Wind* the nature of what happened there dawned on me. It was a transformation.

We were headed back to the modern world of fast food, electronics, and high speed reality—a culture in many ways not well connected to the Earth.

8

I saw that Grandfather Semu was old school (he was born in 1904.) At *Red Wind*, away from most elements of our modern culture, Grandfather was able to [emotionally] take me back to a place in time when people held a different set of basic values. On a subjective level I feel he showed me a vision of an indigenous worldview, which could have been in some ways thousands of years old. What appeared was a natural compassion for the earth and all of its beings.

At that point we were many miles from *Red Wind*, back in the world of cars, roadways and small towns. We drove on, stopping often, heading north on the beautiful Pacific Coast highway taking in the tremendous coastal mountain and shoreline views. We were headed back to the bustle of San Francisco.

Around noon we took a break for lunch near the multi-hundred-foot-tall stacks of the huge Moss Landing Power Plant near Monterey Bay. This place was a thousand-plus megawatt monster with a massive, growling presence that seemed to want to surround and possess you, but it was too heavy and too big to move. It was the size of a small town, but functionally it was a single machine. Its (obvious) essence was environmental defiance.

Sacheen looked at the place for a while and then turned to me and said in a prayerful tone: "please get rid of it, grandfather." What a strange sentence. She sounded like a little girl. It truly felt like someone else was talking . . . from a long, long time ago.

Her unusual request has stayed with me. It sits in the background of my mind as a memory that prompted the writing of this book about a different kind of physics.

The journey of those few days left me with the understanding that for an Indian, the flow of life is holistic and all encompassing.

> The Great Spirit is in all things; he is in the air we breathe.
> The earth is our Mother. She nourishes us; that which we
> put into the ground she returns to us...
> ~ Big Thunder, Algonquin tribe, c. 1890.

> Before the white man came to this land there was no Great
> Spirit. There was only spirit.
> ~ Unattributed

There are specific and subtle views of Totality implied by these quotes. The figurative vantage point from which these views are taken reflects the most profound condition of existence described in Tibetan

Buddhism, called "*Mahamudra*" or "*Dzogchen*". It took me over thirty years to confidently discover an apparent similarity between certain Native American and certain Tibetan ultimate viewpoints. The cultures are vastly different, but they both appear to taste a similar holistic ultimate reality.

> *Dzogchen* means Total Perfection and refers to the condition of primordial potentiality of each individual. The method through which we enter into the knowledge of *Dzogchen* and discover our real condition is called "The *Dzogchen* Teaching." It is considered to be the summit of Buddhist teachings. The knowledge of *Dzogchen* goes back to very ancient times.[11]

A BUDDHIST WORLDVIEW

It was easy to follow an alternative lifestyle in Marin County during the 70s. I managed to make a living at it (sort of) designing and building stained glass windows. I made about 60 pieces—all my own design. Some of them were major constructions up to eight feet across with many hundreds of pieces. I enjoyed the work. I would cut glass and solder lead for hours in my studio, listening to music. Around that time my brother gave me several audiotapes by Ram Dass (a.k.a. Richard Alpert). I was fascinated. I had never heard that sort of logic before. It was Vedic (or Hindu) philosophy and stories from India. As I understood it, Ram Dass was speaking of how a belief system could consciously be used to trump (what was seen as) reality. More on this will come later.

After my time as a stained glass artist, a couple of friends and I started the Redwood Hot Tub Company of Mill Valley, California. We were pioneers. We may have been the first hot tub company in California, as I don't remember any others. I always have enjoyed engaging in cutting edge projects. I designed the systems from scratch. The pumps and heaters came from swimming pool technology. All of the tubs were made by a traditional cooper who had moved to our area from Oklahoma. Constructed out of two-inch thick, solid heart California redwood, the tubs were beautiful! We put out fliers that advertised a new and different experience: ". . . get into a giant tub with your friends and hundreds of gallons of hot bubbling water." (Advertising like this was perfect for Marin County in the '70s.)

Our little company installed about 50 tubs in all. Most were put in back yards and small places where they just barely fit. There are many steep hills in southern Marin County—which meant the tub had to sometimes be positioned on top of a custom built wooden tower in order to be level with a hillside deck or veranda. I liked designing and building the required geometries of the piping and woodwork.

We tried to sell a tub to the Green Dragon Zen Temple located in a canyon near Muir Beach, just north of the Golden Gate Bridge. It was part of the San Francisco Zen Center. The monks didn't buy a tub, but I did begin to attend their Sunday morning lectures. The lectures were held in a large, refurbished horse barn—very austere. About 60 people would show up. We would listen to a lecture and then sit in *zazen* meditation. Most of the people would sit on chairs and the others would position themselves on round black pillows (called *zafus*) with their backs held straight for 30 minutes or so. The monks in residence were American, not Japanese; and the Zen master was American-born Richard Baker. His title was "*Roshi*" (master). He was a lineage holder in the Soto sect of Zen. This was the beginning of American Zen.

For a long time, I specifically chose not to learn the practice of Zen meditation, somehow thinking it would distort my perspective of the world. I just attended the lectures, listened and thought about what was said. I was trying to "figure it out" intellectually, and I felt that they did not describe the "nature of mind" adequately. I now understand that such a thing can't really be done because the process of "figuring" is a part of the puzzle; and a description of the nature of mind may be impossible. (More on this below.)

Baker Roshi showed me how to bow in the Zen tradition. It felt very powerful. As I see it, the action has to do with offering respect for the person (or object) to which you are making the bow; and to offer respect for all of that person's (or object's) relations and connections in time and space. It's a recognition of the person's (or object's) interconnectedness with the totality of the universe. In this way, the bow becomes an internal personal practice for the one making the bow. The respect offered by the person making the bow extends through the receiver and interconnects with the totality of the universe. In a sense the receiver drops out and the person making the bow joins with totality. This is the way I understood it.

In early 1979, I stopped attending the *zazen* sessions at the Zen temple. There seemed to be nothing more for me there.

In October, I sold an old house I had lived in, fixed up and refurbished. I was very much "burned out" from the experience; however,

11

I had made some money on it. I was living in my VW bus and waiting for my passport to arrive for a planned trip to India. I just happened to attend a small gathering in San Francisco where a visiting professor from Italy was giving a lecture. He was a brilliant expatriate Tibetan Buddhist lama who had been schooled in a most extensive fashion in his home-land. By invitation, he immigrated to Rome in 1960 and soon after be-came a professor at the University of Naples. This was Professor Nam-khai Norbu who is now recognized as one of the world's leading experts on the history and culture of Tibet as well as a prominent master of the Buddhist *Dzogchen* teaching. (He has become my long time teacher and I regard him as a great friend.)

On the California trip, Professor Namkhai was accompanied by a group of his students from Naples. It was easy to fall in with this bunch; and San Francisco is a wonderful city to "show off" to visitors (especially Italians). The group of us had an extraordinarily good time going to restaurants, sightseeing and generally just being together. At night, about a dozen people "camped out" on the floor of a rental house in Berkeley. I told my new friends that I was planning to go to India. One of the group members said (I remember the words[12]): "Don't do that. You'll just get sick. Come to Europe with us." I changed my plans.

My new friends and I met up again six weeks later in London just before Christmas. It was the first time I had visited Europe. Nam-khai Norbu Rinpoche had traveled from Italy to teach at a gathering that some of his students had set up. It was held in the ex-Cambodian em-bassy located in the St. John's Wood section of London. This is an ex-clusive part of the city containing great, old, brick and stone mansions. The building was occupied by "squatters" who—as the story goes—had moved in the day after Pol Pot's Cambodian government was toppled by the Vietnamese army. (English law provides for this sort of occu-pancy.)

As grand and beautiful as the mansion was, the squatters had budgeted no money for heat. We all wore heavy clothing, and Norbu Rinpoche taught us a Tibetan technique for generating inner heat (called *tummo*).

In London I realized that I, like many of the others in the group, was "pursuing the *Dharma*." Ram Dass had talked about this. A person can get caught in the process.

Chögyal Namkhai Norbu in Paris, New Year's Day, 1980[13]

Chögyal Namkhai Norbu born in Tibet in 1938, is one of the primary living masters of *Dzogchen*, an ancient spiritual teaching developed in Tibet within the Tibetan Buddhist tradition. As a child he was recognized as the reincarnation of the Tibetan *Dzogchen* Master Adzom Drugpa (1842-1924).

The title of "Chögyal" is honorific, accorded to Namkhai Norbu because at the age of five he was recognized as an emanation of Ngawang Namgyel, the 17th Century Tibetan-born founder of Bhutan.[14]

While still a teenager he completed the rigorous program of traditional studies in Tibet. He left Tibet at the time of the Chinese Cultural Revolution and later moved to Italy. In Italy he taught for more than twenty years as a professor of Tibetan Language and Literature at the University of Naples.[15]

In one sense, pursuing the *Dharma*[D] is actually not possible because the *Dharma* is one's life (thus one would be pursuing the pursuit). *Dharma* is also described as an ethical life path and/or reality for a sincere

---

[D] In Sanskrit the word *Dharma* means "phenomenon", and to be interested in the *Dharma* means to be interested in a teaching that enables one to know the real condition of all phenomena, which is emptiness in terms of Buddhism. This is knowledge that cannot be arrived at in an intellectual way by maintaining a dualistic view of subject and object.

Buddhist practitioner. Another definition of *Dharma* is "a cosmic principle of truth." However, for me it was not that cognitive; it was just something I had a desire to do, maybe even a sort of predisposition. It was easier to do it than not do it.

I see some people in the general Buddhist community trying to maintain a pursuit, but I think they are missing the point. If you have to try, you're going about it incorrectly. It has been more than 30 years now that I have attended to the *Dharma* (in terms of having identified the concept).

The '70s and '80s were the beginning years of the International *Dzogchen* Community, a broad, worldwide association of people brought together by a common interest in the teaching of *Dzogchen*, as taught by Chögyal Namkhai Norbu. The loose confederacy of students who make up the *Dzogchen* Community has become my great extended family.

My interaction with the Community in the early 80s was mostly in California. Almost every year, Chögyal Namkhai Norbu would come from his home in Italy and give week-long summer "retreats." We camped out in different places around the state taking in the warmth and beauty of the California summer.

During these years I became a marginally successful videographer in the San Francisco Bay Area. I did it all: I was a camera operator, a grip, a mini-producer, and script writer. It was interesting work that took me on several international trips. On one, I served as camera operator at a professional gathering in Kyoto, Japan. Another trip was in open canoes along the coast of British Columbia, Canada to visit a Kwakiutl Indian village.

THE LAND OF TIBET

In 1988, I used these same skills on a great adventure across Tibet. This trip was not a matter of employment, though; instead I was on a pilgrimage to Mount Kailash. (I must admit I didn't know what a "pilgrimage" truly was at the time.) Mount Kailash is considered to be a sacred mountain by Buddhists, Bonpos, Jains and Hindus. It is in the Trans-Himalayan mountain range, just north of the Himalayas.

There were about 65 of us on the trip along with another 20 Chinese and Tibetans for support. Chögyal Namkhai Norbu organized it. People came from many countries to join together in Lhasa.

This was a tremendous adventure. In general, the actions of our group could be described both as wonderful and terrible.

14

It was wonderful because we actually finished it without any great interpersonal problems or injuries. It was two months of daily on-the-go traveling in busses and trucks on rough dirt roads. Along the road we slept in tents or in the open. There were no toilets, showers, kitchens, or decent food. Near the beginning of the trip we waited over a week on the river bank because we could not cross the monsoon-swollen Tsangpo River. We were then forced to backtrack and follow an alternate route far to the North and then West along the old Silk Road following the Northern edge of the great Taklamakan Desert. Altogether it was a three thousand mile detour. We often had to get out to repair impassable roads using piled rocks or push the busses over mountain passes 16,000+ feet high (5,000 meters) where the engines lost their power.[E] When fording a river, everyone usually got out of the busses and waded across. It was amazing that we actually got to Kailash and back.

It was terrible because most of us missed the opportunity to make the journey one of great moral significance. In this fashion, the journey itself could have become a tool for profound internal practice. It could have become a "way of being" which served as an impetus for continuing internal awareness. Each of us could have more effectively turned his/her awareness inward towards seeing the self in the context of the difficulties. Instead we mostly looked outwards toward the adventure and the conquering of the problems. This is analogous to the difference between being intently present while moving within the flow of a river or just power-boating around the rocks.

Upon reaching Mount Kailash we did the traditional clockwise circumambulation of the mountain (called a *kora*). The *kora* took three days. The trail is 32 miles long (53 kilometers), climbing to 18,200 nearly-breathless feet (5,500 meters) at its highest point.

After the *kora*, with seven members of the group, I participated in a further expedition where we rode horseback with yaks carrying the gear. We were looking for a "lost city" that Chögyal Namkhai Norbu had learned of from his research in the ISMEO archives in Rome[F]. I served as a camera operator.

What we found were the ruins of *"Kyung lung dngul mkhar"* (Kyung lung)—*The White Silver Palace in the Valley of the Garuda*—in the

---

[E] People jokingly said that we were doing a "five klick bus push." The five klicks (five kilometers) was not how far we pushed the bus, but rather how high we were.
[F] ISMEO, "The Italian Institute for the Middle and Far East".

Himalayas at 14,000 ft. (4,300 meters). The "Garuda" is the spirit of the energy of the raptor, a very old deity. This cave city was an ancient and important capital of the old kingdom of Zhang Zhung in western Tibet. Chögyal Namkhai Norbu with his team were the first to identify these ruins for what they were; the palace of Ligmigya, the last king of Zhang Zhung who was (likely) assassinated in c. 645 AD, effectively ending the political kingdom of Zhang Zhung, and initiating the kingdom of Tibet.

Members of expedition to Kyung lung, 1988[16]. From left to right: (top row) Alex Seidlecki, Enrico Dell´Angleo, Chögyal Namkhai Norbu, Judith Allen, Paulo Brunatto, (bottom row) Jim Raschick, James Casilio, Brian Beresford.

There is good reason to believe that Khyung lung was also the palace of many kings before Ligmigya. Downhill, below the palace, there were other constructions and more than 100 caves that were probably the dwellings of the city's population.

An excerpt from the cover fold of Chögyal Namkhai Norbu's book, *Zhang Zhung, Images From a Lost Kingdom*, explains the impetus for the expedition to Khyung lung.[17]

> The Kingdom of Zhang Zhung, with the venerated Mount Kailash as its center and heart, was an ancient realm which originated more than three thousand years ago, corresponding geographically to the western Tibet of today.

Rooted in Bon, the pre-Buddhist religion of Tibet, the kingdom was famed in its time, but subsequently its name became
virtually unknown even to Tibetans who regarded it as only
the surreal setting of myths or legends. Chögyal Namkhai
Norbu, however, discovered in his decades-long research into
Tibetan history that this realm was the true cradle of Tibetan
culture...

The religion of Zhang Zhung was Bon. In the time of Zhang
Zhung, a Bon master was considered to be the greatest of shaman. The
Bon had many techniques for working with and controlling the energy
of the world. They were thought of as the most powerful magicians;
and, for the people of Zhang Zhung, a Bon master acted as an interme-
diary between the natural and the super natural world.

It appears that the ancient Bon religion was not a religion as we
think of such a thing today; but instead it very much described "the way
of things." It provided a reason and description for the workings of the
everyday world as it unfolded from moment to moment—something
like the way we think of physics today. For the inhabitants of Zhang
Zhung it may have described, for example, why the wind blows.

"The White Silver Palace in the Valley of the Garuda"[18]

17

Khyung lung is astonishing; a ruin perched high up the side of a river canyon. Massive areas of a stratified limestone conglomerate that gleam in the bright sun and appear silver.

What is left of it are a complicated set of the caves that looked to have had wood balconies, stairs, doors, and maybe windows. I saw many individual dwellings, typically with sleeping areas, a main room and a place to cook. It appeared that higher up, near the top, was the more desirable section [the palace] bigger rooms, better views, higher ceilings. One of those rooms was round, about 6 meters across and had an eight-inch wide red band around the inside wall done in fresco, about a meter from the floor. A single window looked out over a clear drop of greater than 100 meters.

I came to understand that much of what we saw was indicative of a Buddhist culture that occupied the city in the centuries after Ligmigya—after the fall of the Zhang Zhung Kingdom. However there was one special place near the bottom of the complex that is (apparently) preBudhist and was dedicated to gatherings. No one knows what went on there.[19]

Some scholars contend that Khyung lung was an important religious center for Bon in ancient times. For me, to visit Khyung lung was to go back in time. In some of the caves, I could sense what felt like a life force from long ago. The quality of reality appeared to change at Khyung lung. It was a feeling difficult to explain. The best I can say is that when I left Khyung lung it felt like there was a magical pull asking me to stay.

The return journey from Khyung lung was as difficult as getting there. I was sick with giardia parasites every day for two weeks until our bus caravan reached Lhasa. We had to get out and push the bus often, and we lost one truck in a river ford.

After Lhasa there was a tiresome journey to Kathmandu and on to New Delhi. It was difficult because the air flights were intermittent and problematic to secure. One had to get in line and argue with the agents. I managed to get the giardia under control with off-the-shelf medicine from the questionable little drug stores of Kathmandu. After a week in Delhi, I got a 56-hour flight to California with an overnight layover at JFK International Airport in New York. By the time I reached California, I was TOTALLY exhausted.

It was difficult to come back to Marin County after the Tibet trip. I had trouble remembering people's names, and it was hard to get

18

things together to make a living. I felt like I had gone too far. This feeling lasted for some three months before gradually tapering off.

In the early 90s, I was again living in Mill Valley. My housemate was Katy Butler, my writer friend. By then an award-winning author, she explained Buddhist thought and its intersection with modern society. I like to think I picked up something of her point of view.

My father died in the winter of '93-'94 (my mother had died some years before) and I received a moderate inheritance. I wanted to get away; and the following spring I flew to Siberia to attend the first of a string of Buddhist retreats occurring in various locations across Eurasia planned by Chögyal Namkhai Norbu. When I returned home I understood that I was, more or less, finished with California.

HAWAII

From California I moved to Hawaii and started the state's first Internet Hawaiian flower store. The first on-line sale was on Super Bowl Sunday, 1995. Very soon after that I met my wife to be, Kaitlyn. She was with her son, Jude, who was three years old at the time.

I met Kaitlyn on a beach, under a full moon near Kealakekua Bay on the South Kona coast. Some local friends had gotten together for a camp-out. I remember the moonlight showed off the snow-white "lace on the waves" as they washed over the black lava rocks imbedded in the wet sand at the water's edge. We could hear the waves hitting the shoreline all through the night. I fell in love with Kaitlyn and Jude almost immediately. Kaitlyn did not get along with Jude's father. She was very available; and we quickly became partners. In 1999, we were married on the beach at Honaunau Bay, also in South Kona. Members of the *Dzog-chen* Community from around the planet were at the party. (More about the Community later.) The wedding was beautiful. Close to two hundred people attended the luau[G] with hula dancers and an *imu*.[H]

Kaitlyn and I worked at the online flower store for years. We also developed a Hawaiian art web site (HawaiianEyes.com). The web site sold prints of images created by the renowned and venerated Hawaiian artist, author and historian, Herb Kawainui Kane.

[G] A *luau* is a feast of Hawaiian food, usually held outdoors and usually accompanied by Hawaiian entertainment.

[H] An *imu* is a traditional method of cooking where a pig, fish, vegetables and lots of other good things are buried in a pit with hot rocks and wet leaves; and then left for twenty-four hours to slow cook.

Over the 16 years that I knew him, Herb introduced me to the Neolithic[1] Hawaiian culture—as best as I could understand it. I think back and remember the many, many lunches we had together at local restaurants or at his home/studio where we sometimes would talk for hours about art, technology, and the course of human history.

Herb Kawainui Kane in his studio. (1928-2011)[20]

My great and wonderful friend, Herb Kawainui Kane, died on March 9, 2011. In paying tribute to him, United States Senator Daniel Akaka said: "Herb Kane helped the world recognize the history and culture of the Native Hawaiian people through his art. He showed ancient Hawaiians as they were: explorers, seafarers and trailblazers in land and resource management. His beautiful portraits displayed on postage stamps, in National Parks, and in museums continue to inspire people around the world . . ."

His studio was always an interesting place. For a time he literally had paintings hanging from the ceiling on ropes with pulleys, stored that

---

[1] Neolithic: a term that characterizes the last phase of the Stone Age.

way as he would work on one and then another. His awards and Polynesian artifacts fascinated me. A carved whale's tooth pendant hung on a neckpiece made of the finely braided hair of ancestors who were kings and leaders *(lei niho palaoa* in Hawaiian*)*. The whale's tooth carving was an abstraction of a tongue; it signified that the wearer speaks with authority and truth. He told me he received this in a ceremony in one of the South Sea Islands, but it was not his: he was only the caretaker. When he died, it was to be returned.

He also received an award from the Hawaii state legislature in 1987; from the Bishop Museum in 1998; an honorary doctorate from the Art Institute of Chicago in 2008; and in 2009 he was selected by the U.S. Postal Service to create a commemorative stamp celebrating 50 years of Hawaii statehood.

From Herb I learned that the ancient Hawaiian worldview was one where the membership in a group was often more important than a personal conceptualization of "self" as is typically understood today. It was a society where the concepts of "right" and "wrong" were often determined by a system of reciprocity. This reciprocity meant respect for others in the community, for the phenomenal world and for a gathering of spirits (or natural forces).

In the first decade of decade of 2000, I worked at designing and building custom homes; Kaitlyn operated the online stores; and together we raised our son Jude. He graduated from high school in 2010 and is now attending college. He got himself a summer job fishing in Alaska and is now very much on his own.

After Jude left, Kaitlyn and I came to a place in our lives where we really didn't have much in common anymore. In 2010, we divorced. I never really saw my life going that way; but it appears to be for the best. As I think back I can imagine that we could have stayed together following a different track of understanding; but that would have required energies and attention that neither one of us was willing to provide.

I've heard said that: "one must go with the flow, one can't push the river." Also, one must "forgive and forget." The idea is to listen to your heart and try not to hold onto old problems . . . otherwise they will consume you. The energy of life is in the present.

In some ways the course of my life has been something like that of the characters described in Jack Kerouac's novel, *The Dharma Bums*, where the pursuit of the *Dharma* was more important than "success" in the material world; but that perspective may be a bit dated (the book is

21

from the 1950s). It appears that a more contemporary view of pursuing the *Dharma* is to integrate the pursuit with the everyday world.

Over the years, I've spent much time and energy in the pursuit of, and being a part of, this thing called *Dharma*. I have read books, done various spiritual practices and have traveled to many countries seeking an overt experience of the *Dharma.*[J] Looking back, there is a solid realization that it is the journey itself that is the *Dharma*—not the "things that were done." In like manner, at any present moment I try to remember that what is truly important is the "doing-ness" of the journey, not the "I" who is doing it. This distinction reflects a holistic worldview, not a linear one that more typifies how we tend to view things in the modern world.

An illustration of this occurred in 1984 on Mt. Hiei, near Kyoto, Japan. I was working as a camera operator on a documentary video. After the shoot, I and a few others were invited to participate in a nocturnal walking meditation associated with a Tendai Buddhist monastery located high on the mountain.

About ten of us visited the monastery for three days. In the evenings we received a simple meal and then retired early on futons unrolled for us on a mat-covered floor of an old, post-and-beam, traditional style Japanese building. At midnight we would arise and begin walking on a narrow, circuitous 20-mile long trail through the mountain forest. Along the way, we would stop to bow and show respect at places along the path.

I asked our guide to explain when and where to offer respect.

His answer; "...give respect to those things which deserve respect."

These were things such as an old temple, a statue, or a large bell. Sometimes we paid respect to natural formations such as a unique boulder, a tree, or even a valley. Along the path these things were simply obvious.

This was the Tendai School of Buddhism which has a certain special relationship with Shinto, the old native religion of Japan. In Shinto there are myriad spirits called *kami*—which can be seen as an as-

---

J It's not so hard to find the money to travel if travel becomes an essential part of what you see as important in your life. One may have to live very inexpensively, of course.

pect of the Buddha nature according to the Tendai School. I recall asking if the sophisticated video camera I had been using had a *kami* associated with it. I never did get a confident answer.

Our guide instructed us not to use flashlights.

He said: "Become the forest and the night."

He was completing his seven-hundredth (more or less) consecutive, nightly circumambulation. He explained that once during the winter he slipped on an icy portion of the trail and fell; but fortunately he only broke a rib and was thus able to continue the nightly walk without interrupting his schedule. After one thousand circuits he was to undergo a series of ceremonies and continue on to more advanced Tendai endeavors which, I'm sure, required much focus, awareness, and fortitude.

The trail wound around the mountaintop and gradually lowered in altitude. The walking practice was energizing. By the fourth night everything felt dynamic and alive. It seemed as though the forest itself was a living entity. The circumambulation would finish at around 9:00 am with a long, 400 ft. climb back to the mountaintop monastery. On the last morning I remember asking our guide's permission to run ahead of the group in order to get to the top faster.

He laughed and consented.

I am not sure why, but it seemed important to me. I was so eager to get there! I ran up the hill, reaching the top ahead of everyone. Much excitement, but there was no one was around. No congratulations and no acknowledgement, nothing special at all. The beautiful monastery was empty and the adventure was over. I remember right then experiencing a sharp realization: "It is the journey—not the end point—that is the essence of the process."

I have come to the understanding that on our planet today there are generally two different worldviews or belief systems. One reflects the traditional indigenous cultures of our planet and the other reflects the cultural demographic of our modern societies.

From this point forward I describe worldviews as belief systems because the book generally describes information as a *culturally intermingled system*.

The indigenous cultures are each *very* different in form; but appear as generally similar in their **holistic belief system** or view of the universe and reality as a whole. It states that: "We all come from (are a part of) the Earth (the Mother, the One) and to that we will return (or

23

continue to abide)." For me those indigenous cultures where information has been most easily accessed are the Native American culture; the Neolithic Hawaiian culture; and the traditional indigenous cultures of Asia. The historic indigenous cultures of Asia are those such as: China, Japan, India, Tibet and Southeast Asia. In these cultures it has been the Buddhist and Vedic scholars who have best recorded their histories and philosophies.

The belief system reflecting the cultural demographic of our modern societies is one that is generally dualistic in nature. I'm calling this a **linear belief system** of the universe and reality as a whole. Modern science has arisen out of the linear belief system. It is an understanding of reality where, in general the premise is; "I am separate from you, you are separate from me; and all things are separate from one another." This statement stands in opposition to the holistic model.

At base this book is a discussion of belief systems and how to work with them. However, knowledge can be both a doorway and a fence. For example: when I was at the University, I had a job working in one of the physics labs and befriended several of the professors. I once posed a question to one of the brightest and sharpest of them.

I asked, "What is the possibility of an anti-gravity device?"

"Not while I'm alive," was his answer.

He was telling me that the concept of anti-gravity was impossible in terms of physical science as he knew it.

For a long time the various Buddhist practices I have been doing felt like the right thing to do, but didn't quite make sense in terms of the "laws of science" as I knew them.

This is the predicament. One needs the knowledge to understand and yet that same knowledge system often acts as a barrier to further understanding. This book attempts to reconcile the predicament by presenting a proposed alternative paradigm that reaches beyond the box of space and time that science currently defines.

We live in a technical epoch. We should learn to see technology as part of the *Dharma*.
~ Chögyal Namkhai Norbu

1.2 - TOTALITY

Obviously there's something out there that feels like time going by. It's generally described as the background fabric for the great display that is the stuff of reality in motion. However, a major premise of this book is that there are no such things as phenomenal reality, mental events or even the flow of time—there are only the experiences of these things, and the experiences are an illusion. True reality is something else. The idea of it being an illusion does not mean the world isn't there, instead it means that its true nature is not as our experiences imply.

This premise is a major feature of the foundation for the unusual philosophic/geometric structure that will be built as you read on. Virtually this structure can be viewed from many angles. One of those viewpoints is a discussion of the nature of the flow of time in relation to the individuated self.

We can begin with a look at the possibility of time-future information being evident in time-past.

ToEs AND A ToT

Throughout all of history, as far back as the very existence of humankind, it appears that people have had dreams, intuitions, hunches, premonitions, precognitions and visions that seem to foretell events that will occur in the future. In order to talk about this phenomenon, we must first be very clear about what constitutes the past, present and future.

Generally, in this writing, events that occur in time will be described according to a geometric position rather than as a function of a "flow of time." The terms "time-future" and "time-past" are used to promote this concept of position.

In order to conceptualize a logical system where time-future information is a part of the present, the overall nature of reality is described in terms of a totality. It is a totality which contains all known physical phenomena and all thought—existing in the past, present and future. This conceptualization is put forth as "something like" a Grand Unified Theory, or a **Theory of Everything** (which is sometimes referred to as a **ToE.**)

There have been many theories similar to a ToE. The first was perhaps in 1864, when James Clerk Maxwell published his famous paper on a dynamical theory of the electromagnetic field. Around 1930 Einstein pursued, what he called, a Unified Field Theory but he didn't succeed. Many ToEs have been proposed but none have been confirmed experimentally. Each ToE explains the nature of reality in a different way.

> [A valid Theory of Everything would] …provide an encapsulation of all of the laws of nature into a simple and single representation.[21]
>
> A ToE mainly refers to the desire to reconcile the two main successful physical frameworks, general relativity which describes gravity and the large-scale structure of spacetime, and quantum field theory, …which describes the small-scale structure of matter…[22]

Not everyone agrees that a ToE is possible. For example: Stephen Hawking was originally a believer in the Theory of Everything but, after considering Gödel's Theorem, concluded that one was not obtainable. Gödel's incompleteness theorems are two theorems of mathematical logic that establish inherent limitations of all but the most trivial axiomatic systems capable of doing arithmetic. The theorems were proven by Kurt Gödel in 1931.[23]

A scientific theory meets certain basic requirements—it makes testable predictions; it provides consistent and fruitful explanations of natural phenomenon; and it adds to our body of knowledge of the world around us—most ToEs do not offer the opportunity for testing predictions, yet the things are still called theories. In this way the term *"Theory of Everything"* is used only in a putative sense—it's not truly a theory.

In general terms, a Theory of Everything is typically described as fully explaining and linking together all known physical phenomena, and predicting the outcome of any experiment that could be carried out in principle.[24] The need for the proposed "something like a Theory of

27

Everything" arises from the argument that the concept of a normal ToE is incomplete. It should also include thoughts, feelings and emotions, herein called **mental events**, because such events exist in time and without them the definition of any experiences associated with physical phenomenon could not be verified as existing.

This of course begs the question: do phenomenal objects exist without an experience of the objects. The objects may exist (in a certain way) but the essence of this book's overarching argument is that such existence are not part of reality in terms of space and time as we know it. In terms of a grander view (call it totality) the questioned events are a probability or potentiality. Accordingly the reality we live in is defined by the experiences (thoughts) that are associated with physical phenomena, thus a grand theory should include those experiences.

For example: Our Sun is more than an immense thermo-nuclear hydrogen furnace acting as the gravimetric center of the solar system. Among other things it's also very beautiful! The beauty is an experience that is very much a part of the experience of our world, but it is not included in a ToE.

Another example: When a being dies, its body may still be a "thing" but it will have no mental activity. Therefore a comprehensive ToE should fully take into account this possible change of state of the "thing" that is the body and the complexity of mental activity, which can be described as the full possible range and content of human thinking. Thus it must also include the mental events entitled: "awareness of the flow of time", "self-awareness" and "causality arising from an individuated self"

In this fashion, what we are talking about here is bigger than all known physical phenomena. To indicate this I use the term Totality (with a capital "T") to describe the "total" picture. Hence this Theory of Everything becomes a **Theory of Totality**—referred to with the acronym "ToT". The ToT (unlike all ToE's) does offer a testable prediction (see below.)

Do Gödel's incompleteness theorems apply to the ToT? I am not sure. The phenomenal universe, according to the ToT, is based on a very simple set of whole numbers which is described as finite. And, behind the number set and the axiomatic definitions there is a clear statement that the true nature of Totality is *shunyata*, i.e., "Emptiness" in Sanskrit [more on this below.]

28

The ToT has a wide reach, drawing from various teachings, philosophies and scientific knowledge. It arises out of an understanding of holistic belief systems in general and, in particular, Buddhist thought and philosophy; however the ToT is not meant to be an explanation of any existing philosophy or viewpoint. It is ultimately an opinion. It is a collection of ideas which are based on an interpretation of the writings and teachings of others.

In this light, the ToT is a coherent Theory of Totality but may not be a precise description of the elements of Buddhism or any other indigenous or holistic culture. I try to point this out where the distinction occurs.

The ToT ultimately proposes a conceptualization of a *true* state of reality that stands apart and distinct from an *apparent* state. This distinction is characteristic of Buddhist thought; but some of the conceptualizations made about the distinction do not necessarily come from Buddhism.

The distinction between true and apparent states of reality is a primary feature of Buddhist thought. It is sometimes described by stating that substantial reality and the "self" do not inherently exist of their own nature.

It can be seen in the following statements attributed to Nagarjuna, an Indian philosopher who was the founder of the Madhyamaka school of Mahayana Buddhism (c. 200 CE)[A]. Nagarjuna speaks of the true essence of reality:

> All philosophies are mental fabrications. There has never been a single doctrine by which one could enter the true essence of things.
> Don't mistake understanding for realization.
> Don't mistake realization for liberation.
>
> ~Nagarjuna

The ToT incorporates the distinction between true and apparent nature of reality; but on the surface an obvious problem remains: the ToT is a mental fabrication. Nagarjuna tells us that a mental fabrication will not allow us to enter the true essence of things. In the full scheme of the human condition this statement is correct; however the ToT is

---

[A] The acronym **CE** refers to the term "currant era". It's synonymous to the acronym **AD,** which is typically not used in non-Christian time-scapes. The acronyms CE and BCE ("before currant era") are used through this book.

29

not a pathway for entering the true essence of things on a personal level. Science does not do this. Science works with the concepts, and the conceptual aspects of the ToT do not apply to the true essence of things.

In Buddhism, the true essence of things is equated with the ultimate reality. In the Pãli[B] language the ultimate reality is noted with the term *paramatthato*.[25] In certain Tibetan teachings it is referred to with the term *Mahamudra* or *Dzogchen*.

Nagarjuna (150-250 CE). Golden statue at Samye Ling
Monastery, Dumfriesshire, UK.[26]

If we take Nagarjuna's statement to its logical end, all of Buddhism and all other teachings would be an impediment to *Dzogchen*. Why? Because they are philosophies or mental fabrications. The ToT

[B] **Pãli** is a Middle Indo-Aryan language of the Indian subcontinent. It is best known as the language of many of the earliest extant Buddhist scriptures.

is both a philosophy and a mental fabrication. It will not let us taste the true essence of things. However it does:

- o Provide a conceptual analogy for all that is not the true essence; and
- o Provide a functional representation of Nagarjuna's admonition by describing how the essential nature of a thought cannot be conceptualized.

Thus the ToT does not give us a full description of Totality—it is not meant to. At best it provides an analog for the essential nature of reality and goes no further.

> *Dzogchen* is the self-perfected state of all beings.
> ~ Chögyal Namkhai Norbu

> [*Dzogchen* is] the ultimate nature of all sentient beings... said to be pure, all-encompassing, primordial awareness or naturally occurring timeless awareness.
> ~ A Dictionary of Buddhism [27]

THE STOR

In the ToT the terms "phenomenal world", "phenomenal reality" or "substantial reality" refer to solid reality and associated forms of energy identified by the physical sciences. The ToT defines the phenomenal world (as it appears to be) as an *illusion*; and then it describes how it intermingles with the equally *illusory* realm of mental events. Mental events are feelings, emotions, dreams etc., all elements of reality that have no phenomenal existence (they are experiences... that is all.) These two groups appear to transpire within a flow of time and together they form apparent overall reality, or [what I call] the **stuff of reality**. As you read on you will find numerous, somewhat wordy, definitions explaining important features of the ToT's philosophy. For the sake of brevity in writing they are often denoted with an acronym. The acronym for the "stuff of reality" is **Stor**. It's part of the lexicon of the ToT.

> The classification of substantial objects versus mental events is very much a description of the "Cartesian dualism", (or substance dualism) which is important historically for having given rise to much thought regarding the famous mind–body problem in Western philosophy. Substance dualism is a philosophical position compatible with most theologies which

claim that immortal souls occupy an independent "realm" of existence distinct from that of the physical world.

The Stor consists of both types of experience; phenomenal reality, and mental events. The second includes the experience of "the flow of time".

When considering the illusory nature of the elements of the Stor we might think of it as similar in meaning to the term "apparent reality"; however the definition of the Stor includes *all* possible expositions of reality. This includes all possible universes across the entire (apparent) expanse of time and across the (conceivable) multiverse. The described *illusory* nature of the elements of the Stor is not meant to suggest a hallucination; instead it's a statement that the Stor is not a true depiction of the nature of reality. The true nature of reality cannot be expressed in terms of the world around us (substantial objects, time, and mental events.) Thus the elements of the Stor are real, but they are not as they appear to be—their appearance is an illusion.

The concept of the Stor is similar to parts of the concept called the *trikāya* found in Tibetan Mahayana Buddhism. The *trikāya* doctrine was systematized in the Yogacara school of Buddhism around 300 CE.

The doctrine is a teaching on both the nature of reality and the nature of the Buddha. It essentially describes the three bodies of the Buddha, which bespeak the nature of the three conditions of reality for beings in general. The *trikāya* is made up of the *Dharmakāya*, the *sambhogakāya* and the *nirmānakāya*. According to the *Dzogchen* teaching the three are aspects of our own potentiality that we all have forever possessed and will always posses.

1. The *Dharmakāya* or "truth body" embodies the very principle of enlightenment and knows no limits or boundaries. It is beyond form and anything concretely determined. In the *Dzogchen* teachings, it means the absence of self-nature, or, emptiness of a conceptualizable essence.
2. The *sambhogakāya* or "subtle body" of limitless form, or a body of bliss or clear light manifestation;
3. The *nirmānakāya* or "created body" which manifests in time and space.[28]

The Stor is a representation of the second and third designations. The first, the Dharmakāya, is essentially what the ToT describes

32

as beyond the veil of conceptuality. In its entirety it appears to be similar to the ToT, in the sense that it describes all of Totality—in total it is the true expression of reality.

In terms of the *trikāya* all the phenomena of the world are not something other than perfect enlightenment, they are an emanation of the perfection of the Dharmakāya. Even though the essence of the Dharmakāya is beyond the veil of conceptually, seen in full flower it is the source and true nature of all phenomena, and thus philosophically it rests in both the relative and absolute conditions of reality.

In this way the Dharmakāya is said to provide conceptual and non-conceptual wisdoms, all of which can be features of a path to enlightenment for a practitioner.

The ToT follows the *Dzogchen* description of Dharmakāya (where it displays an absence of conceptualizable essence.) In the ToT, the essence of the Dharmakāya best describes the domain of Awareness and primordial substance, which are the stated ontological meta-components of an Experience, and thus can never be an Experience in and of themselves. In terms of the ToT the relative condition is comprised only of Experiences.

. . . .

The *Mahamudra* teaching describes the external world as a vision that is: "a *mental error* that is essentially like a dream where the only movement is thought." This quote speaks to the illusory nature of the Stor. It's found in a translation of a *Summary of the Mahamudra* (see the Appendix.)

> *Mahamudra* is a set of spiritual practices found in the Kagyu lineage of Tibetan Buddhism that can accelerate spiritual attainment. The creation of the *Mahamudra* practices is generally attributed to **Tilopa,** a tantric practitioner and scholar who lived in India (988–1069 CE).

Within the ToT, the term Totality describes an all-encompassing singularity (a *oneness*) made up of two factions. One of them is the Stor; and the other is the true essence of reality.

All aspects of an "individual apparently existing in space and time" are part of the Stor. This "individual" is associated with the terms or concepts of the "ego," the "I," the "self," a "single being," the "body" etc. These terms are almost always (and incorrectly, according to the ToT) described as strongly associated with the seat of awareness of an individual; a conceptualization that defines all of the terms as mental events and places them within the Stor.

In the ToT the point of presence of Awareness lay with the true essence of reality, outside of the Stor. As you read on you will discover that the mind-body problem of Western philosophy (re: Cartesian dualism) takes on a different meaning when the point of presence of Awareness (self awareness) is placed completely outside of all elements of the Stor—a figurative position that is outside of observable reality, beyond of any concept of the observer, and completely separate from the flow of time.

PRECOGNITION AND A 5-SPACE VISION

Consider the concept of time-present awareness of time-future information. I have discussed this topic with many people during the course of this writing and found that almost everyone has encountered some sort of premonition, precognition, vision or idea about the future that appears to have subsequently come into being. If not themselves, they know of someone who claims to have experienced this sort of thing. These stories do not establish the existence of premonitions, but they do point to a general interest in the concept. Dreams are often the source of premonitions. Within the lexicon of the ToT, all such experiences, whether awake or in a dream state are referred to as a **5-space vision**. The reason for the choice of words will become evident. For now it's just a title.

In 1901 Sigmund Freud published his seminal work entitled *Über Den Traum (On Dreams)*.[29] In it he described a "dream day" as the source environment of the recent impressions that lead to the instigation of a dream. The dream day is the time spent awake that precedes a dream. This is usually the span of time ranging from after the most recent dream to before the new dream that is instigated by the events of the dream day.

Simply stated, the dream day is the time period that is the day before the dream; but it may also be somewhat longer, perhaps a week, depending on the strength of the events that may instigate a dream. The dream day refers to the recent past in which there may have been strong events related to a dream.

In this context, the ToT hypothesizes a "symmetric dream day" which includes the events that may occur subsequent, as well as predicate to the dream. Paralleling Freud's definition, a symmetric dream day also

34

includes the dream day that follows the dream. In this way it accounts for the presence of time-past and time-future information in a dream.

Sigmund Freud in 1921, (1856-1939). [30]

Freud considered the true source of the dream to be not a function of the dream day, but instead to be in the subconscious. The true source manifested by virtue of a relationship which he called "displacement." According to the ToT, displacement simply speaks of the incredible complexity and relational nature of the karmic milieu which unfolds and forms a depiction of reality (more on this below).

It appears that Freud described the time-future portion of a symmetric dream day as an environment of wish fulfillment. If the ToT is correct and Freud was as astute an observer as history implies, he probably saw many physical phenomena that gave him pause (like a dream that included the premonition of a time-future life-threatening random accident). How a symmetric dream day can functionally occur is a major feature of the ToT.

Expanding on Freud's thesis and terminology, the perceived events occurring within a symmetric dream day can contribute to the instigation of a dream. Thus, a dream may contain references to events that have happened in the past or that may happen in a possible[C] future—because the mental events within a dream may be a function of time-past events or of time-future events.

In terms of the ToT, mental events may occur during a sleeping dream or during a waking state; and if the mental events contain references to a perceived future it is called a 5-space vision. The problem of course, is to distinguish between what is past and what is future. History appears to indicate that people can and do make this distinction. There exist many historic examples of foretelling the future according to dreams, premonitions and intuitions. The ancient Greek oracle at Delphi is one example that historically dates back to the 8th century BCE.[D] In the Bible (the book of Genesis), Joseph interpreted the pharaoh's dreams of future events. History cites many, easy-to-research examples of dreams and intuitions that have foretold future events. Pompey the Great, Calpurnia (Julius Caesar's wife), Constantine I, Genghis Khan, Nostradamus, Hannibal, Napoleon, Elias Howe, Black Elk, Crazy Horse, August Kekulé and Abraham Lincoln are a few historic personalities recorded as having prophetic dreams or intuitions.

There are various oral histories (stories) that go back to the Neolithic Hawaiian culture (which ended c.1800 CE). Many of these narratives are still told today within local family traditions. According to these stories, most people living in that culture frequently felt that they had experienced precognitions of time-future events. A Neolithic Hawaiian *heiau* (temple) sometimes included an oracle tower, which is called an *anu'u* in Hawaiian. It was a place where a *kahuna* (a priest) could speak with the spirits and gain information about time-future events. The stated common occurrence of these events and temple architecture dedicated to precognition suggest that the people of that Neolithic culture also had the ability to distinguish between 5-space visions of the future and dream instigations occurring owing to past experiences.[31]

[C] According to the ToT there are multiple possible futures.

[D] The acronym **BCE** refers to the term "before currant era". It's synonymous to the acronym **BC,** which is appropriately not used in non-Christian time-scapes. The acronym **CE** refers to "currant era" and is synonymous with the acronym **AD**. The acronyms **BCE** and **CE** are used throughout this book.

In the culture of Tibet, it is considered that many dreams arise from *pagchag*—a Tibetan word describing impressions, tensions, emotions and leftover remembrances from the past (often the day before but maybe earlier). As a counterpoint, the Tibetan belief system also tells us that some dreams occur as a result of our clarity. Dreams of clarity exist for everyone, with varying frequency. They can tell us something about ourselves and/or the future.[32]

A specific example of the elucidation of time-future information in the Tibetan culture is the Nechung Oracle, a disembodied personality who, through a medium, acts as an advisor to the Dalai Lama. The oracle provided crucial time-future information that helped the Dalai Lama escape from Chinese soldiers in 1959.

> "In 1947 Lobsang Jigme, the Tibetan State Oracle, prophesied that in the Year of the Tiger, 1950, Tibet would face great difficulty. [In 1950 the Chinese army defeated the Tibetan army in a crucial battle. This led to an official recognition of the sovereignty of China over Tibet.] ...later, in 1959, after predicting the Dalai Lama's flight, Lobsang Jigme spent two months walking to India with His Holiness."[33]

BELIEF SYSTEMS

The concept of a belief system is an important element in the description of the ToT—with respect to the *apparent* functioning of the natural world.

The first time I met Chögyal Namkhai Norbu in San Francisco, he explained a certain point of view in the initial few minutes of his lecture. Here I paraphrase: *Believing in something with faith can be very useful, but awareness is most important. One should be aware of what it is he or she believes in and know when they are exercising this belief.*

Belief systems rely on specific axiomatic definitions; and it appears to me that they usually reflect or attend to faith-based agendas (which are often associated with a religion).

The ToT has a unique set of primary axioms, but this does not mean that the ToT is incompatible with belief systems found in any of the religions of the world. It simply means that it offers a different view of reality, not an alternate conceptualization of God or of a Supreme Being. Thus it does not offer a different view of what is beyond conceptual reality—it simply states: that which is beyond this world is indescribable in terms of this world.

The ToT offers a philosophy describing a different paradigm for understanding the nature of the physical and subjective universe. As a further distinction between a philosophical paradigm and a faith-based belief system it appears that eventually, any new paradigm will become obsolete; however some sort of *conceptualization* based on faith that addresses that which is beyond understanding will continue to exist in some form as long as there is something that is classed as beyond understanding.

Nicolaus Copernicus (1473-1543)[34]
Portrait from Town Hall in Thorn/Toruń, Poland. 1580

For example: In 1543 Copernicus put forth a new cosmological paradigm with his heliocentric conceptualization of the universe.[35] His idea that the sun rests in the center of the universe was much different from the previous paradigm where the earth was described as the center of the universe. Since then cosmology has undergone many changes. In terms of today's understanding, it appears that the sun is merely one star among several hundred billion stars that comprise a single galaxy—and that galaxy is one among two hundred billion plus other galaxies physically existing in a four dimensional, folded, spacetime universe which has no natural geometric center.

However, for most Westerners (and it appears many scientists) the hand of God is still seen as the creator of the universe, just as it was before Copernicus. This tells us there is a general belief that the current explanations of the workings of the universe, as given by the sciences, are incomplete—but this is a common statement. What is uncommon is a philosophical revision of these ideas that allows for a paradigm shift of understanding and yet still includes room for an intersession by the proverbial hand of god. I believe the ToT supplies such a revision.

As you read on, in the succeeding chapters, you will encounter successively more expansive explanations of the universe. An interpretation of a passage from the Bible may stand as a possible viewpoint for discussing the nature of the universe at the depth attempted by the ToT.

> Render unto Caesar the things that are Caesar's and
> unto God the things that are God's.
>
> ~ Matt. 22:21

During a speaking engagement on the island of Maui,[36] the Dalai Lama said that members of certain religions sometimes describe Buddhists as atheists; and atheists sometimes call Buddhism a religion. [He went on to say that this may be an advantage because Buddhists can act as a go-between among the two groups.] The crux of this distinction arises from what appears to be the Buddhist viewpoint of time as well as the lack of a Creator in the Buddhist tradition. The phrase ". . . from beginning-less time" is often heard in Buddhist prayers. This phrase speaks to the lack of an acknowledgement of a creator God. I once asked a Zen master about this aspect of Buddhism. He said: ". . . we have stuff, but no stuffer."[37] This is a good phrase, but to effectively use it one must define the nature of the *stuff*, which in the ToT is defined as the Stor.

The logic of the ToT argues that considerations about the creation of the universe (sometime in the far time-past) and the flow of time *per se* are moot because the "flow of time" is essentially an illusory aspect of the true reality.

In this context the term illusion does not at all imply non-existence. Very much to the contrary it describes a complex, grossly multi-dimensional [apparently dynamic] projected image which is an exact analog for the true nature of existence.

In the lexicon of the ToT all of the elements of the illusion are called the Stor; and they are best thought of as an information set. Within the set all of the understood laws of physics appear to manifest and operate.

In the Sanskrit language the term for what is very similar to the Stor [the projected image] is *maya*. *Maya* is the apparent phenomenal universe of separate objects and people, along with all facets of our sub-jective reality. For most beings, what *maya* describes is seen as the only true reality; however *maya* is defined as an illusory projection of true reality.

Maya is a lesser reality-vision superimposed on the "true" condition of reality. In Buddhism, the nature of the lesser reality is often de-scribed as a function of the mind.

> Just as a picture is drawn by an artist, surroundings
> are created by the activities of the mind.
> ~Attributed to Buddha Shakyamuni

This statement reflects the viewpoint of the ToT which describes reality as an illusion. It doesn't exist as a reality unto itself. Any apparent "realness" is totally a function of the "person"[E] who has the experience of it. The true nature of the universe in which we exist is something much bigger, much richer, much more profound and much more com-plex than what we see as the apparent universe around us.

I once saw a quote from the 16th Karmapa. He said: ". . . the world is simply not there." In terms of Tibetan Buddhism this statement means the world has no reality unto itself. It is very real, but not as it is portrayed by our senses.

A simple analog for this concept is a cinematic motion picture. We can easily become very engrossed in the special effects, the cinema-tography, the expert acting, the superbly-crafted story line, etc., of a well-made motion picture.[F] For short periods of time we may forget that it's only a play of light on a reflective screen; however in essence there is no substance or innate reality in a motion picture. With respect to the reality of what is depicted on the screen—it is simply not there, i.e. it doesn't exist as a reality unto itself. Any reality that it may appear to have is totally a function of the person watching it. Thus any implied reality is a function of the awareness of the beholder—and that awareness is much grander than any image reflecting off of a screen.

[E] The word "person" (as it is used here) has a very special meaning in the ToT be-cause the definition is relative to his or her momentary condition and surroundings. See below.

[F] For me the movie, *Avatar* (3-D version), is a good example of this.

40

The 16th Karmapa, Rangjung Rigpe Dorje[38] (1924-1981),
one of the most notable reincarnate Tibetan Lamas.

Similar to this motion picture analog, the ToT describes apparent reality [the Stor] as an illusory projection. Like a motion picture, the apparent reality of the Stor is totally a function of the awareness of the beholder. The question then arises: "what is the nature of the awareness that is much grander than any aspect of the Stor?" This is a prime topic in the next chapter; but at this point there is more to say about the Stor.

KARMIC VISION

The term **karmic vision** is a concept found in Tibetan Buddhism. It is in some ways similar in meaning to the Stor except it is described in terms relative to the predicament (or viewpoint) of an individual being (or a group of beings.) The Stor is the illusion in general and a karmic vision is what is (apparently) experienced *by the beholder.* Each human has a unique karmic vision; and a group of humans together share a karmic vision (as a group). Every cat has a unique karmic vision;

41

all cats share a karmic vision (as a group); and all humans and cats together share a karmic vision (as a group composed of cats and humans). In short, karmic vision is the experiential milieu of reality that is perceived as the surrounding universe and subjective reality, with some experiences being shared and some not. For example: in a group consisting of cats and humans, the humans do not experience having tails; the cats do not experience having opposed thumbs; but both humans and cats may experience seeing a certain object, such as a tree; or experience certain aspects of reality, such as air; or the satisfaction of it being time for dinner.

According to the ToT, the **shared karmic vision** reflects the reality we all share—which is the physical planetary/environment-al/biological make-up along with all of the thoughts, desires, and emotional predispositions we share as beings on the planet.

The **noosphere**, a beautiful word coined by Teilhard de Chardin, can be used to describe a circumfluent planetary blanket of shared karmic vision. It is as if looking through a set of virtual glasses colored by contemporary culture, thought and feelings; however the noosphere does not include phenomenal reality, which is also a part of the shared karmic vision.

> In 1922 Pere Pierre Teilhard de Chardin wrote an essay with the title *Hominization*: "And this amounts to imagining, in one way or another, above the animal biosphere a human sphere, a sphere of reflection, of conscious invention, of conscious souls (the **noosphere**, if you will)" It was a neologism employing the Greek word *noos* for "mind."

THE FLOW OF TIME

The nature and occurrence of time-future events is not always what we expect them to be; they are sometimes unexpected and generally we don't know what's going to happen. The concept of information transfer against the flow of time typically runs counter to scientific and cultural understandings. Time is seen to continually move in one direction, irreversibly and asymmetrically. It is an idea that is incorporated into some of the most fundamental laws of modern physics.

One of the earliest recorded discussions about the nature of time comes from Zeno[G], a philosopher who lived more than two thousand years ago. Zeno questioned the notion of time being continuous and argued against it being a feature of motion.

An important event in Western history is the portrayal of time as an absolute physical reality that is independent of consciousness. This was apparently initiated by Isaac Newton some 300+ years ago. His ideas were groundbreaking when they were first published and subsequently they became the basis of modern science and an original and influential feature of the present Western cultural (linear) belief system.

Sir Isaac Newton in 1689 (1643-1727)[39]

One of the ideas posited by Newton was that no matter what you think, feel, or do, or how you view time, it does not change; rather, it continues to flow at a fixed, immutable rate in one direction.

It appears that generally before Newton's era it was thought that the experience of time could be different for different people and in dissimilar or diverse places. For example: one could imagine a conversation in a 16th century English pub that described time as moving slower in France!

[G] Zeno of Elea, c. 495-435 BCE (interestingly about the same time as the Buddha Shakyamuni).

43

Later in the eighteenth century a philosophical idea that time moves in one direction arose out of early demonstrations of basic physical laws that eventually led to what we know as thermodynamics.[H] This concept was later termed the **arrow of time**. It describes linear, monodirectional, flowing time.

When Einstein's theories came forward they made time and space active co-players. Later in the early 20th century, geniuses such as Planck, Bohr and Heisenberg ushered quantum physics onto the stage. Both classical physics (Newton, Einstein, et.al.) and quantum physics recognize time in some fashion as a dimensional component of the phenomenal universe. This characterizes the three dimensions of space together with time as a concept called spacetime—which is a four-dimensional conceptualization. With spacetime the phenomenal universe may be observed as a combination of solid reality and forms of energy that *move* and *change* over periods of time.

THE VANTAGE POINT OF THE "SELF"

The most obvious problem in the sciences with measurement of the flow of time is the figurative blind eye turned toward the nature of the vantage point from which the measurements are made. Ultimately this is what stops a ToE from becoming a true unified theory; because researchers deem the observer as capable of objectively judging elements of space and time, while being immersed in space and time. For these measurements to be objective, the observer must have some sort of independent vantage point from which to consider the elements it is judging—this is generally called the "self". The concept of the "self" describes a very interesting, seemingly imprecise observer that exists in spacetime and, at the same time, has the ability to be aware of elements of the universe as well as itself.

Within the ToT the term "self" is enclosed in quotes. The term refers to its commonly understood meaning. Dictionary.com defines the word (noun) "self" as: "the ego; that which knows, remembers, desires, suffers, etc., as contrasted with that which is known, remembered, etc."

Researchers persist in maintaining that an individual maintains an awareness of the "self" and the surrounding universe; and that somehow the "self" serves as an independent objective vantage point within

---

[H] Thermodynamics is the science concerned with the relationship between heat and mechanical energy, and the conversion of one into the other. (Dictionary.com.) Early researchers were Joule and Carnot c.1750.

space and time. This is like a person in a boat at night trying to measure the velocity of a smoothly flowing river when they cannot see the shore or the bottom and they feel no wind—obviously this doesn't work. The nature of the objective vantage point must be clearly defined.

The sciences generally accept the idea that the seat of awareness exists within (and is a part of) the physical body of the researcher asking questions. This is problematic because the physical presence of an individual is a part of the phenomenal universe (spacetime); and at the same time elements of the physical body are purported to be objectively judging facets of the phenomenal universe without prejudice or bias. Logically, the seat of awareness cannot do this purely if it is enmeshed in the thing it is judging.

All areas of physical science incorporate various protocols for dealing with the possible biases brought into the mix by the researcher. However, none of them appear to address (or question) the predisposition to accept the concept or nature of the flow of time as a possible bias on a subjective level. This appears to occur because the concept of the flow of time (described as a mental event) is not considered to be a part of the phenomenal universe, and thus cannot be a part of a physical experiment.

What is called the mind sciences have various protocols for dealing with the bias of the researcher. These types of science may include concepts as variables; however the flow of time is seldom, if ever, dealt with as a concept.[1] Instead, it is seen as a background, constant, unchanging feature of reality. This may seem to be an obscure (or even silly) distinction to make; but it lies at the heart of an understanding of the ToT.

For example: for a researcher to make an observation, the act of observing must have a duration; it cannot be *instantaneous* (because, prosaically, the act would not last long enough to be recognized).

> One might think that the exception to the concept of the impossibility of existence being *instantaneous* is the instancy described as a mathematic limit point, but that is a virtual—admittedly not real, hypothetical, inferred from indirect evidence, i.e. a concept that cannot exist in spacetime as we know it.
>
> Conversely, instantaneous existence is an axiomatic feature of the ToT. More on this later.

---

[1] The exception to this is in relativistic equations.

Another way to look at the issue is to recognize the phenomenal universe as a part of the Stor—which is an illusion. The seat of awareness cannot exist in the context of illusion, because the seat of awareness, which recognizes the illusion, cannot also be a part of the illusion. An illusion always exists with respect to something else, i.e. an illusion does not recognize itself.

In the ToT the seat of awareness is described as having the ability to (instantaneously) parse multiple episodes of "time-past" simultaneously. The word "simultaneous" has implicit in its root meaning the concept of the flow of time—which is not the manner in which the word is used in this context.

> The meaning of this word "simultaneous" touches the heart of trying to describe a timeless reality using a language that is a feature of a time based culture. The word "concurrent" is another candidate but it also has temporal connotations. The word "parallel" might be more appropriate however it doesn't fit grammatically. In this document the word "simultaneous" is to be understood as being applied without temporal connotations; as if it describes the elements of a geometric sequence.

For example: a person might say that they are aware of the movement of time because they can simultaneously *remember* multiple visions of grains of sand in an hourglass changing position. Thus the constituents of time-past are considered to be a part of memory and the sequential episodes in memory are seen to occur simultaneously.

The concept of different positions for the grains of sand is with respect to the instant of the present reality, the moment of the "now" at which the assertion of awareness is made—and that assertion of awareness is an experience described as "being aware of the movement of time." Therefore any experience of the movement of time is a function of memory. In this way the cognizance of time is a result of memory. This is a logically valid statement; however it is said with respect to when? According to the physical sciences the observer is purported to be the seat of awareness; yet the observer can never identify the instant of "now" that is not memory. Thus, whenever the nature of "now" is considered, it is a little bit in the past.

This leads to the (logical) conclusion that it is only the instant of the present that affords the vantage point from which a being can be

46

aware of time. However, when one intuitively asks the question "what is the instant of the present?" there comes an uncertain answer that is a function of another question: "being that the duration of the present is instantaneous, where (or how, or when) does the seat of awareness exist?" An obvious conclusion is that existence of the seat of awareness must be of zero duration otherwise it would include memory; and memory is the stuff that is being looked at, so memory cannot also be part of the thing that is the seat of awareness.

The idea of existence being instantaneous may be difficult to grasp from the perspective of spacetime. The concept is however axiomatic in the ToT and thus logically sound in that context.

A scientist does research on the phenomenal universe. To do this properly, the seat of awareness of the researcher must function as a relevant vantage point from which to observe and make decisions. A ToE is described as a complete and coherent explanation of everything (a "unified theory"); yet, the nature of the seat of awareness is generally not included in the unified theory! This is a major error.

In simple terms, the scope of what is being theorized within a ToE is necessarily incomplete because; without a defined and examined seat of awareness (that exists outside of spacetime) there is no vantage point from which to assess the elements of spacetime—a major problem for science as we know it!

The ToT addresses this problem.

THE AWARENESS OF TIME

Researchers do not have a clear answer to the question: "what is the nature of an awareness of the flow of time?" As a result, an ill-defined seat of awareness is given as the default platform from which to do research.

To say this another way: any action, such as a scientific observation, requires a duration. Logically this action implies a seat of awareness that is nontemporal in nature (i.e. outside of the flow of time). This would allow the seat of awareness to objectively and accurately measure the duration of the observation.

An illustration that highlights this apparent contradiction is the comedy movie released in 1952 entitled *Son of Paleface*.[40] I remember it from my youth. The movie was incredibly insensitive to the social conditions of Native Americans; however it contained a very interesting scene. The movie starred Bob Hope, Jane Russell and Roy Rogers. At

47

one point, Hope and Russell are riding in an antique, open-topped automobile and are being chased by a band of Indians on horseback across an open plain. Hope is standing in the back of the car shooting at the Indians and Russell is driving. During the chase, the rear wheel somehow becomes loose at the hub and the wheel begins to spin off, eventually becoming detached from the axle. At the last moment, Roy Rogers rides alongside on his horse and lassos the wheel-less axle with his rope, and in so doing, holds up the back corner of the car and keeps it from dragging on the ground. The chase continues with Roy Rodgers on horseback galloping alongside the three-wheeled vehicle with the rear axle lassoed. Meanwhile the displaced wheel has rolled off ahead of the moving car. Suddenly Roy Rodgers proclaims "I'll get the wheel. Here, hold this!" He gives the rope supporting the rear of the car to Hope (still standing in the back) and rides off after the wheel. Hope is left holding himself and the car aloft while Rodgers retrieves the wheel. Hope says to Russell, "I hope he's quick about it. This is impossible!"

Bob Hope's predicament is analogous to the situation facing the various sciences when they try to make measurements without accounting for the nature of the seat of awareness that is supposedly a part of the physical reality that they are describing. It appears they (figuratively) have no place to stand because the seat of awareness cannot logically exist in the spacetime universe.

This is not a cautionary statement that can simply be addressed by being aware of the subjective coloring the observer may bring to the table. What this means is that a researcher cannot control the effect of variables just by being aware of their scope and nature. A coherent explanation of Totality must, by definition, answer the fundamental question: "what is the nature of the perception (or the awareness) of the flow of time?"

The answer to this question is embedded in the information of the Stor. When this information is described as a karmic vision it can form a belief system or a "reality map", depending on one's point of view.

BELIEF SYSTEMS AND REALITY MAPS

The ToT describes elements of reality as the Stor and then discusses them at a very profound level. The results of this discussion can serve as doorways to greater understanding or as barricades (*i.e.* conflicts) to ideas that don't fit in with an already accepted "way of things."

People deal with what is beyond their understanding in various ways. Some people study and contemplate; others embrace an organized religion or believe in something with faith. Religion and faith can be wonderful, comforting and life sustaining. A personal relationship with God is profound, genuine and empowering. For some, matters of faith amount to a relationship with a community of similar believers; for others it may be a relationship with a guardian deity or a heart-felt concept of a hoped-for different reality; and for others it can simply be a profound respect for the wonderment and beauty inherent in the natural universe.

Each of these scenarios can be described as a belief system or a belief system to the degree that adherents believe in and rely on basic axiomatic definitions; but such a description implies there is a "self" who is doing the believing. In the ToT, the "self" is identified as part of the information of the Stor—this is a problem with respect to the distinction between the observer and what is being observed. Therefore in the ToT there is instead the concept of a **reality map**, which is a combination of a belief system and the "self" who is apparently doing the believing.

> The definition of a belief system does not include a statement of the nature of the observer or the location of its seat of awareness.
>
> The definition of a reality map specifically states that the concept of the observer, the apparent "self", *is part of* the information of the Stor; and the seat of awareness *is not part of* the illusory nature of the Stor.
>
> A reality map is defined as a collection and organization of ideas and beliefs through which an individual ostensibly interprets the world[J] and interacts with it. The term "ostensible" is used because in the ToT, the makeup of the "self" (the apparent observer) is a part of the reality map; and the "self" includes primary concepts that allow it to (apparently) observe and (apparently) interpret the world.

A reality map may exist with respect to an individual being or a group of beings. The description of an individual reality map ranges across a variety of interactions with the surrounding universe and with

---

[J] **"The world"** is a colloquialism. It describes the concerns of the earth, its affairs, its inhabitants, all things upon it and the conceptual view of the universe and how it operates.

personal thoughts and ideas. However, it is defined as always containing one or more **primary concepts**.

Primary concepts are defined as those essential concepts that are *a priori* assumptions, that is, they need no verification—they are accepted epistemologically, without verification. The *existence of time* and the *existence of a "self"* are typical primary concepts.

The distinction between a belief system and a reality map is subtle and is especially important within the confines of the ToT. Henceforth the term "reality map" will generally be used in place of the terms "belief system" or "world view".

Within the context of the ToT all beings are described as necessarily operating according to some sort of reality map.

The differences in the descriptions of reality maps are generally classed according to the nature of the primary concepts they include in their logical base. Humans generally embrace a coherent gathering of concepts that allow them to (ostensibly) interpret and interact with the world around them. Specifically, each living being has a unique reality map as part of his/her makeup.

A reality map is a pattern of protocols that describe how the events and stuff of reality exists and works. Generally, people learn it from childhood and it is strongly linked to the culture in which they live. For example: consider a person living in the Neolithic age of Hawaii, as a nomad on the plateau of Tibet, as an ancient Native American, in medieval Europe, or in our modern world [which relies on classical physics and quantum mechanics]. Each of these groups has a collective reality map, which is a generalization that describes the workings of reality as characterized in that group; and in general, each group is different. However, the term reality map, *per se*, always reflects a single individual.

> A primary axiom of the ToT is: For a person (a being) to be alive means there is an intrinsic absence of doubt that his or her reality map is a valid description of existence. This is always the case; if not, the pattern of protocols will be supplanted by something else. This is the nature of existence in reality as we know it.
>
> This axiom is particularly important when considering that, in the depths of an understanding of the ToT, it is obvious that there is no real place to stand in reality as we know it (more on this below).

SCIENTIFIC METHOD AS A REALITY MAP

Among scientists and lay people the tenets of scientific method generally are not viewed as a reality map; instead they are usually seen as objective tools with which to test other systems. Scientific method is fundamentally based on the idea that data may be gathered, empirically analyzed and used to objectively test a hypothesis by independent observers. In this way scientific method, in its most basic guise, is interpreted to mean that reality is revealed systematically through the experiences of its practitioners. Thus it can occur only within the flow of time.

These experiences are the outcomes of empirical observations that are based upon hypotheses or theories. Subsequent experiences result from repeated testing—which may or may not yield the same results. For scientific method to function, a researcher must believe that the nature of reality is revealed through experiences that ultimately rely upon the human senses. Specifically, the experiences associated with the senses may be a function of the tools employed, such as measuring devices, computers, video cameras, etc.; but ultimately the acceptance of the nature of reality is a matter of the senses having a seminal relationship with experiences. This generally describes scientific method. In terms of the ToT it's also an unquestioned, primary axiom found in the reality map of a scientific researcher.

The characterization of scientific method as a reality map may be a hard sell to a scientist. However, as described above, within the sciences there appears to be an unstated, not-analyzed agreement on the basic nature of the existence of the observer who has the experiences.

Here I am not speaking about the possible bias of an observer making an observation; instead I am drawing attention to the overarching, unquestioned belief that experiences actually reveal the nature of reality. The Buddhist scholar and writer Elias Capriles-Arias noted that:

> "…physicists, while believing that they are probing the physical universe, are in fact probing the patterns of reality which lead to the illusion of the solid world interacting within itself.[41]" In this case the term *itself* includes the apparent "self" that is the researcher.
>
> ~ Elias Capriles-Arias

According to the ToT the belief that "an experience actually reveals reality" is seen as merely a primary concept taken as an epistemological truth within the shared reality map of the sciences.

Another way to express this is to say that there appears to be a set of unacknowledged limits to the empirical nature of modern scientific method that allows practitioners to probe and question the nature of the universe while avoiding discussions about the ultimate nature of the continuity of the "self" in time. Such discussions are typically shuffled into various categories like "...the unknowable mind of God", "...the realm of the soul", or "...the immensity of the unconscious". As best that I can determine, almost all existing Theories of Everything do not include a reasonable explanation of the nature of the observer with respect to time.[K]

In the sciences as they now sit, faith-based understandings of the universe may thus exist peacefully unexamined, side-by-side with empirical disciplines of the sciences. If empirical disciplines are based on a foundation of axioms; and if those foundational axioms are well defined, then subsequent systems of logic built on those axioms become generally agreed upon as rational and "scientific." Conversely, if the axioms are not well defined (but are still accepted), the result is generally agreed to be "belief in something via faith"—which is sometimes framed as religion.

For instance, the theorems of Pythagoras are an axiomatic basis for the science of geometry. In contrast, it appears that the concept of intelligent design is not an example science. We can see why this is if we compare the basic axioms. The Pythagorean theorems are a definition of a very precise set of axioms; whereas the axiomatic basis of intelligent design is imprecise and appears to be something like:

> The universe is far too complex and uniquely in balance to have occurred by accident (according to proponent's purview), therefore there must be an intelligence behind it (or in it). However, the nature of that intelligence can't be explained and the mechanism of its function cannot be determined because it is far beyond the proponent's ability to conceptualize.

Therefore, with respect to any individual reality map, it appears that the more basic and the more precise that the foundational axioms

---

[K] The exceptions to this are holistic Eastern-based theories and perhaps ideas put forth by the physicist David Bohm: See: David Bohm, *Wholeness and the Implicate Order*, 1980.

are defined, the more comprehensive the example of science that will occur.

From this logic follows the idea that a Theory of Everything would be more comprehensible if it more precisely defined the basic axioms upon which it is based. To do this it must include an explanation of the "self" that sits in judgment of a proposed Theory of Everything. When this is done, we have a Theory of Totality, and the path to accomplishing this follows the logic of describing parity between traditional mass/energy and mental events.

TWO CLASSES OF EXPERIENCE

This segment is a more in depth look at what was discussed above. The ToT divides experiences into two classes: one that involves traditional mass and energy, and one that doesn't. Together they form the Stor.

Experiences in the first class involve the phenomenal universe and are experiences of physical objects, velocity, momentum, various accelerations,[L] and every kind of electromagnetic energy. The other class of experiences are subjective and do not directly involve the phenomenal universe. Examples of this class are: hope, fear, love, hate, happiness, art appreciation, the love of music, etc., all of them classed as mental events.

A parallel to this distinction is found in the Heart Sutra[M], a text found in the Prajñāpāramitā sutras[N] of Buddhism, where form and feelings etc., are described separately:[42, 43] The Prajñāpāramitā Sutras are a class of sutras that suggest that all things, including oneself, appear as thought forms (conceptual constructs). The oldest Prajñāpāramitā sutra is entitled "Perfection of Wisdom in 8,000 Lines", which was probably put in writing in the 1st century BCE.[44]

[L] "…various accelerations" include: gravity, radial acceleration, linear acceleration and perhaps some atomic level forces.
[M] In Buddhism, the term *sutra* refers mostly to canonical scriptures, many of which are regarded as records of the oral teachings of Gautama Buddha. A translation of the Heart Sutra can be found in the appendix.
[N] "Suttas [*sūtras*] are not meant to be 'sacred scriptures' that tell us what to believe. One should read them, listen to them, think about them, contemplate them, and investigate the present reality, the present experience with them. Then, and only then, can one insightfully know the truth beyond words." Quote from Ajahn Sumedho. An excerpt from the Prajñāpāramitā sutras can be found in the appendix.

"...form does not differ from the void,
and the void does not differ from form.
form is void and void is form;
the same is true for feelings,
perceptions, volitions and consciousness."[45]

~Prajñāpāramitā sutra

A unique and fundamental feature of the ToT is that, at a very basic level, both of these classes of experience are expressed in the same terms. In this way the ToT finds an equivalency between: 1) traditional mass and/or energy (phenomenal reality) and 2) mental events.

We will discover that finding parity between these two classes of experience is what allows the ToT to become a true unified theory of reality. For example: consider a handful of gourmet coffee beans. The ToT accounts for the physical complexity of the coffee molecule *and* the subjective satisfaction experienced when drinking a cup of coffee prepared from beans composed of those molecules.

DIFFERENT REALITY MAPS

Modern populations largely agree on the contemporary paradigm of science that explains and facilitates our relationship to the phenomenal universe. It's considered to be pretty much "the way of things;" and thus it's a major part of most people's reality map. Science generally serves as the operational paradigm for the phenomenal universe. However, there are other (more localized) operational paradigms on the planet.

In my 1988 trip across the high plateau of Tibet (the *changtang*), I was able to visit briefly with some nomadic people. For them, fundamental concepts of nature and the universe operate in an immense holistic pattern that is in concert with their individual existence... it is very different than my reality map.

Yak with solar collector near Mt. Kailash.[46]

Their fundamental concepts textually translate as "space, air, water, fire and earth." The precise understandings of the meaning of the words relate to Tibetan culture and the local history and provide a useful and workable explanation of the universe. For more than four millennia, these (or similar) concepts have in all likelihood provided a set of understandings that allow people in this region to live and interact with the world around them.°

I videotaped our trek around Mount Kailash for a documentary. Our equipment was carried on the backs of yaks, and I had strapped a solar electric collector panel to the top of one pack load. This was the only way to charge batteries on the trail (a generator would have been cumbersome). This was immediately accepted and understood by our nomad yak drivers. I quickly understood that they saw the fire element (associated with the sun) somehow going into the batteries, which then allowed me to use the video camera and take specific images of the mountains, etc.

° The concepts were still viable and useful in 1988—however things are changing fast and this may no longer be the situation.

While this alone is not remarkable, I also perceived that they understood this exchange of sun energy for camera energy as a natural and acceptable balance. It was explained that I must have the right karma because the mountain was allowing me to make images of it.

In terms of the local Tibetan reality map, if somehow an image was not to be made, then the battery would likely not have received a good charge. It was a holistic situation involving the totality of the environment and the situation. (This was my interpretation.)

Arial view of Uluru, Northern Territory, central Australia[47]

Another trip was a weeklong Land Cruiser excursion in the central desert of Australia. We went from Alice Springs out into the desert, stopped at Uluru, the huge red rock protruding from the desert floor, and ended up back at Alice Springs five days later. Uluru is a special and sacred place for the Aboriginal people.

Our small journey, moving in a circle, was indicative of the routes used by the ancient Aboriginal inhabitants. They took much longer routes and moved more slowly than we did (maybe a year or two). The routes were called "song lines" partly because they were known by oral histories described in song. Their path and intersection points were also described by complicated metaphysical stories mixed with dream experiences.

For the Aborigines, the song lines served as agreed-upon patterns of inhabitance which tribal groups would slowly follow on a seasonal basis. This helped to keep use of the desert's sparse natural resources under control. These song lines and their associated stories have served as workable operational paradigms that have kept groups of semi-

56

nomadic Aboriginal people alive in a brutal environment for perhaps 40,000 years, likely longer.

During the Australian trip I talked with an Aboriginal man who was much respected for his knowledge. He spoke of what he called "one time." His description left me with an understanding of the nature of a long ago era where the concept of progress or social change was never a consideration. Things just continued. The way of things was prescribed by the song lines—which were an integrated part of the landscape, the culture and the people's dreams. In the larger sense, nothing ever changed in the repeating cycles dictated by the song lines. For perhaps 40,000 years it was one time. This was their reality map.

Pele, Goddess of Hawai`i's Volcanoes[48]

The Hawaiian Island chain was formed by volcanoes over millions of years. Today most of these volcanoes are long gone or dormant; but on the island of Hawai`i there is still today the continuously active volcano known as Kilauea. It's usually fuming hot gases and flowing red lava—in a gentle fashion (if that term can be applied to a volcano). I have spent many hours hiking out on the lava flows, sometimes when it is only a few days old. There are no trees or grass on the just-hardened surface of a new flow; it's just black stone, sometimes incredible rough and sometimes smooth and undulating. Occasionally you may have to step over cracks that hold still glowing red lava in their depths. If you are hiking near the ocean on a clear, open sky day with the trade winds blowing, there is immense sense of the elements—fire, water, sky, air and space. In such a place one cannot help but think about Madam Pele, the goddess of Hawai`i's volcanoes.

Presently, according to modern lore and similar to ancient times, there is a loose set of protocols relating to the goddess Madam Pele. Certain actions are considered to offend her and other actions are deemed to please her. If one lives on Hawai`i Island, it is obviously not good to offend Madam Pele, she may take your home with a lava flow or give you some other sort of trouble. (For example, at this time there is a lava flow slowly moving across the main street of my town, Pahoa, on its way to the ocean). This could be called superstition; however, according to members of the local community it is a completely valid operational paradigm—part of the Hawaiian reality map—for dealing with the phenomenal universe.

For example at the time of this writing, on the island of Hawaii, there is a proposal to build a great Thirty Meter Telescope (thirty meter diameter mirror) on the top of Mauna Kea, the near 14,000 foot high mountain at the center of the island. There is considerable opposition to the construction by some in the Hawaiian cultural community.

The scientists involved see the telescope as a state-of-the-art crown jewel of modern technology capable of peering further into the cosmos than any device constructed to date. In contrast, in terms of the native Hawaiian reality map, I've heard it described as "a piece of junk". The Hawaiian reality map includes a sincere belief that the ancestral life-lines (the connection with their cultural, spiritual and physical history) is physically embedded in the mountain itself. This is not simply rhetoric; instead it is the definition of the mountain as something like a naturally occurring church and repository that incorporates the continuing life-lines of the Hawaiian culture and blood-lines dating back more than 1500 years.

The Hawaiian reality map sits opposed to the reality map of the scientists that incorporates a paradigm that is arguable little more than two to three hundred years old. A scientist might say that the telescope technology deals with facts that apply to everyone; and the Hawaiian viewpoint is a religious belief system, not based in fact, that applies to only a few people. A Hawaiian might say that the facts of the Hawaiian physical and cultural heritage are irrefutable and the attendant belief system is as valid as the one associated with the sciences.

We shall see that according to the ToT, both the scientists and the Hawaiians are espousing reality maps that are patterns laid over a deeper *actual reality*; and that it is the Hawaiian system that may best express an understanding of *actual reality*.

A LINEAR REALITY MAP

Our modern, collective reality map provides an explanation of the universe on an analytical level and on a cultural level (the two more or less being described as the sciences and the humanities). It outlines a generally agreed upon path of discovery into the future. At this time there is a global problem relating to energy use, population and the environment. It is universally expected or hoped for (in cultural terms, without analytics) that new discoveries and implementations of science will be a major part of the solution to the problem. Learning to live together will also help a lot.

Our contemporary scientific paradigm has arisen, for the most part, out of the historical Western philosophies whose roots date back to pre-Greco-Roman times. These reality maps served as the basis for the development of the theories and methods of modern physics.

The sciences (as we know them) have historically employed an understanding of nature that relies on a methodology of verification based on the senses operating in nearby space and time. This perspective has allowed the scientists of the last three-hundred-plus years to study parts of the world in isolation from the rest of it and then, subsequently, put the pieces together. This resulted in an underlying intuition that researchers could analyze the world and understand a part without knowing the whole.

For example, the early 19th century researchers Hans Christian Oersted, André-Marie Ampere, Michael Faraday and others each made individual and unique discoveries relating to the nature of electricity and magnetism.

Some years later in 1861, James Clerk Maxwell synthesized and expanded these separate insights into a set of equations that unifying electricity, magnetism, and optics into the overarching understanding called electromagnetism.

After that, Maxwell's equations together with other understandings of movement (kinetics) and advances in mathematics were understood as a whole and set the foundation for the fields of special relativity and quantum mechanics. In this way various parts of the puzzle of "natural science" were discovered individually and then the parts were put together into a grander understanding.

This is quite different than the traditional holistic cultures where maps of reality assume all aspects of Nature to be intrinsically interrelated. In these cultures, a panoply of influences predominate and interact with one another to form a complicated interdependent whole. This view of Nature is reflected in the Buddhist philosophical reality map. In Buddhism there is no Creator—*i.e.* no formal beginning or end to the universe (in other words: the universe has always existed). In the cultures of the East, the traditional emphasis in the study of the universe is the realization of the nature of a holistic Totality (popularly called *enlightenment*). This perspective would naturally make scientific study more difficult because the underlying *intuition* (afforded by the Western reality map) that one can study parts is not predominant.[49]

It is against a background of these different reality maps that inventions and discoveries have occurred—with the great majority having occurred in a milieu characterized by a **linear reality map** generally found in the Western cultures.

All creative thought occurs against a background of existing constructs—else what is there to creatively alter, build upon or compare to? Historically, whatever has been invented, created, or discovered was with respect to a then contemporary set of understandings, because some thing or some situation always precedes an invention; otherwise it is like a found pebble on the beach—it is new but not yet contextualized and therefore not so important.

Intuitive leaps that seem not to relate to the local environment, such as described by Rupert Sheldrake, still require a background against which to be judged. Without it, they would not be recognized as intuitive leaps. They would likely be ignored.

Facets of a reality map affect the process of discovery and the subsequent interpretation of the discovery by the culture at large.

Suppose we were back in 1687 in England with Sir Isaac Newton. Would Newton have perceived and described the nature of gravity differently if the society he lived in had been Buddhist rather than Christian? We can assume the realization of the inverse square relationship between centers of mass at a distance, and the calculations thereof would have been the same; however his descriptions of gravity and the fashion

60

in which society may have assimilated that understanding very likely would have been different. The English society of Newton's time was overtly Christian with a commonly respected omnipresent God, who was the creator of the universe. God was perceived to be generally standing apart from and looking "down on" his creation. Newton, a devout Christian, thought of gravity as a part of God's creation, where objects reacted with one another according to a defined force described by immutable laws of motion—all of which were constant and separate from the individual.

If Newton had lived in a Buddhist society, it is arguable there may have been much less of an emphasis on a God or a deity "looking down" on the world as it is held together by gravity. Instead the concept of gravity might have described "a relationship within the totality of objects, emotions and being." For example: Neem Karoli Baba, the primary teacher of Ram Dass, described gravity as an example of Earth's love.[P]

Buddhist philosophy is representative of a traditional reality map of a holistic belief system —which describes reality as a great dance of relationships. It is a continuing interplay of awareness and being, where the phenomenal objects and energies of the universe are considered to be intimately related to the senses and, ultimately, are seen as an illusion, when considered from the perspective of a vantage point outside of the illusion.

A HOLISTIC REALITY MAP

In a typical Western reality map, reflecting the sciences, first there is an object and then there occurs the sensation of the object—it's a causal relationship. In a **holistic reality map**, exemplified by Buddhist thought, it's different. There are *senses* and there are the *objects of the senses*, called sense-objects. In terms of the ToT these pairs always exist in a codependent, *timeless* relationship.

> Commonly the word "timeless" (ironically) appears to be almost always expressed as a situation where reality is frozen while an awareness continues to exist in some kind of alternate personal flow of time. This "personal flow of time" vantage point allows the viewer to experience a duration of

---

[P] Neem Karoli Baba was not Buddhist but his traditional roots are easily described as holistic in nature.

awareness which has a quality described as "timeless." In general this process appears to be an un-analyzed, internal rhetoric that comfortably sustains an illusion.

Logically this definition of "timeless" is incoherent, and it is not the definition used in the ToT. In the ToT we find a concept more aligned with what I have sometimes seen expressed as graffiti: "time is nature's way of keeping everything from happening in a single moment".

Within the ToT a sense-object is considered to be an exposition of the Stor, which is an illusion reflecting an unseen "true" reality, which is described as something other than an illusion. This sets a stage for a very different description of the phenomenal universe than is found in the scientific paradigm of spacetime physics.

In the ToT the sense/sense-object pair are called the "Experience" and the "Experience-object". The non-temporal (timeless) relationship between the Experience/Experience-object pair is astoundingly different than the causal relationship between an object and the sensation of that object (described in terms of a typical linear reality map)—more on this in the next chapter.

The scientific paradigm, a linear reality map, is always evolving. This is evidenced by the continual and rapid advancements in technology and the ever-increasing understanding of the universe in terms of space and time. Good examples of this are the multitude of changes in our understandings of cosmology and quantum mechanics over the last one hundred years. Conversely, the more holistic reality maps of traditional societies appear to have changed very little since ancient times.

The core of the ever-evolving Western collective reality map acts to provide a reference against which changes continue to occur. The strength of this reality map is much related to the figurative fences it describes as the boundaries of physical reality. However, these same fences also act as a barricade that resists certain changes in the current scientific paradigm.

To wit: the existing scientific paradigm does not accept the concept of (what is described as) mental events as being a necessary feature of the essential description of the physical universe. Also, it does not directly address the concept of the nature of the "self" as existing outside of the bounds of space and time (a concept that could be part of a religion, but not a scientific belief). In this way the adherents of contemporary physical sciences may be approaching the limits of their collective reality map. This does not mean that modern physics is on the "wrong track" or that it could have evolved in a more appropriate fashion. In fact it may be that the most expedient historical route to a grander, more inclusive Theory of Everything (herein described as the ToT) has occurred in a most perfect fashion.

It could be that the first baby steps towards a truly comprehensive ToT were best taken with the Newtonian-based physics that came into being within the European Christian society of the 17th century.

The mathematician John D. Barrow asserts that ". . . a successful study of natural laws needs to start with the simple linear problems if it is ever to graduate successfully to the holistic complexities created by non-linearity."[50] It could be that the holistic approach was simply premature in relation to the past three-hundred-plus years of scientific discovery. To embrace the holistic approach initially would have entailed leaping over the linear, item-by-item discovery chain that maps the history of physics. It would have meant that from the start there would have been an attempt to create a ToT that described Totality as non-linear while including all understandings of contemporary physics. This seems highly unlikely if not impossible in terms of a Western reality map. Within a holistic reality map of the East it would likely be called "enlightenment", and in terms of today's world, not many taste it.

However many do taste the concept of information being communicated in a direction that is opposite the arrow of time, a phenomena not easily explained with a linear reality map. Conversely such information transfer is a prime example of Totality expressed as non-linear in nature.

The researcher Rupert Sheldrake proposed the concept of a "morphic field"[51] that can, in one interpretation, describe the nature of similar abstract forms occurring in cyclic patterns. In that view it appears that the morphic field *may* be seen to explain precognition. For this to occur the elements of an existing cyclic pattern must in some way be similar to a time-future abstract form—and thus the contemporary cyclic pattern elements could somehow comprise a precognitive awareness. The ToT does not include the concept of fields and therefore stands apart from Rupert Sheldrake's work. However, in the ToT there does exist a description of shared quantum bits that are responsible for Experiences. The overall pattern of the (sometimes repeating) relationship

between these bits is geometrically similar to Sheldrake's concept of a morphic field.

Precognitions are a barely a viable concept within the paradigm
of contemporary science. Thomas Kuhn[52] speaks of the impossibility of
understanding one paradigm through the conceptual framework and terminology of another rival paradigm. The idea of information moving
counter to the arrow of time rivals the dominant scientific paradigm on
the planet, yet it seems to occur every time an individual experiences a
premonition.

The problem may be that the shared reality map in play (rooted
in Western culture) may inherently deny the formulation of the tools
needed to provide reasonable answers to the above questions. This leads
to the idea that answers (to this problem and others) might be provided
using tools existing in a reality map historically different from the one
presently in play. The ToT is defined as pointing at such a set of tools.

1.3 - NO TIME AT ALL

There is a profound understanding that has roots back to the oldest forms of Buddhism.[53] It describes a view of existence more basic than is found in all of the sciences that have evolved from Western philosophy and religion. It's known as the **two truths** and has become a principle doctrine of Mahayana Buddhism. The Dalai Lama describes the two truths as referring to "...the philosophical view that there are two levels of reality. One level is the empirical, phenomenal, and relative level... the other is a deeper level of existence beyond the [relative level] which is often technically referred to as 'emptiness.'"[54]

> The true nature of things is void. Spacious and naked as the sky; the clear light of emptiness without a center or a circumference; the dawning of the awareness of pure consciousness.
>
> ~Tibetan Book of the Dead

CONDITIONS OF REALITY (THE TWO TRUTHS)

The concept of the two truths is associated with the Madhyamaka School, whose origin is credited to Nagarjuna, c. 200CE. He was the first to express the two truths in its complete form.

The two truths of Buddhism are often described as the **relative condition** and the **absolute condition**. A clarifying analogy for the two truths is to compare the elements of the everyday physical world around us with an image of the same reality as seen on the atomic level. For example: compare a vision of the earth, the sky, sunlight, radio waves, sound etc. with a vision of the same things made up of atoms, sub-atomic particles, various types of energy and mostly empty space. We have been taught that both are true, yet in very different ways. The first example is the way we generally perceive things; and the second is what might be thought of as (supposedly) the way it really is. Both are considered to be true. This is an analogy. It does *not* express the Buddhist concept.

The 14th Dalai Lama, Tenzin Gyatso (1935--)[55]

From the viewpoint of absolute truth, what we feel and experience in our ordinary daily life is all delusion [it has no reality of its own]. Of all the various delusions, the sense of discrimination between oneself and others is the worst form, as it creates nothing but unpleasantness.
~ His Holiness the Dalai Lama

Similarly, the ToT also posits two truths (or conditions of existence)—the relative condition of reality and the absolute condition of reality. What we generally believe to be the phenomenal world around us in which we exist, think and act, is the relative condition—*i.e.* that which is (apparently) portrayed by our senses.

The ToT considers the absolute condition to be the "true" condition of reality. However this condition eludes us because we have no way to conceptualize it using information found within the relative condition—except with the possible use of mathematics (as is done in the ToT) where we may occasionally point at a constructed analog of the absolute condition.

Mathematics may be uncomfortable for some readers. However it is important understand that from its beginnings mathematics has been a tool to define patterns. Those definitions can be presented on paper using numbers and symbols; or as a textual description of a relationship.

For example: consider the relationship between the number of times a person blows into a balloon and the size of the balloon. That is a statement of a mathematical relationship and an expression of a mathematical concept. Textual descriptions such as this are what are often used in this writing to describe relationships between experiences that are (apparently) a result of the senses. When these experiences are described as collections of geometry and elements of phenomenal reality, standard mathematical notation is brought into play.

The concept of using mathematics to describe features of the absolute condition is a feature of the ToT. It provides surface validity for the primary thesis. However, according to traditional Buddhist thought, any concept of the absolute condition is misleading. In this light, keep in mind that the concepts put forth herein merely "point at" the absolute condition.

EXPERIENCES

The idea that the senses are not providing a true picture of reality is not a new idea in Western philosophy. It was put forth in the midfifth century BCE. At least three philosophers, Parmenides, Zeno, and Melissus, are noted for having this view. They lived in what is now southern Italy, near a city named Elea. Historians call them the "Eleatics".[56] In general, they rejected the concept that perception by the senses can be a method of determining truth. Melissus, in particular, argued that what is perceived by the senses is an illusion. However, their ideas did not prove to be a pattern for the mainstream shared reality map that evolved with Western culture.

It was within the holistic belief systems that similar concepts evolved into what is known as the two truths—the relative condition and the absolute condition.

The ToT describes the first of the two truths, the relative condition of reality, as being made up of basically two parts; the phenomenal universe and mental events. Together they form the Stor, which is all of the elements of reality according the tenets of the relative condition. Additionally, within the relative condition, the nature of the phenomenal universe and the nature of all mental events are axiomatically described as Experiences.

For example: the nature of a tree is not defined as solid, instead it is defined as an "Experience" of a solid object; and the nature of an appreciation of Art is not defined as a mental event, instead it is defined as an Experience of a mental event.

The term **Experience** is a unique part of the lexicon of the ToT and it is written with a capital "E" to denote it is a noun—not a verb. Henceforth throughout this document the word is used in this fashion except in certain circumstances where it is describing a verb, in which case it is denoted with an asterisk (for example experience*). This is done because the essential nature of Totality is defined as time-less; therefore there is no time in which a verb-described action may occur and the distinction between Experience and experience* is crucial. This is also done with other verbs when they are used in terms of the relative condition.

In the ToT all of reality is defined as a set of Experiences—that is all. Consequently the Experience of something is prime and the "object of the Experience is a function of the Experience. The former is called the **Experience-object**" (it's hyphenated to denote its unique stature in the ToT.) Typically, in the world as we know it, an object is described as the cause of an experience* because the object's existence is understood to precede the perception of it. This is not the case in the ToT. In the ToT, there is an ontological distinction but there is no temporal relationship (or interval) between the Experience and the Experience-object. In other words; in the ToT the existence of the object does not *precede* the experiencing* of the object in the flow of time. Normally (when we speak of the nature of reality) there is an object which exists, and then subsequently that object is perceived*.[A] This is not the case in the ToT.

The object of the Experience of a mental event is a bit more subtle. The ToT makes a distinction between the mental event and the Experience of that event. Within the ToT they are conceptually separate concepts—which is not generally the case in the normal phraseology of

---

[A] The verb **perceived*** (past tense) is denoted with an asterisk to describes existence as if within the illusion of the flow of time.

the English language. Consider the Experience of an "appreciation of Art." In the ToT it is paired with an Experience-object that has the (illusory) quality of existing within the flow of time. In this case the Experience-object is the "appreciation"—a mental event which is a verb apparently occurring in a span of time. Both the Experience and the Experience-object are considered to be part of the Stor.

In the ToT the adjective **syncategorematic** is used to describe the simultaneous and instantaneous relationship between the components of an Experience/Experience-object pair.

> It's important to note that a syncategorematic relationship is instantaneous.

One of the translations of the Mahayana Buddhist term *Pratītyasamutpāda* (Sanskrit) is "interdependent co-arising".[57] This is close to the meaning the ToT ascribes to a syncategorematic relationship, but the Sanskrit term does not appear to specifically imply an instantaneous situation.

> Syncategorematic is defined as: "of or pertaining to a word or symbol that has no independent meaning and acquires meaning only in the context of other words or symbols…" [Dictionary.com].

For each Experience there is a unique associated Experience-object. In the ToT Experience-objects never have a substantial existence, whether they are mental events or elements of the phenomenal universe. Both are essentially concepts that are in essence an illusion. This is in concert with Buddhist philosophy which specifically states that there is no substantial existence.

In the ToT Experiences are nouns, never verbs; and both Experiences and Experience-objects, as a feature of their illusory nature, appear to exist in the flow of time, but the pair is always instantaneous in nature.

TIMELESS AWARENESS

In general, contemporary philosophy places the seat of awareness of the individual in (what appears to be) the reality of space and time. Buddhism calls this the relative condition; and declares that our true nature lies in the absolute condition. In like manner, the ToT defines the relative condition to be illusory; and therefore places the true seat of awareness wholly in the absolute condition.

> According to the ToT an illusion cannot be the location of the seat of awareness.

The physicist, David Bohm, was one of the few modern Western scientists who did not describe the seat of awareness as being solely in the relative condition (although he does not use that term). In his book, *Wholeness and the Implicate Order* (1980), he describes the universe in terms of ordered elements. On the quantum level there is neither space nor time and the order of things is described as *implicate*. At the level of reality where things are perceived to "exist" and where there are mental functions, the order of things is described as *explicate*.

However, Bohm appears to ultimately describe the "self" as the seat of an experiencer* who exists in terms of patterns relating to both implicate and explicate order. Thus it appears that for Bohm, the seat of awareness of reality is not clearly defined and is left to exist in the relative condition *and* in the absolute condition. This is quite different from the ToT, which specifically points out that any description (of reality) is an Experience, which by definition is given only in terms of the relative condition. Therefore, an Experience cannot represent the absolute condition as it truly is; and of course cannot in any way be the seat of awareness, because the elements of the relative condition are an illusion. In the Tot there is no substantial existence, and the seat of awareness of reality rests totally in the absolute condition.

In Buddhist teaching, the absolute condition is never described—it is defined as beyond concept. Within the ToT, the absolute condition is hinted at using geometry and analogs—which is probably the closest we can come to an explanation of a grossly multi-dimensional, **non-local** and timeless concept; if we try to describe it in terms of space and time. In this way the ToT poses conceptual analogs that point at the absolute condition.

> The term non-local indicates that there is no primacy ascribable to any direction or set of dimensions, and that there is no measurable distance or direction whatsoever—any dimensionality is due to an overlain concept indicative of the relative condition.

Some Buddhist teachings speak directly of a timeless awareness and others allude to it. An environment without time is difficult (if not impossible) to describe using verbs. [This can be a problem for a Buddhist (or any!) teacher.]

It is difficult to communicate the idea of a realization (enlightenment) because it will likely be understood commonly as an experience*. However, Experiences (or experiences*) are defined as part of the relative condition—whereas the goal of a Buddhist teacher is to communicate a path to the realization that all perspectives are within the absolute condition. To do this the teacher may use an analog, a metaphor, an implication, physical practices, mantra or even an example of a condition of reality. For instance, the words of a certain Zen mantra give the speaker a vow to "...*taste* the truth of the [Buddha's] words." The word "taste" implies a delicate use of the active verb, which (for me) encourages a consideration of the timeless state.

The ToT conjectures a universe that is in some ways similar to Bohm's description; however the ToT places the seat of awareness totally in the absolute condition, such that *all* awareness lies only in the absolute condition. The Experiences associated with that awareness manifest as features of the relative condition. These manifestations include time, the phenomenal universe, mental events and the concept of the "self."

The "I" or the "self" is a relative concept and is usually seen as the apparent seat of awareness in terms of space and time. They are usually defined as the agent that perceives all of the elements of reality; however, according to the ToT the "self" is simply an Experience-object resulting from an Experience (common noun). It is not the *perceiver* of reality, but rather it is a *piece* of reality—i.e. a part of the illusion.

In Buddhism the seat of awareness is different than what is typically perceived as the "I" or the "self" in Western culture. For example: Robert Thurman, a Buddhist philosopher and teacher, offers a refreshing description of the "I." He describes it as the "self habit." The word "habit" implies something ongoing and therefore within flow of time, thus placing it firmly within the illusion. Another example is a description given by Nagarjuna.

> Our physical and psychological identity arises from
> the false idea of an "I." It grows from an illusionary seed, so
> how could it possibly be real? Just as you can't see your own

face except as a reflection in a mirror, so the "I" does not exist apart from your illusionary identity.

~ Nagarjuna

When we describe reality as containing *no "self"* (another tenet of Buddhism) we begin to see how the *concept* of karma, in terms of the relative condition, is intertwined with the *concept* of an individual performing actions in space and time.

KARMA AND *SAMSARA*

For the most part the ToT is based on the *Dzogchen* teaching, described as one of the highest teachings in Mahayana Buddhism. At its core it is effectively timeless in nature and beyond causality. Many other teachings in Mahayana and Theravada Buddhism do not overtly bespeak these concepts—therefore in various teachings of Buddhism definitions may be differ.

How then does one then practice a non-causal path? Most perfectly, they hold a continuing awareness and work full-time in all forms of practice (as each appears appropriate according to the situation at hand), while knowing full-well, without doubt, that it's all an illusion—never forgetting that! In this context, as you read on, you will discover some discourses and explanations that appear to exist in space and time and others that do not. It will be obvious that those that do, lead in a direction pointing toward a realization of those that do not.

In terms of space and time (the illusion), karma is something like "a balance of actions". A common interpretation is: "what you do to others-and-the-world will follow you". People often understand this to be a functional description of reality where a certain act will (somehow) manifest as a certain set of circumstances or events in the future—which implies that we "create" karma, and karma then "creates" or is "responsible for" aspects of time-future reality. This is a reasonable description in terms of the constraints of the space and time where there is a "self" that is apparently responsible for actions performed. This view is evident in the commonly heard Buddhist aphorism relating an understanding of: "...karma, cause and effect." For example, a common Buddhist perspective is: "No event can be fixed or predetermined; because if it were enlightenment would be impossible."

In terms of the illusion of the relative condition, an individual's experience* of the apparent natural way of things results in what is called a being's karmic vision (this was described earlier). Thus, in terms of the relative condition, every time a person reacts as if the illusion is the true reality, he or she creates relationships within his/her karmic vision. These relationships are called **karmic traces**. The creation of karmic traces results in subsequent continued involvement within the karmic vision—which can be judged as either positive or negative. The idea of good vs. bad, sadness vs. happiness, pain vs. secession of pain, etc. is a relative judgment on the part of the person who believes the illusion is truly reality.

Padmasambhava[58] (c. 8th century CE). Image of a statue that was at Samyé Monastery. It was made from life, and upon seeing it (so the story goes), Padmasambhava said: "it looks like me." [B]

If the teachings are not understood, the idea of "I" remains, then come the concepts of good and bad creations leading to better or worse rebirths.

~ Padmasambhava

[B] Padmasambhava (the name means "The Lotus Born") was also known as Guru Rinpoche (which means "Precious Master"). He transmitted Tantric Buddhism to Bhutan and Tibet in the 8th century CE.

74

The ongoing striving (actions) to lessen the negative and increase the positive creates karmic traces that maintain the cycle and tend to reinforce the idea that the illusion is real, which causes a person to continue to be caught in the illusion. Explained and understood in this fashion, the illusion (the Stor) describes what Buddhists call, **samsara**.

Samsara is described as continuing across an enormous number of lifetimes with its attendant karmic traces unfolding, manifesting, and then reestablishing in different fashions, continuing on in perpetuity unless something is done about it.

According to Buddhism, the "something that can be done . . ." is to practice in a manner that leads to a realization of one's own true nature. Buddhists believe that such realization can bring an end to suffering within the relative condition. This is the essence of what the Buddha taught.

THE FOUR NOBLE TRUTHS
- The Truth of Suffering.
- The Truth of the Cause of Suffering.
- The Truth of the End of Suffering.
- The Truth of the Path leading to the End of Suffering.

The Buddha's famous first sermon was to a group in the Deer Park near Varanasi, India. He spoke what has come to be called The Four Noble Truths. They sum up, in a systematic formula, the central teaching of the Buddha; and they propose a "road map" for a practitioner of Buddhism to deal with (or transcend) the concept of *samsara*.

Samsara is a feature of the relative condition, because it describes making judgments of apparent situations relative to other apparent situations and to the actions that ensue because of these judgments. All beings in the relative condition are to some degree enmeshed in *samsara*.

The beings reading this book are those who are in the "human condition," a sub-set of the relative condition. Another part of the relative condition is, for example, the "animal condition"—cats, dogs, birds, fish, insects, etc. All of this is simply nomenclature.

The human condition is very real, powerful, beautiful, terrible, exhilarating, destructive, nurturing—all of the things that are human—but it is an illusion. As such it is defined as simply not there, in terms of the way we normally think of it. It is generally accepted among humankind to be the true nature of existence, but it is not. It is *samsara*, and it is illusory. This is the view of Buddhism and a basic premise of the ToT.

Bhavacakra or Wheel of Life. Tracing of a Tibetan
Temple-fresco of Sankar Gompa, Leh[59]

The image is "…a symbolic representation of continuous existence in
the form of a circle. The Bhavacakra is a symbolic representation of
samsara (or cyclic existence) found on the outside walls of Tibetan Buddhist temples and monasteries in the Indo-Tibet region."[60] The Bhavacakra is popularly referred to as the wheel of life. This term is also
translated as wheel of cyclic existence or wheel of becoming. The cycle
of existence is *samsara* continuing across an enormous number of lifetimes with its attendant karmic traces unfolding, manifesting, and then
reestablishing in different fashions, continuing on in perpetuity

In the ToT the "I" or the "self" is an illusion formed out of a
collection of information that is viewed from a perspective outside of
space and time. The perspective rests in the absolute condition.

76

NAKED SPACE AND ITS WARPS

The ToT conceptually defines the absolute condition of reality (that which is *not* illusory) with an analog. How else could it possibly done?—being that all concepts are said to be part of the illusion. The analog serves as the virtual perspective from which the illusion is defined. Axiomatically, the absolute condition is the "true" nature of reality.

In the ToT the absolute condition is the genitive source of the totality of all possible information—all that ever has been (time-past) and all that ever conceivably can be (time-future) is completely and totally in a state of timeless co-existence coming together in the moment of the "now".

In the context of the relative condition information is ultimately binary—zeros and ones. In the context of the absolute condition there are no concepts, thus information is expressed analogously as a smooth continuation of warped "naked space" with no defining concept of where one warp starts or ends. It is only when the warps resolve to the relative condition that they gain their dualistic, binary aspect where a concept exists as relative to another.

In the ToT this distinction describes the metaphorical edge that defines the veil between the dualism of the relative condition and the non-duality of the absolute condition.

In Buddhist thought, the absolute condition of reality is described as the "Void", s*hunyata*, or "primordial space". A possible translation describing these terms is "free from permanence and nonexistence" [Tibetan: "*tak ché dang dralwa*"]. This is one of the most profound understandings in Buddhist thought.

The ToT maintains a slightly different view of the Void etc. In the ToT it is described as **naked space**—its existence is independent of any Experience.

In physics the word "space" indicates a real expanse or volume to which coordinates may be applied, and thus it is the background canvass against which substantial reality and attendant forms of energy play.

Naked space is the *virtual* canvas upon which the basic quanta of reality are painted. It's *virtual* because it cannot actually provide a set of coordinates stating a location for the quanta. Functionally the quanta have a location only with respect to one another, and such information is only expressed when it is a salient "Feature" of the EQ (see below).

Naked space extends endlessly but it is not limited to the three dimensions of substantial reality, instead it is axiomatically defined as infinitely dimensional.

Such dimensionality is, of course, impossible to envision or literally conceptualize but we can embrace the logical concept of consecutively greater dimensions to a number beyond all bound. Consider for example, the two dimensions of a flat plane, the three dimensions of the space around us, the four dimensions of space and time, the five dimensional idea of another degree of freedom on top of the four and ultimately, continuing to stack additional dimensions, higher and higher beyond all bound. Thus naked space is defined as infinite in breath and infinite in dimensionality. It is by nature *beyond concept* and not part of the relative condition. Naked space is the essence of the absolute condition.

According to the ToT the essence of reality is the defining warps figuratively painted onto the blank canvas of naked space, with the ensuing patterns being the genitive source of what resolves to the Experiences of reality. In the ToT each tiny warp forms a single quantum bit (building block) of the universe. The pair, the warp and the quantum bit, exist in a syncategorematic fashion similar to the way mass is described as a partner to a warp in space according to relativistic spacetime physics.

Each of the quantum building blocks reflects a single warp in one of the dimensions of naked space. The warps are indefinitely large in number, but not infinite. In terms of the relative condition, each quantum bit (building block) resolves to a quantum of information that is the smallest part of an Experience, which in turn is an information set.

Logically naked space itself is empty; but if we think of the quantum bits and their associated warps as occurring simultaneously, each a reflection of the other, we have a logical "start point" for existence. A creation point if you will, however because the concept of time is an item of information contained within the quanta, there can be no before or after *creation*. The warps and the quanta cannot *occur* simultaneously. All just exists—for a single instant or for eternity, there is no difference. The verb "to occur" does not enter the picture.

This is the closest to a "start point" that the ToT defines.

A CHAIN OF EXISTENCE

Relativity theory tells us space is warped by any phenomenal object that occupies it. Consider an area of space being warped by, for example, a single phenomenal object (imagine a baseball size sphere of iron). The warp can be accurately described in terms of contemporary physics however, in the ToT there are no phenomenal objects, there is only the Experience of those objects. Thus in the ToT an object does not warp space, instead in a timeless, syncategorematic relationship, a warp in space is linked to the Experience of the object (which is an information set). Thus we can envision this situation with the ball of iron in either of two ways; 1) in terms of contemporary physics (what the ToT calls **spacetime physics**); or 2) in terms of the ToT.

1. A ball of iron *exists* in space and time causing: an experience* of the ball for an observer and; a warp in space.

2. A warp in the naked space of the absolute condition instantaneously resolves to: a relative condition Experience (an information set); and its Experience-object pair, the illusory ball of iron.

In the first instance existence is defined as in spacetime and causality is described as a function of time flow. The experience* is a verb occurring in time.

In the second instance existence is instantaneous and the relationship between the warp, the Experience (an illusion of a noun describing an object) and the Experience-object (an illusion of an object) is timelessly syncategorematic in nature. The components existing in a non-temporal, sequential relationship—that is called the **chain of existence** in the ToT; and it belies a causality resulting from a position in a static, non-temporal sequence, *not* from a position in time flow.

This is an example of **sequential causality.** It will be explained in detail in the last part of the book; but for now simply understand that this alternate description of causality naturally arises out of the ToT's alternate definition of reality, where there is no substantial existence, and where existence is described as instantaneous in nature. Thus the causal relationship described in the ToT between phenomenal objects and the warping of space is very different than the (temporally based) causal relationship described by relativistic classical physics. Additionally, in the ToT the warps in naked space are causally related to every type of Experience; be it an Experience of mental events or of phenomenal objects.

Generally, the relationship of an Experience to its associated genitive quanta is inferred by the verb **to resolve**—even though all elements of the chain of existence (all things and events) are axiomatically described as ultimately coexisting instantaneously in a time-less condition of reality. Therefore the use of the verb is a textual accommodation that allows an easy reference to a nontemporal relationship. Thus a primary quantum of reality (an "EQ") is said to resolve to an Experience. The full definition of "Experience Quanta" and its acronym "EQ" follows below.

SINGULARITY

The totality of information characterized by the absolute condition is of course, far, far beyond the boundaries of any specific definitions in the relative condition. In the absolute condition we all exist as the genitive source of one great set of Experiences—all of us conglomerated together—spatially, temporally and emotionally. All beings, all phenomenal objects, all mental events, across all of time, the total and complete essence of the relative condition exists as one great absolute truth—a singularity of information—the source of which, in the ToT, is defined as the absolute condition. It is the seminal potential of all possible information.

In this context, the concept of a single being (a "self" existing in the flow of time) is an absurdly tiny sub-set of information. Naked space is infinite in dimensionality; and the limited (non-infinite) dimensionality of the warps therein reflect the finite nature of relative condition.

In the following chapters you will discover that the elements of the relative condition (the Stor) are defined as information sets expressed as resolving from virtual mathematical objects (math objects) describing the EQ relationships in the absolute condition. These math objects (which are geometric in nature) describe Experiences that manifest as the illusory world-scape of the relative condition. In this context it is quite conceivable that there are certain possible Experiences that no being ever has had or ever will have, thus the Stor is finite. Naked space on the other hand is the infinite background fabric upon which the information (the geometric math objects) is figuratively laid.

To say this another way: in the ToT naked space (the essence of the absolute condition) is infinite, nontemporal, unchanging and non-local; and has the quality of being able to be warped in infinite possible ways and infinite possible dimensions. Thus it includes all manifestations that comprise the Stor (i.e. the relative condition)—but that doesn't mean that all *possible* warps manifest in the relative condition, thus the Stor is finite while naked space is infinite.

What's been said to this point is (hopefully) sound logic; but there may still remain some uncertainty about the logic of how the basic quanta of existence become Experiences. This figurative process follows from my understanding of an idea put forth by the physicist David Bohm in his 1980 book *Wholeness and Implicate Order*. He noted that the prevailing view among physicists is:

> . . . the world is assumed to be constituted of a set of separately existent, indivisible and un-changeable 'elementary particles', which are the fundamental 'building-blocks' of the entire universe. ...there seems to be an unshakable faith among physicists that either such particles, or some other kind yet to be discovered, will eventually make possible a complete and coherent explanation of everything.

For me this statement posed the question: Why must the elementary particles of existence resolve to solid reality? Why do they not resolve to Experiences of solid reality (and also Experiences of mental events)? There is no *a priori* reason to accept one versus the other.

This question prompts an assessment of the nature of the elementary particles of reality, which in the ToT, is very different than is found in classical or quantum physics.

PRIMAL CONCEPTS

The absolute condition refers to the absolute nature of all that exists. According to *Yogācāna* School of Buddhist philosophy (the *Mind Only School*) the most basic, most primal concepts that can be understood in terms of the relative condition are labeled "primordial awareness" and "primordial substance".[61] In this school "...only consciousness, pure non-duel cognitive potentiality, has absolute existence." The ToT contains a similar logic but it does not follow this school's line of thought exactly.[62]

The terms primordial substance and primordial awareness have unique and richly nuanced definitions that have been discussed and debated for over a millennium. It is not the purpose here to accurately portray the Buddhist definitions; however the ToT does contain two primary overlays that are similar to the *Yogācāna* School. In the ToT they are named and defined differently. Primordial awareness is called simply, **Awareness** [with an upper case "A"]. Primordial substance is defined as quantum in nature and the quanta are denoted by the acronym "EQ".

Notably, the ToT also defines the relative condition in a slightly different fashion than the *Mind Only School*. The ToT recognizes that it is only concepts that reside in the relative condition; however, because EQ and Awareness are the basic formative elements of concepts, they are classed as being part of the absolute condition. Obviously they are concepts in the sense that they are described in this writing, but the concepts these words portray are analogs that point at the functional formative elements of *all* concepts; and thus, in essence they cannot be concepts themselves. This argument also applies to naked space and its warps.

> Note: Only those warps in naked space that have a syncategorematic relationship with Experiences of the relative condition are defined as EQ—all other possible warps are considered to be incoherent.

In the ToT, EQ and Awareness are both seen to be appropriately part of the absolute condition in that they fulfill the definition of *shunyata* ("free from permanence and nonexistence"). By definition they exist; and they are free from permanence in that they exist outside of time [time is a concept] and thus they can be neither permanent nor impermanent. They are all pervasive and ethereal in nature [because they are *non-local*, which means they have no implicit dimension]. This is the description of Awareness and EQ in the ToT. Together they form the sole ontological subset of naked space—which is the ultimate source of all existence, and designated the absolute condition.

THE BASIC QUANTA OF EXISTENCE

Within the ToT each basic quantum of existence is called an **Experience Quantum**—a term unique to the ToT lexicon. Both an Experience Quantum and its plural, Experience Quanta, are denoted with the acronym "**EQ**". These quanta are not to be conceptualized as a substance in the relative sense—they have no size (length, width etc.) or specific qualities (*i.e.* odor, color, charge, mass etc.) They also have no temporal qualities (*i.e.* they don't move or change). They are not part of the relative condition. We can conceptualize them with an analog—tiny warps in various and multiple dimensions of naked space.

Together they can be thought of as single indivisible whole that exists in an infinitely large number of dimensions with a unique defining characteristic in each dimension. Or, they can also be thought of as an indefinitely large collection of quanta that are the primary, most elementary, building-blocks of the universe.

If they are conceived to be a large collection of quanta, their nature is: tiny, grossly multi-dimensional, warps in naked space. However this description must be seen as an analog because these quanta are defined, singularly, as that which resolves to an Experience, which is the smallest possible concept that may occur—thus an EQ is the item that is the basic building block of a concept cannot itself be a concept. This is self-evident.

Therefore, unlike all other conceptualizations of basic quanta in spacetime physics, these quanta (the EQ) never resolve to phenomenal reality; they resolve only to Experiences.

In the ToT, EQ are one of the two most basic features of naked space. The other is Awareness.

AWARENESS

In the ToT the description, not the definition, of Awareness is much the same as the description of empty multi-dimensional space. If one thinks deeply about it, empty space is a unique and illusive concept to define. It is a riddle: it is nowhere and everywhere simultaneously. The same is true for Awareness. This is axiomatic.

If Awareness existed in some sort of temporal environment we could say it "parses" an array of the warps in naked space. However in the ToT the essential nature of existence is instantaneous, thus the verb "to parse" will not apply. Instead Awareness is defined as a nontemporal "mirror" resting in figurative opposition to *all* of the EQ. This description (...the "mirroring") is meant to emphasize that many or all of the EQ may be viewed simultaneously, and thus simultaneously they resolve to *many* or *all* of the Experiences that comprise the relative condition, be they time-past or time-future. All of this is axiomatic, and expressed colloquially it's "everything is happening at once". Therefore in this rendition of the ToT, to make for an easier read, this meta-verb is described with the term **Parse** (with uppercase "P").

Awareness is "something like" the idea of *self-awareness*—which is another axiomatic concept (and one that much of spacetime physics depends on.) Awareness is similar but without a self. Awareness is defined as beyond concept because there can be no information defining it (it exists at the genitive level of concepts). We can only point at it, describe it with inference and say what it is not. Awareness is "onto itself"; thus there is not "something" or "someone" that has an aware-ness (noun) or has the ability to "be aware*" (verb).

Henceforth the word **aware*** or **awareness*** is the form used as a verb describing a relative condition situation occurring in time. It is spelled with a lower case "a" and in-cludes an asterisk.

In terms of the relative condition, Awareness just *is*—all-perva-sive, infinitely multi-dimensional, nonlocal, and timeless. It stands strik-ingly apart from its relative condition parallel, "self-awareness".

Self-awareness is a concept that is almost universally described among all humans, as the point of presence for viewing reality. The concept of self-awareness is generally accepted with unquestioned cer-tainty and very little apparent thought or regard for the idea that self-awareness is axiomatically defined. [Perhaps this is because there is no obvious, easy to understand, alternate explanation].

We commonly consider the "self" to be the agent that is aware* of reality. In other words, awareness* is described as an attribute of the "self"; but this logic doesn't work in terms of the ToT. Recall that the "self" is identified as an Experience-object; and therefore an illusion that cannot be an agent that is aware* of itself or any other Experience-ob-jects.

The world around us is information formed as an illusion of re-ality. Who you think you are is an illusion. Illusions do not have Aware-ness; they can include the concept of awareness*, but that is a mental event (a verb) and it is part of the illusion of the relative condition.

The description of Awareness in the ToT addresses the classic question: "if a tree falls in the forest and no one is there to experience* it . . . does it make any noise?"

The answer according to the ToT: "The tree does not fall (*i.e.* it doesn't exist in the form of an illusion of reality) if there is no one there."

Awareness Parses in parallel. In its grandest interpretation it can, in a single timeless Instant, view all information comprising the Totality of reality. It does this from a point of presence that is not a part of the information being viewed.

Imagine sitting in meditation considering all the ele-ments of reality... you continually find that none of them are the "self". No matter how long you search, you can't seem to find something that is the *viewer* of reality and not the stuff that is viewed. You consider more and more elements, grouping then into larger and larger clusters, sorting and striping them away from an elusive core (some say it's like peeling an onion)—but there is still no "self". You give up. You stop trying. There's nothing left, yet Awareness is still present.

This is an approximation of a meditative process which may lead to a realization that Awareness is "non-personal"

In the ToT, ultimately *who one thinks they are* is characterized as information, and all beings share some information to a certain degree—for example: one or more of the Experiences of earth, sky, water, heat, air and space are generally shared by all beings. These Experiences arise directly from the interplay of Awareness and EQ.

Functionally, within the relative condition, an Experience is described as being the product of the syncategorematic combination of Awareness and EQ. In the ToT these are the two most basic ontological subsets of naked space—which is the ultimate meta-concept describing information, and the essence of the absolute condition.

SAMANTABHADRA

Samantabhadra and Samantabhadri[63] detail of thangka.

85

In the Nyingma School of Tibetan Vajrayana Buddhism, Samantabhadra is considered the "Primordial Buddha of timeless awareness, awakened since before the beginning" and not subject to limits of time, place, or physical conditions.

An image of Samantabhadra can be seen at the top of some *thangka*[C] paintings depicted as deep blue, naked and in indivisible yab-yum union with his consort Samantabhadri. The blue color indicates the element of space, and the nakedness indicates a total lack of associated conceptualities. In the *Dzogchen* teachings the pair, in essence, represents the unity of Emptiness and Awareness. In terms of the ToT, these qualities are seen as EQ and Awareness.

Out of this intrinsic, inseparable, syncategorematic union comes the full expanse of all conceptual phenomena—which in the ToT is the Stor.

. . . .

The rest of this book is a conceptual slicing and dicing of Awareness and EQ (the basic quanta of existence). This culinary-like procedure allows a logically consistent display of these concepts in a fashion that is congruent with contemporary Western philosophy and science (spacetime physics); and with my vision of Buddhism.

The most primary feature here is that *all* Experiences can be defined generically the same on a quantum level, whether they be Experiences of phenomenal objects or of mental events (thoughts, emotions etc.) However for this to occur the point of presence of Awareness must be *outside* of the universe being described by the quanta—in the same way that "self-awareness" is considered to be objectively *outside* of the physical universe.

The described component patterns and pieces of Totality are not to be considered as "cast in stone." Instead they are simply analogs for elements of the Stor and pointers to the nature of the absolute condition. They are tools created to facilitate an explanation of the principles of the ToT—which is an analog for Totality..

[C] A thangka is a Tibetan scroll painting that can be rolled up when not on display.

PATTERN CHART

ABSOLUTE CONDITION	NOTES	RELATIVE CONDITION	
Patterns Described as Warps in Naked Space		Patterns Described as Information	
In terms of…EQ		*In terms of…* MIND-MOMENTS	*In terms of…* EXPERIENCES
primordial substance	∞ dimensions	NA	NA
Information in a single dimension of an EQ (dimensional info.) a **Feature** of an EQ	The info. associated with a single dimensional warp.	NA	A facet (one dimension) of the info comprising an Experience…
EQ (Experience Quanta)	An EQ is comprised of levels of dimensional warps.	NA	A single **Experience…**
A group of EQ	Contains only nExperiences	A **Mind-Moment**	A single **Thought** A group of Experiences
A Cloud A set of EQ groups or a collection of EQ.	A relative self contains both nExperiences and oExperiences, (The flow of time is an oExperience	A **time route** An instant view across a set of MindMoments. An instant 4-manifold.	A **relative self**, the time-past section of a time route. A set of Thoughts or a collection of Experiences. A time route.
A meta-Cloud A gathering of Clouds, or a gathering of sets	By definition the grandest expression of the individuated SELF. A rendezvous of Thoughts	A **Sheaf** A time route bundle. An instant 5-manifold.	A **5-space vision** The Experience of simultaneous or disparate incidents in multiple flows of time—past & future—extending from the nexus of a time route bundle.

HIERARCHY OF PATTERNS AND DEFINITIONS FOUND IN THE ToT

Chart describing the component patterns and pieces of Totality according to the ToT. The elements are not to be considered as describing an array of "cast in stone" components; instead it is a logically consistent summary of concepts that are basically congruent with contemporary Western philosophy and science, and with the author's vision of Buddhism. Ultimately this chart represents a collection of concepts attached metaphorically to that that is more profound than any possible conceptualization—which is the nature of naked space.

1.4 - REALITY MANIFESTS

According to the ToT, a conception of Totality is a paradox. It's self-contradictory because the EQ themselves are the generic building blocks of concepts. It's impossible to have a concept of the essential building blocks because any description is comprised of the building blocks themselves. Thus, we can never truly see beyond the veil that marks the limit of the relative condition, nor describe what may be there; but we can make analogies.

The paradox here parallels the Buddhist statement that the essential nature of reality is beyond concept. Ultimately, in order to *taste*[A] that essential nature, one must taste Awareness in its essence—a goal in the Buddhist path to realization. The ToT contains no direct description for the components of the absolute condition; however, it does contain geometric analogs that become talking points. In this way, by default, it wholly fulfills its role as a putative Theory of Totality.

This chapter is a collection of definitions that describe a way of organizing information. These definitions ostensibly explain the "way of things and thoughts"; but what they really do is let us conceptualize a very complex system of information. Ultimately, a valid description of the true nature of reality is "in the wind", so to speak. It is definitely onto the realization of the beholder and beyond any concept found in

---

[A] The term *taste*, as it appears in this paragraph, is a careful use of the verb as an analog that points at a *realization* of something beyond concept.

spacetime reality. Thus what is written here is simply one of many possible allegorical explanations.

Recall that in the ToT, Awareness and EQ are defined as the sole ontological subsets of naked space; and they are analogs for that which is beyond concept, i.e. the components of the absolute condition of reality. The relative condition is nicely described with mathematical objects which all have names and descriptions. The "Pattern Chart" (found a few pages back) contains a list of the definitions set forth in this chapter that relate to the ToT.

MATHEMATICAL OBJECTS

Within the ToT each basic quantum of existence is called an Experience Quantum (acronym EQ.) EQ are nontemporal—they do not exist in time. Think of them as the smallest unit of information that is possible. There is no quantity of energy or specific physical quality associated with an EQ. We can conceptualize their virtual existence as tiny warps in various and multiple dimensions of naked space. This was described above.

> Note that EQ are similar in concept to a "space particle" described in a very ancient Kalachakra tantra. In that tantra[B] they are described as the smallest of particles.[64]

In the ToT an EQ is a described as a multi-dimensional mathematical object.

> A **mathematical object** [math object] is an abstract object arising in the philosophy of mathematics and in mathematics. ...It may include numbers, permutation and relations. Geometry, a branch of mathematics, has mathematical objects such as hexagons, points, lines, triangles, circles, spheres, polyhedra, topological spaces and manifolds.[65]

An EQ is defined as occupying a finite number of dimensions; however the environment in which it exists, naked space, is defined as infinite in dimensionality. Each of an EQ's dimensions of existence describes a unique piece of information, and each dimension is orthogonal to every other dimension of its existence. *Orthogonal* means at a right angle or perpendicular, thus the information in any one dimension is unaffected by the information in any other dimension that is orthogonal.

[B] The term **tantra** describes "a system of thought or set of doctrines or practices".

Each EQ has a unique set of **Features** (with upper case "F" in the lexicon of the ToT) that generically describes the information resident in a respective set of dimensions. A single Feature is associated with a single dimension. In this way, each slug of dimensional information in an EQ resolves from the nature of a single Feature in that EQ. The Features of an EQ resolve to the elements of an Experience in the relative condition. When speaking about an EQ we can, for example, say that in terms of the relative condition:

- o It is by nature formless; therefore it may have three Features that resolve to an Experience of a three-dimensional form.
- o It is by nature nonlocal; therefore it may have a Feature that can resolve to an Experience of a quantum change in position (see below).
- o It is by nature timeless; therefore it may have a Feature that can resolve to an Experience of a quantum unit of time (see below).
- o It is by nature emotionless; therefore it may have a Feature that can resolve to, for example, an Experience of different qualities of happiness—such as delight, ecstasy, humor, contentment, etc.; or of any other emotion.
- o It is by nature colorless; therefore it may have a Feature that can resolve to an Experience of color.

Note that these are only a few examples of an indefinitely large possible number of Features.

The Features describing a three-dimensional form are easy to conceive of—think of the standard three orthogonal directions in space (width, height and depth). When the number of dimensions is greater than three it becomes more difficult. For example: imagine the shape of a five-dimensional object (you probably can't do it!) Instead it's better to consider each of the orthogonal dimensions of an EQ to be degrees of freedom indicating different values, or qualities of information, and the information in one degree has no effect on any other degree.

Recall that EQ are definitely *not* the building blocks of the phenomenal universe in the manner that is typically explained in spacetime particle physics.

In the ToT, an Experience is always a noun, never a verb. An Experience and its associated Experience-object are part of the relative condition; and they resolve from the inter-play of EQ and Awareness, both of which are resident in the absolute condition. An Experience-object may be a phenomenal object or it may be a mental event.

THOUGHTS, CLOUDS AND RELATIVE SELVES

A **relative self** is a core element in the explanation of reality within the ToT. It has a unique and unusual set of attributes that require extensive explanation; hence the Pattern Chart can be a helpful reference for the pages that follow, as it lists the hierarchy of nomenclature, elements and patterns that comprise the ToT. An understanding of the described patterns will unfold as you read on. The elements of the chart describe the functional relationship between a great many concepts that, taken together, comprise major features of the ToT.

In the first column of the chart, see that the EQ are the basic quantum components of existence, and that they are comprised of **Features**, one for each relevant dimension of the EQ. A single EQ (in the absolute condition) may resolve to a single Experience (in the relative condition); and a "group of EQ" may resolve to a single **Thought**. A "set of EQ groups" or a "collection of EQ" is called a **Cloud**. A Cloud resolves to a relative self. The column on the right of the chart uses terms of the relative condition to describe the patterns that "show up" as the world around us; and in those terms a relative self is a *collection* of Experiences. [As a matter of nomenclature, a *group* of Experiences is a Thought.]

The term Experience is often used as a synonym for the Experience-object that it is associated with. This is not done to ignore the syncategorematic relationship between the Experience and the Experience-object; it's simply a matter of textual expediency. [Hopefully this tactic does not confuse the meaning and it tends to make the sentences easier to read.]

The chart tells us that a group of EQ resolves to a single Thought and that a set of Thoughts make up a relative self. It's interesting that the set of Thoughts (comprising a relative self) is always presented as a sequence.

The sequence of Thoughts, as a whole, is always instantaneous but individual Thoughts appear as if within the flow of time—from the vantage point of a relative self existing in spacetime. This illusion of time flow occurs in the instant of the present. In that instant a sequence of time-past Thoughts (memories) appears to have occurred predicate

93

to (leading up to) the present moment; . Thus the Experience of time flow is always a time-past Experience and the instant of the present is a sequence of memories. (More on this below.)

The concept of the instantaneous nature of the sequence of Thoughts that comprises a relative self is a primary feature of the ToT. It's described by the tenets of the **Instancy principle**.

THE INSTANCY PRINCIPLE

Within the ToT the "flow of time" is defined as an Experience-object and thus it is part of the Stor. (The flow time is a mental event, not a substantial object). The idea that we should accept only what we experience* or observe* for ourselves is a statement attributed to the Buddha's teaching. Generally such observation tells us we exist in the flow of time, but if you think about it deeply you will observe that the Experience of time flow is based on a memory of the past. For example: consider the motion of the second hand of a clock—you perceive* there is a flow of time because you remember the hand being in a different place a short time ago "in the past". The Experience of the perception occurs in the instant of the present; or we could say: "The Experience of the *memory* occurs in the instant of the present". Thus the Experience of time flow occurs in a single instant, i.e. the Experience is instantaneous. If this weren't true the Experience would have to be part of some sort of time flow in which the Experience is embedded, and then we would have to define a duration for that Experience, which would imply another (alternate?) definition of time flow.

The idea is that there is no true flow of time; instead there is only an instantaneous Experience that is "a memory of a duration." From that memory we naturally infer a false condition called "the flow of time"; but according to the ToT, the space and time universe (as we commonly know it) is actually a static set of memories, which truly exists only in the instantaneous moment of the present. This begs the question: How, then, can Experiences of substantial reality (as we know it) "continue to exist" in an illusory flow of time?

An understanding of the concept of a static universe is facilitated by a small story.

> Long, long ago a very powerful magician was engaged in a great war with his brother leading the opposing forces. The magician won the war and gained complete control over his brother's life.

94

He said to his brother: "I am going to take your life; but because you are my brother I will not take all of it. I will leave you with a single instant in which to be alive. In that Instant, you will have, first, all of the memories of having lived a full and interesting life; and second, the idea that you will continue to be alive for some (indefinite) time to come. These two concepts will, of course, give you the idea that time is still flowing (but it won't be)."

The brother said: "When will my moment of existence occur?"

The magician replied: "It already has; and it includes this explanation."[c]

We exist in the instant of the "now"—which has no duration and is solely comprised of the static set memories. Usually included in that set of memories is the idea of multiple, possible time-future Experiences [i.e. Experiences "yet to come"].

Together, the memories of time past and memories of expectations of what is yet to come make up the illusion of the flow of time. This group of Experiences in memory is called a relative self and it is Instantaneous. Every sentient being is a relative self, therefore at the instant of the present there are as many relative selves as there are living beings. This is a very large number (considering all living beings, not just humans); and it is with respect to only a single instant!

This description of the set of single instants comprising memory is the lesser part of the Instancy principle, because there is a bigger Instant.

More precisely, the term **instant** (w/ lower case "i") applies to every remembered instant in time-past and every postulated instant in time-future. As a counterpoint, the term **Instant** (w/ upper case "I") applies to the great meta-Instant of the moment of the "now". The Instant is the containing package holding all of the lesser instants. Thus there are always multiple examples of instants, but there is only one Instant.

All understandings of the meaning of the term indicating the "great meta-instant" (the Instant) are written with

---

[c] As I understand it, the background temporal concept alluded to in this story is an interpretation of the Tibetan word *lundrub*—in that it will instantly manifest *any* aspect of apparent reality in a single, non-duel moment of the Now.

95

an upper case I. When the word refers to a lesser, single instant, it's written normally, in lower case. This terminology is held from this point forward.

An Instantaneous collection of instants may be a difficult concept to initially accept; and it is made even more difficult when you recall that each Instant contains a full collection of all beings (relative selves) that are alive. This viewpoint, of course mandates that existence be defined as simply "in the moment"; and the moment must be defined as with zero time duration[D]—i.e. existence is ultimately nontemporal in nature.

The ToT, with axiomatic pragmatism, describes existence in this way, and thus defines the Instancy principle.

A Dzogchen practitioner may find the Instancy principle interesting in light of its effective description of an unchangeable universe. This of course is a viewpoint had from a very grand overview. More on this below.

AN INFORMATION PACKAGE

Imagine a relative self composed of a set of Thoughts that amount to the process of walking from point A to point B. Imagine the moment of the halfway position (between point A and point B). At that instant the relative self may contain the Experiences of having taken the most recent few steps or (possibly) the Experience of the expectation of taking the next few steps. All of these Experiences will be part of a memory describing the relative self at the moment of the halfway point.

Experiences have an interesting description in the ToT. A relative self (an individual) is defined as not really *having* Experiences; instead he/she *is* the Experiences. The Experiences are grouped into unique information sets peculiar to each relative self. Thus a relative self is solely comprised of information.

To take this a bit further: in the ToT a memory is an Experience, therefore, it follows that an individual doesn't really *have* memories; instead the relative self *is comprised of* the memories. Thus a relative self (an individual in terms of the relative condition) is solely an information

---

[D] This is a fine example of Ockham's razor, from William of Ockham (c. 1287 – 1347), a principle of economy used in logic and problem-solving. It states that among competing hypotheses, the hypothesis with the fewest assumptions should be selected. Wikipedia.

package. "Self-awareness*" is a mental event (an Experience) and part of the package. Awareness—which is an element of the absolute condition—is *not* part of the package. The relative self is an illusion, and an illusion cannot have awareness. Instead the relative self is simply an information package.

You are the information!

In the ToT, a relative self is merely an Instantaneous information package. The belief in an ego or "self" is an Experience and an element in the information package making up the relative self.

In the relative condition Experiences, in the guise of the Experience of a memory, appear to be sequential, spontaneous and self-arising—existing within the flow of time. In terms of the absolute condition all of the associated EQ and EQ groups are defined as existing simultaneously.

Prosaically a person *is* their memories; they do not *hold* their memories. This is an important feature of the ToT.

CLOUDS

The relative self often contains an Experience of a "self" that appears to be an entity existing within the flow of time and is apparently the seat of awareness* that perceives the phenomenal universe and mental events. However, the "self" is not the true seat of awareness*. It is simply another Experience which is a part of the collection of Experiences comprising the relative self.

The apparent "realness" of all of reality is an illusion—it is only a great collection of Experiences. The phenomenal world is an illusion. Space is an illusion. Time is an illusion. Mental events are an illusion. The physical laws describing the universe are not what they appear to be. All of these concepts are instead expressions of pattern relationships between quanta of a much more basic genitive nature. In the most fundamental fashion, these concepts are not to be thought of as relationships between real objects, mental events, and/or phenomena. They are instead patterns of math objects which have no substance. These patterns are called **Clouds**.

97

A Cloud is a collection of EQ that resolves to a single relative self existing within the apparent flow of time in a single universe.[E] However, if we look at it from a different angle we can see that Clouds can overlap and produce interesting results. Consider a single Cloud that resolves to an individual named Fred and another Cloud that resolves to a second person named Alice. We are now talking about multiple Clouds that resolve to separate beings.

> A Cloud is comprised of a collection of EQ that resolves to Experiences of both a being's body and personality; and to Experiences of external objects and events.

Consider a situation where Fred's Cloud and Alice's Cloud overlap and share the same EQ for the environment, but they do not share EQ that resolve to either's body and/or personalities. In this case, the shared EQ resolve to external objects and/or events. If two beings are (for example) looking at the same tree or hearing the same violin play, then the shared information may be "very similar;" but the information does not reflect the body or personality of the beings represented by each Cloud. In this way, different relative selves may be comprised of nearly the same Experiences of external objects or events—the differences could be expressed as due to slightly different Features for the same EQ. Remember; a relative self is ultimately a "point of view" had by Awareness. It has no substantial reality or awareness* of its own.

A further example of shared Clouds: A group of people are attending a party. At any given instant, each individual will be defined as a unique relative self, and each will be describable by different collections of Experiences. Some may have a memory of a long ago past event, some may have a consideration about the surroundings (*i.e.* the bright color of a wall, etc.) and others may have a consideration of some time-future event such as "when will the food arrive?" All of the people (relative selves) are represented by a collection of Experiences indicating similar surroundings (the room) but they are also represented by Experiences of different memories, associated perceptions*, or possible futures. In this way, some of the EQ are shared (concerning the room) and some may not be shared (individual physical bodies, memories, and/or considerations about the future); however, each person in the room is represented by his or her Experiences simultaneously, in the

---

[E] The ToT contains multiple universes.

same Instant. This Instantaneous representation is each person's unique relative self, and it is a Cloud in the absolute condition.

> We believe we are in a body and separate from
> one another… isn't that absurd?
>
> ~ Nancy Cramer[F]

With respect to any single Cloud, other Clouds may be very similar but they will never be the same, because by definition a Cloud is a virtual concept that encompasses a *unique* collection of EQ. Two Clouds may include many of the same EQ, but there will always be some differences. Recall that EQ are axiomatically declared to be the most elementary description of existence. The EQ simply exist; and a Cloud is a virtual construct or pattern that lies over a very small portion of the total grand array of EQ existing in naked space.

There are, of course, many possible patterns; however the patterns that are of specific interest are the patterns that constitute the Clouds of EQ that resolve to a relative self; and there are only a few patterns that do this. Conceptually the vast (emphasize *vast*) majority of the EQ patterns are untenable—that is, with respect to the human condition they are noise. Most patterns are not of a sufficient complexity and coherence of information to resolve to a functional relative self and be called a Cloud.

> Imagine an ox's yoke adrift on a vast ocean, and a
> turtle happens to poke its head through the hole. This is
> how rare and extraordinary it is to be born a human being.
>
> ~ Longchenpa [G]

The total distribution of EQ can be envisioned as an enormous chaotic system. Within the chaos there are only a small number of EQ which will resolve to coherent information sets. These sets are called Clouds; and by definition a Cloud *always* resolves to what is termed to be a sentient being (a relative self) in the relative condition. This is axiomatic.

Think of each of these Clouds as an "island of certainty" within an overall chaos of the distribution of EQ. This

---

[F] Nancy Cramer is a philosopher friend who lived in Pahoa, Hawaii when she made this statement.
[G] Longchenpa. He was a major teacher and Dzogchen master in the Nyingma school of Tibetan Buddhism; who lived in the first part of the 14th century, 1308–1364.

concept and terminology stems from the work of Ilya Prigo-gine.[66]

A Cloud *always* resolves to a sentient being within the V.1 uni-verse. This is crucial to an understanding of the illusory nature of the relative condition. In terms of the relative condition, it is only a sentient being (a relative self) that is the information set Parsed by Awareness; because it is only a relative self that contains the Experience of "self-awareness", and thus can (apparently) be cognizant* of reality. It's a "chicken or egg" situation. Prosaically… it is only a sentient being that can consider* itself to be alive* and able* to be aware* of and interact* with the universe it believes* it inhabits*, and thus it is only for a sentient being that the universe may exist*.

Within the nomenclature of the ToT, any reference to the term Cloud indicates that it is a coherent pattern of EQ that resolves to a collection of Experiences that function as a relative self.

THE PROXIMITY PRINCIPLE

In the ToT, the definition of the term **proximate** and its adverb **proximity** are given with respect to the absolute condition. This is a virtual construct that describes nuances of multiple EQ patterns. The term "proximity" is a statement of the number of EQ Features that are shared between two Clouds, not a statement of location. Recall that Clouds are patterns of EQ that overlap and consequently may resolve to similar Experiences in different relative selves. Thus a relative self is considered to be proximate to another relative self if their associated EQ Clouds are overlapping and share EQ. This is the **proximity principle**.

A value of proximity is always a positive integer or zero. A value of zero for the proximity of two Clouds, means that no EQ are shared. A value of 9, for example, means that nine EQ are shared. The concept of sharing is with respect to the information associated with a certain dimension (*i.e.* Feature). A shared Feature means that a *version* of the respective potential information is shared.

The value of proximity between two Clouds is directly related to the number of shared EQ populating the two Clouds. The term "shared" is to be understood as the sharing of EQ that produce essen-tially the same Experience, even though the Experience according to each relative self will be slightly different. For example, two people may have an Experience of the same tree from slightly different angles, or they may both have an Experience of a feeling of security from having the same type of insurance policy. In each case the Feature (degree of freedom) resolving to the "shared" Experience is identical but the information in that dimensional package may vary. In the case of the tree, each person has a different viewpoint; and in the case of the feeling of security, the personal history relating to financial security needs may be different.

Therefore, with respect to a certain dimension, the value of proximity between two associated Clouds is a function of the number of Features within the EQ Clouds that are shared between the Clouds. The greatest value for proximity between the Clouds would indicate that one less than the total number of EQ in the smaller of the two Clouds is shared.

....

What does the proximity principle look like in terms of the relative condition?

In the mid-1990s I visited Ulan Bator, the capital of Mongolia, to attend a retreat with Chögyal Namkhai Norbu. At one point we were hosted by Doliin Kandro Suren, an elderly Buddhist healer, *Chöd* practitioner and spiritual guide for thousands of people in Mongolia and Russia. She was 83 years old when we met and she had been a practitioner (more or less) through all of the 70 or so years of the Mongolian Communist regime. [H]

> The *Chöd* is a spiritual practice found primarily in Tibetan Buddhism. Also known as "Cutting Through the Ego," the practice is based on the Prajñāpāramitā or "Perfection of Wisdom" sutras which expound the "emptiness" concept.

She had invited a few of us to visit her home located in a small village about 50 kilometers outside of the city. We drove out across the green rolling steppe, a vast, treeless, grassy expanse of land that covers most of Mongolia. It's like an ocean without water. The Mongolians appear to have a relationship with the land akin to that of the Native Americans. It was explained to me that the steppe has never been "owned" by anyone in the sense of being real estate. I don't know what modern times will bring, but it appears that for Mongolians, the concept of owning the steppe has never been especially viable in terms of their reality map.

[H] A documentary video about Doliin Kandro Suren was being made at the time. See: *Where the Eagles Fly,* (1998).

Doliin Kandro Suren's home was a large yurt constructed in traditional fashion with inch-thick felt hand made from the hair of local horses. Our little group was treated to a party after which she led a *chöd* practice. She was dressed in a traditional Mongolian long red robe. She also wore a large headdress that was purportedly made out of the hair from Genghis Khan's favorite consort (who was considered to be an emanation of the goddess Tara). Those who may be familiar with the *chöd* practice understand that it involves lots of loud recitation, horn blowing, shouts and drum beating throughout. At different times, as we continued with the practice, Doliin Kandro would drink a small amount of vodka, eat a lump of brown sugar, or take a bit of tobacco snuff. She was amazingly robust for someone her age.

Doliin Kandro Suren (1910-1995)[67]

When we had finished the practice, I moved closer to her to say thank you. She had a compassionate and happy presence. As she motioned me even closer she whispered into my ear, giving me a mantra— it's a small ritual that many lamas do. The exchange was very private; no one else could hear what was said. This was a very personal incident; however the mantra was one that I had heard many times before, albeit without the Mongolian accent.

102

I thought: "why did she whisper it? The words of the mantra are not secret." Sometime later I understood that it was a "secret" between Doliin Kandro and me. It was a connection with her and a way to remember her presence. In terms of the ToT, I would say that she used this small ritual of the whisper to create and/or enhance the proximity between the Experiences that were Doliin Kandro and (subsequently*) Experiences that would be "myself"[1] in the great pattern of **karmic links** at (what appeared to be) some point in time-future.

KARMA AND MATRIX LINKS

As described earlier, karma simply deals with what is. Karma does not have a value of its own. There is not an intrinsically "good" or intrinsically "bad" karma. In terms of the relative self, karma may be seen as the sum of all that an individual has done. Sometimes the word is roughly translated as "action*." From this viewpoint, karma is very much a verb that describes the concept of a continuation of things happening because of relationships over time.

In the general waft of Buddhist thought there is the often-heard concept of "karma, cause and effect" which is described as a basic principle. This might be seen as similar in some ways to Newton's principle that every action produces an equal and opposite reaction (karma however, is thought to produce a *like* reaction). Every time we think or do something, we create a cause, which in time will bear its corresponding effects; and those effects produce more karma which in turn leads to another cause; and so on indefinitely. This is the cyclical repetition of cause and effect that is called *samsara*—which is displayed as the on-going conceptual universe including birth and reincarnation for indefinite amounts of time (in terms of the relative condition). This is a straightforward, easy to understand explanation that "makes sense" in terms of an understanding based on a background concept of a flow of time.

Another view of karma appears in esoteric Buddhist thought where the non-temporal condition of reality is promoted. From this view, karma can be thought of as a static pattern of associations that exists between the karmic visions of many beings. Translating this into the terms of the ToT we can say that: what some Buddhist thinkers call karma, can be described as an intertwinglarity[J] of links within an array of

---

[I] The term "myself" means a proximate Cloud that resolves to a relative *self* that lay in a time-future position of the apparent flow of time. More on this below.
[J] **Intertwingle**, see next section.

EQ Clouds. A grand overview of these links is expressed as a **Matrix** (w/ upper case "M"). It's a term that has a special meaning in the ToT.

To restate: In the ToT the **Matrix links** and the linking pattern in general reflect an intertwingularity of information that is shared between relative selves; and the amount of sharing is an expression of proximity between the elements of the Matrix.

This definition (within the ToT) follows an expression of karma as described in esoteric Buddhist thought. We will discover later that, according to the ToT, these linking patterns manifest as the oExperience commonly described as "compassion."

INTERTWINGLED INFORMATION & TED NELSON

Ted Nelson coined the word **intertwingle**[K] and used it in his book *Computer Lib/Dream Machines* (Nelson: 1974). He wrote:

Ted Nelson, PhD (1937--)[68]
Ted Nelson gives a presentation on Project Xanadu for the *SuperHappyDevHouse* at *The Tech Museum of Innovation*, San Jose, California, February, 2011.

[K] **Intertwingle** is a portmanteau word invented by Ted Nelson to express the complexity of interrelations in human knowledge.

EVERYTHING IS DEEPLY INTERTWINGLED. In an important sense there are no "subjects" at all; there is only all knowledge, since the cross-connections among the myriad topics of this world simply cannot be divided up neatly.

The following comment was added in the revised edition (Nelson: 1987):

Hierarchical and sequential structures, especially popular since Gutenberg, are usually forced and artificial. Intertwingularity is not generally acknowledged—people keep pretending they can make things hierarchical, categorizable and sequential when they can't.

I worked for Ted in the early 1990s managing his small video-editing studio. At the time, Ted was developing a computer-based network and interface called Xanadu that sought to elucidate the intertwingled aspects of human knowledge. Xanadu was commercially unsuccessful at that time but was in many ways similar to the World Wide Web—which was said to be "invented" a short time later by Tim Berners-Lee. However I and many others consider Ted to be the true originator of the Web, because it appears that his was the genius upon which the philosophical framework of the World Wide Web is based.

Ted is not in agreement with some of the features of the Web in its present incarnation. For example, Ted writes:

The "Browser" is an extremely silly concept—a window for looking sequentially at a large parallel structure. It does not show this structure in a useful way.

The Xanadu® project did not "fail to invent HTML."
HTML is precisely what we were trying to PREVENT!
~ Ted Nelson (1999)

It was a unique experience* managing Ted's video-editing studio. The studio was set up in a room below the main deck on a houseboat docked at the Gate #5 Marina in Sausalito, California. Our studio had one of the first Avid nonlinear video editing setups. It was based on early Macintosh computer hardware. At the time, extensive hard drive space was unavailable, and we used magneto-optical drives for media storage (incredibly slow!). The editing studio had high windows, and occasionally kayaks would cruise by with the paddlers looking down at us as we worked. We partied often: If six people or so climbed up onto the flat houseboat roof, and together walked quickly side to side across the beam of the boat, we could get the whole thing rocking—which made the main deck a genuinely dynamic place for dancing.

THE ANTHROPIC PRINCIPLE

Contemporary physics tells us that the phenomenal universe as we encounter it is very special. It has many stars neatly collected into galaxies giving off starlight; it has planets orbiting many of the stars; and it has the Earth that has its own star (the sun) set at just the right distance so as to continuously provide the right amount of radiation for the support of extremely complex molecules and life forms. In terms of the physical sciences, it's all an extremely delicate balance of mass and energy, and that only a very limited set of unique initial conditions would allow the universe to be as it is. In fact, what we have seems quite improbable considering the enormous variety of initial conditions that could have shown up after the Big Bang. A much more probable universe would have been any one of a great number of others, all of which would be boring sameness or some sort of great jumbled chaos.[69]

In terms of probability it is unusual and improbable that we exist at all in the cosmos. This coming together of apparent probabilities is called the anthropic principle in standard nomenclature.

> The Oxford Dictionary states that the anthropic principle is: "the cosmological principle that theories of the universe are constrained by the necessity to allow human existence."[70]

This is not the definition according to the ToT. In the lexicon of the ToT, the **Anthropic principle** (note capitalization) simply states that in the instant of the present "a relative self contains the Experience of being who he/she appears to be, in the context of what is remembered." This is a very simple principle. At the instant this is being read, you (the reader) are the collection of Experiences of being who you are, in the context of what you (apparently) remember.

Simply stated, in the ToT the Anthropic principle means:

> "We see the world as we remember it to be."

> We don't actually "see" reality around us—in this statement it would be more appropriate to replace the verb "to see" with the verb "to be"; and thus the statement would become: "we are the world as we remember it to be", but

this does not read as well. Also, any Experience of a probable future is an element of memory.

The ToT's Anthropic principle might be understood as an expression of what some psychiatrists call "projection;" however, such an understanding is based on the concept of the point of awareness* of the "self" being within the relative condition and within a flow of time.

The Anthropic principle asserts that the universe attends to certain principles given that it is described in terms of the human condition—the situation in which we believe ourselves to exist. Thus it relates to the relative condition because the concept of the flow of time (time-past and time-future) is implicit in the Experiences that imply existence*.

V.1 SHARED UNIVERSES

The ToT also allows for the existence of Experiences within simultaneously parallel universes within a multiverse (you will discover this as you read further)—provided beings somehow exist in them.

From the apparent viewpoint of the relative self, the version of the universe now in play is the version where each of us (each unique, instantaneous relative self) is synchronized with all other relative selves in this version; and each Experience of reality is simultaneous with all others in the same Instant. This is also the version of the universe in which I wrote this book, and you, the reader, are reading it. In essence we are sharing this universe.

In the lexicon of the ToT, a shared version of the universe that we can talk about and have the Experience of existing in is called Version V.1 (or simply V.1). V.1 labels the apparent **shared universe** around us at the instant of "now." It is shared by all beings appearing to exist in that instant; and the designation is with respect to those individuals.

A counter point to a shared universe is the concept of a **solo universe**—which is the universe experienced* only in terms of the viewpoint of a single relative self; more on this below.

There may be other three-dimensional shared universes and it may also be possible to be "alive" in a universe that does not include the restraints imposed by the geometry of the ToT (more about this in Part II). However, none of those versions are now in play according to you, the reader. What *is* now in play is V.1, and all of us who have an Experience of reading these words are in V.1 (as well as many others who aren't reading). We know this is V.1 because we (apparently) exist. This is an exposition of the Anthropic principle according to the ToT.[71]

The logic of the ToT contends that the V.1 cannot be explained within the contextual boundaries of space and time. Instead the explanation must be given using conceptualizations that are functionally not bound by the dimensional and temporal constraints of the universe as we know it; *i.e.* not bound by the constraints of spacetime physics. The ToT attempts to explain the relative condition in this fashion.

LINKING PATTERNS

Scientists believe they are autonomously probing the physical universe; however according to the ToT, this is not the case. Instead, the scientists themselves simply reflect a minor pattern in a Matrix of EQ that, in a large part, resolves to the V.1 shared universe. V.1 resolves from of a great collection of patterns that are *each relative selves*, which are individually comprised of Experiences of the substantial world apparently interacting within itself in a sea of associated mental events.

Modern science describes the phenomenal universe with beautiful, well-tested laws that indicate the basic natural physical condition of our universe. The ToT describes these laws as representations of a linking schema within the Matrix. These linking patterns can also be understood as an exposition of karma—thus reflecting the interconnectedness of all beings and information. This concept is similar to what is described by certain understandings in Buddhism.

> All which is, is as a reflection, clear, limpid and pure…
> without definition and without explanation…
> with a cause, always coming from karma.
> The essence is without dualism and without fixity.
> This is all that exists. Know this!
> ~Attributed to Buddha Shakyamuni

To more clearly understand this, recall that:

o   The Matrix is an unchanging, grossly multi-dimensional array of warps in the naked space of the absolute condition.

o   In the ToT the linking patterns, which describe karma, coincidentally describes coherent information sets that are part of a Cloud.

o   A Cloud resolves to a relative self, in the relative condition.

Therefore patterns of warps (in the absolute condition) resolve to information (in the relative condition); and that information always manifests as an Experience and is always part of a relative self. The question then arises: What is the nature of the Experience that resolves from the *overall* linking pattern described as karma?

Karma itself is a philosophical concept—on the face of it, there is no associated Experience, yet it is described by a pattern of warps. According to the tenets of the ToT, if it's a pattern within a Cloud, it should resolve to some sort of Experience within a relative self. According to the ToT the Experience that resolves from the linking pattern can be either one of two types, depending on the viewpoint: awareness*, or Awareness.

1.   With respect to awareness* it's an Experience in the context of spacetime; *i.e.* couched in terms of the flow of time.   If this is the case the linking patterns will resolve to an Experience-object of *samsara*—continuing on indefinitely, across many lifetimes.

2.   With respect to Awareness it's an Experience in the context of the Matrix, *i.e.* an overview of the linking patterns. If this is the case the linking patterns will resolve to an Experience-object of **compassion**—a mental event.

The term "karma" labels the linking pattern and the terms "*samsara*" and "compassion" labels the Experience-object resolving from the pattern.

There will be more about this special type of Experience explained in Part II.

COMPASSION

In terms of the ToT the Experience of compassion, is much greater than, for example, feeling sorry for a hungry puppy. In esoteric Eastern thought it's sometimes called the "great compassion"[72], and it remains as the seminal core of the Experience of a heartfelt connectedness with all beings.

According to the ToT: compassion is an expression of the intertwining, overlapping, intermingling (nontemporal) aspects of the myriad of interrelationships among all instances of EQ in the context of a Cloud. It is also closely associated with the philosophical aspect of "c" (the velocity of light) being an absolute speed limit within the relative condition (more about this below).

According to Buddhism, compassion or **big-heartedness**[L], (in Tibetan *changchub*) is naturally accorded to (and for) all beings who believe the relative self is real and who therefore attempt to end their suffering with the approach of moving toward what is seen as good, or avoiding what is seen as bad. In this way the Experience of compassion is naturally one of empathy for the predicament of beings trying to deal with pain and suffering in an ineffectual fashion.

Milarepa (1052-1135 CE) [73]

Jetsun Milarepa is one of Tibet's most famous yogis. The above Bhutanese painted thangka of Milarepa, Late 19th-early 20th century, resides in the Dhodeydrag Gonpa, Thimphu, Bhutan.

If a person eliminates all of the attachments and clinging to the concept that the *"self"* or the *"ego"* is the seat of awareness*, then what is left is emptiness—which resolves to the self-arising realization that there is a connection between all beings, and that connection is the Experience

---

[L] The Tibetan word for "compassion" is sometime translated as "big-heartedness." [This information from a conversation with Lama Wangdor Rinpoche.]

of compassion*. This concept is prominent in Buddhist teachings. Milarepa, a renowned Buddhist teacher in old Tibet, said it very well.

> Know emptiness.
> Know compassion.
> ~Milarepa

Atisa, another famous Buddhist teacher, helped establish the Sarma lineage of Buddhism in Tibet during the first part of the 11th century.

> The supreme goal of the teachings is the emptiness whose essence is compassion.
> ~ Atisa

Once, in a conversation with Grandfather Semu Huaute, I asked him if he was going to give his teaching to someone else before he passed on. [Here I paraphrase from memory] He said he would like to but couldn't because he hadn't met anyone who had fully experienced the universal pain being existing in human-kind and all other beings.

He didn't express his feelings in terms of what the ToT calls compassion, but that is what he appeared to say, to my understanding.

It appears Semu Huaute, Atisa, Milarepa, the Buddha and others found (the concept the ToT calls) compassion to be a self-evident facet of Totality. In terms of the ToT the Experience of compassion naturally manifests as an emanation of the linking pattern between the EQ resulting from warps in naked space. This description follows the lead of Buddhist logic where there is an oft-mentioned, difficult to realize association between emptiness and compassion.

REPLETE WITH EMPTINESS

With respect to a relative self, there is often the possibility of an Experience of an enormous amount of space, such as looking out into a clear night sky. It is a concept of indefinitely large universe that (apparently) has existed and will continue to exist across a huge amount of time. It's a concept that helps provide the background fabric of the reality associated with a relative self—which is the Experience of: "continually being enmeshed in a flow of spacetime".

Physics talks about the dimensions of reality and describes spacetime as a four dimensional concept; one dimension of time and three dimensions of space. Consider (what appears to be) the three dimensions of space around us.

How do we think of space? Generally it's the size of objects or the distance between them. We subjectively define the boundaries of the space around us, such as: the size of a room, of a back yard, of the distance to the horizon from a beach etc. Imagine even a greater space, perhaps the amount traversed after traveling one hour in a jetliner? Imagine being on the space station orbiting the earth; on the moon; one light year out from the Sun. How about a vantage point that provides a view of the entire Milky Way galaxy, and so on.

Each of these descriptive visions of space relies on the objects occupying the space. None of the visions are a description of the space itself—which is called *naked space* in the ToT. Recall that naked space has no associated information; it can't be described by itself.

> The naked space found in the ToT is axiomatically defined as being comprised of an infinite number of dimensions, not just the three described here. Naked space is nontemporal (unchangeable) in nature and appears to be analogous to the Void described in Buddhism, which is figuratively replete with "emptiness".
>
> In the *Dzogchen* teaching emptiness is the experience* of the absence of an I or self in all phenomena. It corresponds to the absolute truth of the Mahayana Sutra. At a relative level, everything manifests, but the true nature of every aspect of the reality of phenomena is emptiness.

In terms of normal reality we know that we can define substantial, three-dimensional objects using geometry (they might look like a machine shop CAD[M] drawing.) Then, with another dimension, a fourth, we can easily add time to the group (the drawing might be animated and change shape as we watch the 4D CAD file run on a computer screen.) We also know that geometry is mathematics—thus we have defined a four-dimension mathematical object with the animation. With four dimensions the mathematical objects can be described as resting in "spacetime"—which is the way we (typically) describe the experience* of solid reality around us.

In terms of the ToT a mathematical object also represents an Experience. We can follow the logic of the ToT further and allow for

---

[M] The acronym "CAD" refers to the term "computer assisted drafting".

an indefinite number of more dimensions for expressing information. When we do this we can add mental events to the group of Experiences we are considering. All of these Experiences, from the four-dimensional spacetime substantial objects, to the seriously multi-dimensional representation of mental events, can be described with mathematical objects—and a super-set of those objects together can be figuratively laid onto to a "playing field" of naked space to create a grand analog representing all of reality.

The super-set of mathematical objects is finite in number because it appears that reality *is not* infinite. The naked space upon which the objects are laid *is* infinite in dimensionality and non-local in nature. These two tenets are axiomatic in the ToT.

For me the idea of laying geometries (mathematical objects) onto empty space is a logical representation of the Buddhist *Dzogchen* teaching, because in the ToT *all* such objects are a pure representation of the EQ of the absolute condition. Thus the logical essence of what you are reading may be around two thousand or more years old.

A modern description using mathematical nomenclature came forth in the middle of the 19th century in Europe with the work of the mathematician Bernard Riemann. It's the opening topic of Part II.

PART II

PHYSICS OF THE MIND
Traversing the Shapes of Experience

Perception unfolding as a grand illusion; and
thought forms, framed as geometry.

2.1 - GEOMETRY

In modern times the mathematical concept of laying geometries onto space arguably began with a lecture given in Germany in the middle of the 19th century. In 1854 a young mathematician named Bernard Riemann gave a lecture to the public and faculty of the University of Göttingen near Hanover, Germany. Riemann was somewhat shy but he was urged to give the lecture by his faculty advisor, the famous mathematician Carl Friedrich Gauss.

The lecture was called a "habilitation" lecture and was required in order to become a professor at the university. Such lectures had been a tradition for hundreds of years.

RIEMANN'S HABILITATION LECTURE

Riemann's lecture was entitled *On the Foundations that Underlie Geometry*. Among other things, the lecture was probably the first public instance where space was distinguished from geometry (in Western culture). Riemann described geometry as an additional structure that could be laid onto a space. He was also the first to suggest using dimensions higher than merely three or four in order to describe reality. Some of his work allowed the later development of general relativity.[74]

The idea that geometry and space are separate concepts can be described by an example employing a large empty aquarium and some cooking utensils (a flat griddle and a rounded Chinese style wok). Imagine placing the griddle into the space defined by the aquarium and holding it in the center of that space. The surface of the griddle defines a certain two-dimensional flat plane within the three-dimensional space of the aquarium. The flat plane has a two-dimensional geometry defined by sets of coordinates that are couplets, where an "X" value and a "Y" value will define any point on the plane (X, Y).

Bernhard Riemann in 1863 (1826-1866)[75]

It appears that ancient Buddhists (or more likely the Buddha himself) may have been the first to describe space as separate from the multi-dimensional qualities that may define it. Therefore it could be that unknown to Riemann, a conceptual form of his ideas was originally described publicly several thousand years earlier, albeit without the mathematics as we know it.

In terms of the ToT the flat plane of the griddle surface is a two-dimensional geometry laid onto a background of naked space—if we discount any concept of the aquarium and consider the background space to contain no information other than the flat plane. The geometry of the griddle is called *Euclidian* geometry[A] because it's "flat".

Now, take the wok and its rounded surface. Imagine placing the wok into the space defined by the aquarium. The geometry that is the

---

[A] **Euclidian geometry** is named after the Ancient Greek mathematician Euclid of Alexandria.

117

wok's rounded surface is also defined by two dimensions, but this surface is called *non-Euclidean* (it's not flat). If we extended the wok's surface in each direction as far as it can go it would bend around and run into itself. We would end up with a sphere in the aquarium (if we maintain the curvature and if the aquarium is large enough). The surface of the sphere would have no edges and be finite in size.

The area of the surface of a sphere is given by the formula: $A = 4\pi r^2$.

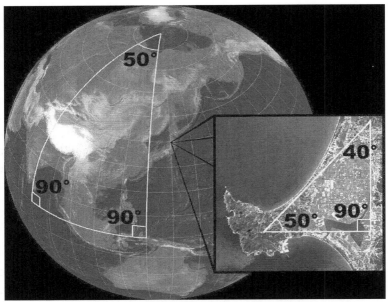

Diagram of Non-Euclidian Geometry

On the surface of a sphere, the sum of the angles of a triangle is not equal to 180°, but locally the laws of the Euclidean geometry are good approximations. In a small triangle on the face of the earth, the sum of the angles is very nearly 180°.[76]

Consider the surface of the Earth as it is generally thought of—a global map that is the surface of a sphere. Two-dimensional non-Euclidean geometry will basically describe it. We measure distances on the Earth's surface two-dimensionally. Typically, we would say that Auckland, New Zealand is 12,500 miles from Madrid, Spain. We would say this because the Earth is (approximately) 25,000 miles in circumference and the two locations are on opposite sides of the planet; therefore they

118

are said to be 12,500 miles apart. However, the two are actually only about 8,000 miles apart if we measure the locations as antipodes—through the center of the planet. But we don't. We consider the surface as extending directionally: north and south, and east and west. We can describe the surface of the wok in a similar two-dimensional fashion.

The surface of both the griddle and wok can be described as two-dimensional; respectively with Euclidian and non-Euclidian geometry. When we place the objects into the aquarium, we will have defined two different, two-dimensional geometries within the three-dimensional space of the aquarium.

The surface of the griddle is called a plane, and the surface of the wok is called a *manifold* (call it the "wok-manifold" in this instance.) We can also say that the curved surface of the wok-manifold has a **positive curvature**. This means that it could, if extended, wrap around to form a sphere. In this way, the extended wok-manifold would become spherical and then be called a **2-sphere** because its *surface* is described by two dimensions. The term 2-sphere defines only the surface of the manifold, not the dimensionality of the interior; which is a three-dimensional volume. Thus, the non-Euclidian geometry of the 2-sphere requires a three-dimensional volume of space in which to exist (which, in the above example, is the inner volume of the aquarium).

Any point on the surface of the wok-manifold can be defined by a set of coordinates (couplets), similar to those associated with the surface of the earth (longitude and latitude).

We have now defined two different geometries within the same space and could define many more geometries within the aquarium. For example, different woks with different radii of curvature—a deep wok or a shallow wok, or perhaps a wok with a dent in it. This concept of geometry being separate from the space in which it exists is what Riemann defined mathematically. However, Riemann defined it in such a way that it applied to all possible dimensions. To use the framework of the above example we would say that his aquariums were not just three-dimensional, but were built using a number of dimensions we can't conceive of in terms of life on earth. They could have been four, five, six or indefinitely more dimensions in scope. The cookware that Riemann would have immersed in these aquariums would have been constructed with equally rich dimensionalities. However, as we can see from the above example, the geometry defining the surface of non-Euclidian (spherical) cookware will always have—at least one dimension less than the space in which it is immersed. This is important to remember.

> It's interesting to note that all of the points defining the surface of the plane, the surface of the wok-manifold or the surface of *any* greater dimensional manifold can be described with a set of binary numbers (ones and zeros)—this is ultimately the nature of information.

N-MANIFOLDS

In the ToT substantial objects and mental events are both described as geometric mathematical objects (manifolds) of various dimensionalities. In the ToT manifolds describe information (ultimately zeros and ones). You can think of them as a graph or chart of many dimensions, not just the two dimensions of X and Y found in a typical graph. The manifolds resolve from patterns of EQ in the absolute condition and become information in the relative condition represented as an Experience/Experience-object pair. This indicates a one-to-one equivalency between the terminology of a manifold and that of its corresponding Experience/Experience-object pair. In terms of the illusory nature of the relative condition, they are both virtual constructs.

As a matter of terminology, In the ToT the term **n-manifold** is be used to describe a geometry of a unknown number of dimensions, where "n" indicates the number of dimensions involved. For example: a 2-sphere is a **2-manifold**. Recall that a 2-sphere has a two-dimensional surface.

In the ToT an n-manifold is information (describing an Experience) virtually "laid onto" ever-present naked space. Thus a relative condition concept is virtually laid onto the absolute condition of naked space. This statement is a bit different that how some Buddhists might say it.

> An interesting practice is to envision being immersed in, and completely surrounded by naked space—space that is absolutely clear of any information what-so-ever. At the same time try and "see" the substantial elements of reality as laid into the naked space. As this is done the elements describe locations, distances, qualities etc. that are separate from the clarity of the naked space.

The Experience-objects associated with the manifolds appear as reality in the relative condition. Consider an Experience-object: the surface of a beach ball (a 2-manifold) for example. We could say that: as the 2-manifold folds around onto itself making the surface border-less, it subtends a volume of naked space; but any apparent volume (distance and/or shape) of naked space that it subtends is defined by the information in the geometry itself. Without the geometry, the naked space has no implicit volume (distance or shape) of its own. Thus the dimensionality and the volume is not that of the naked space; instead it is the information carried by the manifolds that are laid onto it.

The various dimensions and volumes of naked space described by a manifold are termed to be the manifold's **configuration space.**

> In classical mechanics, the *configuration space* is the space of possible positions that a physical system may attain... The configuration space of a typical system has the structure of a manifold....[77]

In the realm of space and time, our worldly substantial environment, the most commonly experienced* manifolds are **2-manifolds** and **3-manifolds**

> The surface of the beach ball is a good example of an experience* of a 2-manifold. Understand that the surface of a 2-manifold is a two-dimensional *surface*, the surface of a 3-manifold (and higher dimensional manifolds) is a *hypersurface*. The hypersurface of a 3-manifold is three dimensional in nature. Our three-dimensional universe can be viewed as the hypersurface of a 3-manifold; and in that context we live on (in) the hypersurface of a 3-manifold. Within that hypersurface we can experience* solid, three-dimensional objects.

We can see* and touch* the solid objects that make up our substantial reality, but the experience* of a mental event is very different. For example: we cannot see* or touch* an emotion. Yet in the ToT both substantial objects *and* mental events are equally represented by mathematical objects described as n-manifolds. Both resolve to Experiences in the relative condition; and both are defined as the illusory constituents of the reality. We don't see* or touch* emotions because the n-manifolds that describes them are not 3-manifolds, they are of higher numbers.

121

The information describing emotions (mental events) is resident in other dimensionalities—the specific indentifying number is unimportant. With respect to Awareness the number merely indicates a placeholder and all dimensions are of equal relevance, with no set of dimensions being preferred.

In terms of the ToT, it is the Anthropic principle that provides the reason 3-manifolds manifest as the illusion of substantial objects. In essence all n-manifolds are simply the progenitors of an Experience. However, the Anthropic Principal mandates that: in a Cloud, a certain type of EQ patterns holding Features that resolve to sold objects are described as a certain set of three and resolve to a 3-manifold. These 3-manifolds are wont to describe substantial objects in V.1, because of the Anthropic principle.

In a similar fashion, another Feature in the EQ set, typically resolves to an Experience of time flow. The Anthropic principle demands that information of a certain type always resolves from the same Feature (dimensional number) of the EQ. The dimension describing time flow expresses an iterative sequence of the Experiences that are each described as a quantum of time. Anthropically it's closely related to the 3-manifold and together they form a **4-manifold** with the "Experience of time flow" information resident on the surface of the 4-manifold.

In the ToT a manifold is the information. There are an indefinitely large number of possible manifolds. All Experiences are represented by manifolds. A relative self is totally comprised of manifolds (*i.e.* Experiences); and all manifolds represent information.

This is the information that describes the tremendously rich symphony of Experiences that make up the human condition; and to a much grander extent the complete relative condition. As you read on you will logically discover that at any Instant you are the information that comprises the universe.

INFORMATION FROM THE VOID

It's notable to remember that (in terms of the absolute condition) an EQ is described by multi-dimensional warps in naked space; and it is only when EQ are Parsed by Awareness do they become "information", in the relative condition. An EQ is the genitive basis of a concept; and it cannot itself be a concept (or information, or an Experience) in any fashion. Thus a warp in naked space is not information; and naked space is axiomatically defined as containing no information whatsoever. After it's Parsed any information is defined is a facet of the relative condition and is no longer a part of naked space. Thus any conceptual discussion of naked space must be by analogy only. [The persistent problem with this description is the intermittent misuse of verbs as the viewpoint switches back and forth between the absolute and relative condition. It's written in this way to make it easier to read.]

Therefore: the warps in naked space are axiomatically defined as resolving to the quantum bits of information that comprise the geometric mathematical objects describing the Experiences of reality of the relative condition.

POSITIVE AND NEGATIVE CURVATURE

Recall that the curved surface of the wok-manifold (the 2-manifold we placed in the aquarium) has a positive curvature. A **negative curvature** manifold is different. If we are still talking about 2-manifolds it's a saddle-shaped curve on the manifold's surface, as pictured below. Such a curved area can describe the side of a peak or a pit that could extend to infinity.

An Experience that is representative of a manifold containing a surface area of an infinitely high peak, or infinitely deep pit would be unknowable in terms of our apparently finite spacetime universe.

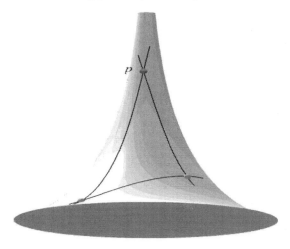

An area of a section of the surface of a 2-manifold with negative curvature leading to a possible infinitely high peak.[78]

It's interesting that a manifold describing a large number of dimensions (a very complex math object!) can also exhibit negative curvature. This idea becomes relevant later when we talk about information expressing higher dimension manifolds.

SIMPLY CONNECTED MANIFOLDS

There is another geometric concept that is important to understand: A manifold can be described as being, or not being, **simply connected**.

The main feature of this geometric concept can be explained using some more familiar objects as props: a desktop model of the Earth (a globe), a large doughnut, and a piece of string. The surfaces of both the globe and the doughnut are two-dimensional manifolds, not flat planes. They are both called 2-manifolds. The globe is also classified as a 2-sphere; and the doughnut is also classified as a **2-torus**.

For compact 2-dimensional surfaces without boundary, if every loop can be continuously tightened to a point, then the surface is described as topologically homeomorphic to a 2-sphere (usually just called a sphere). In this context the word "homeomorphic" applies if two objects can be deformed into each other by a continuous, invertible mapping.[79]

Tie the ends of the string together with a slipknot and make a loop with the length of string. Imagine laying the loop onto the surface of the globe in the shape of a circle. From the position of the knot you will be able to pull the ends of the string together causing the loop to get smaller. The loop will continue to get smaller until the loop is closed. We can imagine it slipping over either the North or South Pole as it gets smaller (depending on the size of the loop and where you put the loop to begin with). As you do this, the points describing the length of the string must always touch the surface of the manifold that describes the surface of the globe—this is a requirement for what we are doing.

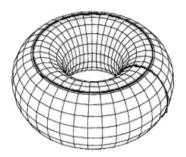

Neither of the darker loops on this torus can be continuously tightened to a point. A torus is not homeomorphic to a sphere.[80]

Now consider the other 2-manifold... the one described by the surface of the doughnut (the 2-torus). We have three basic options for placing the loop.

1) The doughnut is not a sphere but we can still easily place the circle of string on a certain area of the surface (perhaps on one side/edge of the doughnut with all points touching) and pull it together as we did with the globe and get the same results.

2) We can enlarge the loop and lay it on top of the doughnut— as if it's a squiggle of frosting around the top for decoration. Try again to pull the ends together while maintaining the requirement that all points of the string continually touch the manifold. It can't be done. The loop will become smallest with the string sticking to the surface of the doughnut around its inside center hole. We can't pull the loop to a zero point.

3) We can untie the knot, put one end of the string through the doughnut hole and then attach the two ends together again in a big loop. Place the resulting loop loosely on the surface of the doughnut such that the string touches the manifold at all points. As we try to pull the ends together it will obviously tighten up around a circular cross section of one side of the doughnut. Here again, we can't pull the loop to a zero point.

When we do the experiment with the torus we can't always pull the string to a zero point—which means the two-dimensional manifold described by the surface of the doughnut is deemed "not simply connected."

Examples of 2-manifolds that are not simply connected are doughnuts and various pretzels with two or more holes.

125

3 hole torus[81]
Not simply connected

1 hole torus[82]
Not simply connected

2-sphere[83]
Simply connected

Versions of 2-Manifolds

The small thought exercise with the loop of string demonstrates how and why a manifold is called simply connected or not. A sphere is the only simply connected, finite, two-dimensional manifold. All other two-dimensional manifolds are not simply connected.

HOMEOMORPHISM

The terms **homeomorphic** and simply connected are used in the field of **topology**.

> Topology is the mathematical study of the geometric properties that are not normally affected by changes in the size or shape of geometric figures. In topology, a donut and a coffee cup with a handle are equivalent shapes (called home-omorphic) because each has a single hole.[84]

Recall that a geometric object called a 2-sphere is a 2-manifold with a two-dimensional surface that is simply connected (*i.e.* no holes passing through).

Examples of common 2-spheres (simply connected).[85]
These objects are homeomorphic to one another.

The surfaces of certain physical objects are examples of such 2-manifolds. They subtend three dimensions of space. Examples of these are: the surface of a beach ball, the surface of a common loaf of bread, the surface of a Frisbee, the surface of a bowling ball (with finger holes drilled deep enough for the fingers), the surface of a glass for holding water, the surface of a pearl taken from an oyster and the surface of a

126

golf club. These are all objects without holes through them. All of these examples fall into the category of 2-spheres, regardless of their shape. They are all homeomorphic. This is the way things are viewed in the field of topology.

Examples of common tori (not simply connected).[86] The cup and a doughnut are homeomorphic to one another.

Examples of 2-manifolds that are not simply connected objects because they have holes through them are: the surface of a coffee cup (with a loop handle); the surface of a pearl in a necklace (with a hole drilled through it); the surface of a Frisbee that has been bitten through by a dog; the surface of a doughnut; and the surface of a pretzel. All of these are 2-manifolds are called "tori" (plural of torus); and the cup and doughnut are homeomorphic with one another.

In terms of 2-manifolds it's easy to see which are simply connected and which are not; however the concept of a manifold being simply connected applies to all dimensionalities of manifolds—whether they are 2-manifilds, 3-manifolds, 4-manifolds, etc. It is difficult (impossible) to imagine all of these multi-dimensional manifolds, but it offers a taste of what Riemann was dealing with.

TYPES OF SPACE

Geometrically, a 3-manifold is a four-dimensional volumetric object. It is an information package that can be laid onto the four-dimensional hypersurface of a 4-manifold. The hypersurface of the 4-manifold cannot be envisioned in terms of the everyday world—unless time is one of the dimensions. In that case it could be, for example, a ball bouncing—but it's hard to imagine that as a surface.

If we were discussing this topic with Newton, he would likely describe the three dimensions of the space around us as extending indefinitely (along straight lines) in all directions with no bumps, warps, curves or reference to anyone's measure. He called it **absolute space** and described it as independent of any objects that occupied the space.

His understanding requires us to think of space as the unchanging background in which the three-dimensional objects of our world exist.

In the ToT, space is a concept that sits relative to any objects described as being in it. Without occupying objects, there is no space. It's a relative consideration—a conceptual background that is there when needed. Any coordinates we may lay onto it are always relative to a substantial object or concept. In the ToT the only true example of space is naked space.

Newton's idea is perhaps very much like the space Riemann envisioned. However Riemann, being a pure mathematician, saw the opportunity to place virtual geometric objects of various and many dimensions into the space.

To help describe the layers of information intrinsic to the ToT, we can use Riemann's mathematical objects (manifolds) as analogs for the information packages that resolve to Experiences. For example: if the Experience is one of phenomenal objects existing in a flow of time, the configuration space defined by the manifold is four-dimensional (a 4-manifold) and it's called "spacetime" in the vernacular of an English speaking relative self. Therefore, in terms of the ToT... when we do this we are not conceptualizing space as real, instead it is an illusory meta-concept serving as a tool to help describe the illusion of the relative condition.

Historically spacetime is described as four-dimensional **Minkowski space**, named for the mathematician of the same name. Spacetime is the mathematical space setting in which Einstein's theory of special relativity is most conveniently formulated. Minkowski was first to described spacetime as being comprised of three **space-like** dimensions and one **time-like** dimension;[87] but in terms of the ToT each of these defines configuration spaces of manifolds that describe Experiences. Thus there is no "space" in the space-like dimension—there is only information; and there is no "time" in the time-like dimension—there is only information. Also, in the ToT the various dimensional n-manifolds portray Thoughts that describe substantial objects and/or mental events.

Henceforth the terms "spacetime", "space-like dimension" and "time-like dimension" are used only as a convenience to replace the words "the configuration space describing [any of these three terms]".

Hermann Minkowski (1864-1909)[88]

The views of space and time which I wish to lay before you have sprung from the soil of experimental physics, and therein lies their strength. They are radical. Henceforth space by itself, and time by itself, are doomed to fade away into mere shadows, and only a kind of union of the two will preserve an independent reality.

~ Hermann Minkowski, 1908[89]

The quote indicates that Hermann Minkowski was quite pleased with the concept of spacetime.

TEMPORAL AND INSTANT OBJECTS

Spacetime lets us make geometric representations of three-dimensional objects within the flow of time. For example: imagine a pillow—the complete three-dimensional aspect of the pillow, not just the surface. Imagine it being squashed, pressed and fluffed up as it's manipulated throughout a night's sleep—its shape and position changing over time. In the lexicon of the ToT, such an object is called a **temporal**

object.[B] A temporal object is a four dimensional object existing in spacetime. Its existence is described by an array of values in three dimensions of space (width, depth, and height; or in mathematical notation... "X, Y and Z") and in a fourth dimension attributed to time flow (called "T"). In terms of classical physics the term "temporal object" describes a *real*, substantial physical object.

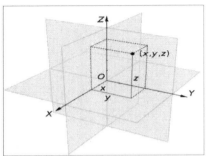

A three-dimensional object defined by three coordinates.[90]
A fourth dimension, the flow of time, is not shown.

Now imagine a single instantaneous example of a temporal object. Imagine it as truly instantaneous with no duration in time. Its representation in the fourth dimension is a single point (indicating zero duration). Imagine an object frozen like a stature, it does not change.

In the lexicon of the ToT this is called an **instant object.**[C] It may also be *real* in terms of modern physics; but in such terms it is an abstraction because what's real generally has a value greater than zero in each dimension of spacetime.

> For an instant object to exist, existence must be *universally* defined as instantaneous in nature... a primary tenet of the ToT, but not a feature of physics.

If we axiomatically accept that some single example of existence is instantaneous, then logically all of existence must be instantaneous. This is obvious because: if we hold that any example of existence can occur in a timeless instant, then any postulation that existence requires time is groundless.

Does it make sense for an instant object to exist? In spacetime physics, where a homogeneous flow of time is the accepted norm, an

---

[B] A **temporal object** is an invented term found in the lexicon of the ToT.
[C] An **instant object** is an invented term found in the lexicon of the ToT.

instant object can exist only at a limit point extrapolation that can never be reached. Thus it cannot exist. In such a belief system a duration is seen as a necessary tenet of existence.

This leads to the conclusion that one can take their pick between systems, but choosing one disallows the other.

. . . .

In terms of the ToT, the information in Minkowski's time-like dimension is not smoothly homogeneous in nature; instead it is quantum and made up of many tiny bits. In this light, a single temporal object is comprised of multiple, discrete iterations of instant objects.

In order to discuss this, let us again mentally take a step down one dimension. Imagine a book with images of a stick figure drawn into the margin of consecutive pages. Each of the drawings is similar and consecutive but with the legs and arms in slightly different positions. When you flip through the pages you will see a moving image of the "same" figure dancing. [We know it's not the same figure, but it sort of looks that way.]

In this analogy, each book page is an instant object, and all of the pages together are a single temporal object. The analogy allows us to envision the changing shape of a *single* three-dimensional temporal object existing in spacetime. It does however lead to the question: is time smoothly homogeneous in nature (as it appears to be in the world around us) or is it quantum in nature (as depicted by the flipping pages of the book)?

The answer highlights a major difference between the ToT and spacetime physics:

- o According to the physical sciences, a single temporal object existing in spacetime can be depicted as smoothly changing its shape across an expanse of a fourth dimension labeled time. Thus time *is not* described as quantum in nature, and existence requires a value greater than zero in the dimension of time.

- o According to the ToT, a single temporal object existing in spacetime can be depicted as multiple, discrete, instant objects occupying consecutive, quantum positions in a fourth dimension labeled time. Thus time *is* described as quantum in nature, and in essence existence is expressed as *always* being a single point in the dimension of time.

131

If we adopt the second scenario an instant object would have all of the normal attributes that comprise a three-dimensional object—an inside, an outside, etc.—but it would constitute a single, "frozen in time" object.   For example: consider a watermelon—think of it as an instant watermelon.   It would have smooth exterior skin surface, a harder area just under the skin, a softer, juicy interior area, and seeds throughout. These attributes would be described using three dimensions of geometry; however, because this is an instant watermelon, there would be a single (quantum) representation of it in the fourth dimension of spacetime; and that representation would not express duration.

We can also think of the surface of a 4-manifold as representing the information resolving to the Experience of a temporal watermelon. The information set would have values greater than zero in each of four dimensions (X, Y, Z and T)—thus displaying four degrees of freedom for the expressed information. The value for T would be a whole number that expresses an iterative sequence of instant watermelons, strung out consecutively across the time-like dimension of the 4-manifold.

From the perspective of a view from the "normal world" we live in, the collection of instant watermelons would be described as the same, *single* melon existing in time. However, from the perspective of Awareness (resident in the absolute condition) it would not be a single temporal object: it would be many instant objects.

We could apply these same powers of envisioning to a group (perhaps a truckload) of temporal melons because the group can be thought of as a single temporal object (called "a truck full of watermelons"). Now think even bigger. Consider a large temporal watermelon patch the size of a football field with a great number of melons lying around still attached to the vine. The fence around the patch, the air above the patch, some insects, the vines, the root system, a few feet of the earth below and the many melons make up this temporal watermelon patch. It can be envisioned as an iterative series of instant watermelon patches arrayed across the fourth dimension. Take this further, apply it to even larger temporal objects like the food stores that sells the melons; it's a chain of stores across the nation. Now think of the continent on which the chain of stores exist; then the planet; then the solar system; then the 300+ billion stars of the Milky Way galaxy; and finally the 200+ billion galaxies which comprise the cosmos as we observe it.

All of these scenarios can be described as occupying the four-dimensional hypersurface of a 4-manifold. The smallest is a temporal watermelon and the largest is a very big 4-manifold called the cosmos of the spacetime V.1 universe. In this way we can think of the cosmos not as a single temporal object but as a tremendous series of instant objects laid out across the quantum structure of the four dimensions of Minkowski space (spacetime)—a 4-manifold.

We can get an idea of the shape of such a 4-manifold by considering the immediate area surrounding the space that you, the reader, occupy. Think of that space as a 3-dimensional configuration space; but you and all of the objects etc. around you are instant objects, i.e. there is no time flow. Think of configuration space as only a small portion of the hypersurface of the very large instant 3-manifold that extends to the furthest reaches of the universe. Out there, as far as you can envision in front of you, at the "end" of the universe, the stuff of spacetime folds around, and in a continuous fashion comes full circle connecting with the other end of the universe extending from behind you—the connection is seamless and it's three-dimensional; thus the concept holds true for every direction you can look out, across the instant 3-manifold whose hypersurface is the cosmos. This describes an **instant 3-sphere**... add time to it and we get a 4-manifold. Thus an instant 3-manifold is a single point on the hypersurface of a 4-manifold describing spacetime.

This mind puzzle has a two-dimensional analog... imagine being anywhere on surface of an "instant Earth" looking horizontally across the land or water. The Earth's surface extends away from you, out and around to the other side of the planet and then returns ending up behind you. This happens in every direction you look horizontally.

In the three-dimensional model, the stuff that comprises the phenomenal universe (an instant 3-sphere) is folding around and merging back into itself on the "other side" of the universe. This means that the universe has a certain finite size in the same fashion in which the surface of the Earth has a certain finite area. However, the surface of the Earth is two-dimensional and the substantial stuff of the phenomenal V.1 universe is three-dimensional. In the same way that there is no end or edge to the surface of the Earth, we could conceivably travel indefinitely in any direction across the cosmos and always return to our starting point. In a similar fashion, if we could look with a very powerful telescope in any direction we would see the back of our head.

Now consider an iterative series of the huge instant 3-manifold that is the cosmos. The series becomes a single temporal manifold describing the cosmos in time—the cosmos becomes a temporal object, *i.e.* a temporal cosmos. The temporal cosmos populates the hypersurface of an instant 4-manifold, i.e. a time-like dimension. It's spacetime.

For me, this is one of the most understandable examples of a 4-mainifold. (It is however given in terms of the ToT where we are working with three *temporal* space-like dimensions, and one *instant* time-like dimension.) If we consider the universe to exist in this fashion, we must understand that the information that is "stuff" of spacetime comprises the hypersurface of an instant 4-manifold; and the geometry of that 4-manifold's surface describes what we are calling the phenomenal universe.

We must wonder what happens with time in this scenario because the time-like dimension is defined as being "instant"?

In this context, considering just spacetime, we might look at Sir Roger Penrose's book ["Cycles of Time: An Extraordinary New View of the Universe" (2012)]. In it he describes the universe as we typically understand it to be a single eon in an indefinitely long, connected string of eons.

Using mathematics Sir Roger expands a picture of the presumed beginning of an eon (the big bang) and compares it to a compressed picture of the totally expanded presumed end of the previous eon. When this is done the images appear as reflections of one another with certain information being transferred across the junction, creating continuity from one eon to the next.

Does the far future merge with the far past? Perhaps it's a great encircling necklace of the eons.

Thus we have a picture of our universe as existing in spacetime, where the time-like configuration space is the hypersurface of a single, instant 4-manifold. If we were to consider a temporal 4-manifold we would have multiple versions of the "same" spacetime cosmos in a single instant—which is where the logic of the ToT is taking us (more on this in Part II).

In the ToT, the *Experience* of time is understood to be quantum in nature. It is comprised of very small jumps, with each jump associated with an instant object. Conversely, in physics, time is seen as homogeneous with no quantum jumps; and thus the flow of time is a feature of existence.

From the viewpoint of the ToT, it appears that it was an instant object that occupied the interest of the respected French mathematician,

Henri Poincaré; but it was not important for him to make a distinction between temporal and instant because, in Europe at the beginning of the 19th century, it appears that the concept of existence required a notion of time flow.

THE POINCARÉ CONJECTURE

Jules Henri Poincaré as a young man (1854–1912).[91]

In 1904, almost fifty years after Riemann's habilitation lecture, Henri Poincaré formulated and published a certain, seemingly correct, mathematical statement; but he did not provide a formal proof. Throughout the 20th century it has been known as the *Poincaré Conjecture*. It was called a "conjecture" because of the lack of a mathematical proof. The standard form of the Poincaré conjecture is:

Every simply connected, closed 3-manifold is homeomorphic to the 3-sphere.[92]

Recall that a 3-sphere is a special case of a 3-manifold. The term *closed* means that it does not have a hole in its boundary or an area of negative curvature that rushes to infinity. The Poincaré Conjecture specifically addresses only 3-manifolds. It does not describe higher dimensional manifolds.

For 100 years the Poincaré Conjecture was the great puzzle that no mathematician could prove. Many of the best minds of the 20th century tried but none succeeded until, in 2003, Grigori Perelman, of St. Petersburg, Russia, was able to provide a proof.

Perelman used a variation of an equation called the *Ricci flow* which "...treats the curvature of space as if it were an exotic type of heat, akin to molten lava, flowing from more highly curved regions and seeking to spread itself out over regions with lesser curvature". Using a procedure known as *Ricci flow with surgery* he was able to mathematically remove the areas of negative curvature that rushed to infinity.[93]

Grigori Perelman in 2006, (1966--)[94] and Richard Hamilton in 1982 (1943--)[95]

In 2006, Grigori Perelman was offered a Fields Medal for his work on the Poincaré Conjecture. The Fields Medal is one of the most prestigious awards in mathematics, often described as the "Nobel Prize of Mathematics." He declined the Medal. Later, in 2010, he was offered the Millennium Prize for his work. The prize was offered by the Clay Mathematics Institute and included a $1,000,000. award. He declined this prize also, saying that he believed his contribution in proving the Poincaré Conjecture was no greater than that of Richard Hamilton (who discovered the Ricci flow equation and suggested it as a method for creating the solution).[96]

Poincaré was speaking in terms of math objects and the many possible static shapes the single definition can describe. Consider the paraphrase of his conjecture: "a closed 3-sphere is the only possible finite, simply connected 3-manifold that may exist."

If we apply this definition of existence to the substantial objects within our universe (V.1) those objects must be seen as existing within the flow of time and, according to the ToT, would be defined as temporal objects, possibly changing shape over time. The paraphrase of the Poincaré Conjecture should then be adjusted to read: "…a closed 3-sphere is the only possible finite, simply connected 3-manifold that may [*continue to*] exist."

The ToT describes our universe as an instant 4-manifold; whose hypersurface contains a set of temporal 3-manifolds. These 3-manifolds comprise the substantial reality aspect of the Stor. An individual instant 3-manifold can be seen as describing an instant object; and an iterative series of instant 3-manifolds a temporal object.

These 3-manifolds are not necessarily 3-spheres (we do have experiences* of doughnuts, pretzels etc.) thus the 3-manifolds are not always simply connected. The adjusted Poincare Conjecture tells us such objects cannot continue to exist; and this is the situation in the world around us. If, for example, a doughnut hole becomes so large that there is no longer any dough around the hole, the doughnut will cease to exist—then there will be no experience* of a doughnut. No problem. There is simply no experience* of a doughnut; but there will remain an experience* of the atmosphere or (if you are outside of an atmosphere) the experience* of electromagnetic radiation etc., i.e. other information.

The situation changes, however, if we expand the example to express, not just the experience* of a doughnut, but instead *all* information in a certain area of reality. This example would constitute a very complex, grossly multi-dimensional math object. A figurative "doughnut hole" in this example would contain *no* information at all. It is interesting to note that this would not be a hole in naked space, instead it would be a hole in the information laid onto the space—it would be a manifold that is not simply connected. This could be a problem because if there is no information, there is no existence (in terms of the relative condition).

There is also the uncomfortable possibility of a temporal manifold that morphs into a shape with an extreme negative curvature that yields a tall spike or deep pit where the hypersurface would rush to infinity. It would no longer be a closed manifold and the open end would constitute a hole in the information (whatever that is!) In any case there

137

would again be an area of no information and no existence, in terms of the relative condition.

The parallel situation in the Perelman-Hamilton solution to the Poincaré Conjecture is dealt with by "cutting out" the problem areas using *Ricci flow with surgery.*

A similar logical path is followed in the ToT. To understand this recall that the basic nature of apparent reality as Instantaneous and is made up of a sequence of instant objects. Portions of the sequence can be figuratively "cut out" or terminated using a feature of the ToT-defined Anthropic principle. The feature is called **anthropic denial** and is philosophically analogous to the *Ricci flow with surgery* procedure. Anthropic denial is explained below, but first an overview of the Instant universe.

THE INSTANT UNIVERSE

In the ToT the information in the fourth, time-like dimension of spacetime is not smoothly homogeneous; instead it is quantum in nature with each quantum incident representing a single, static, three-dimensional instantaneous version of the universe—call it an **instant universe**. An instant universe is the largest possible instant object in the V.1 universe. V.1 itself, in its entirety, is the largest possible temporal object, with respect to V.1.

The information describing the substantial V.1 is represented by the hypersurface of an instant 4-manifold designated the "time-like dimension". The instant universes are described as discrete and consecutive with each one indicating a self-contained incident of reality having a single point in the dimension designated as time-like. Each of these points, of course, represents a single instant in the Experience of the flow of time. However, with respect to Totality the complete set of instant universes arrayed across the time-like hypersurface occurs within a single, grand Instant (note uppercase "I").

A primary axiom of the ToT is that there is no *a priori* reason for the apparent reality of any substance, energy field, emotion, or concept etc. other than that which is Instantaneous, or instantaneous.

Within the relative self every Experience is instantaneous in nature and produces the illusion of an *instant* substantial object or an *instant* subjective event. A sequential iteration of instantaneous Experiences produces a meta-Experience of single **temporal object** or **temporal event**. Such a meta-Experience is called an overlain Experience (more on this below). Each iterative single Experience that comprises an over-lain Experience is slightly different. In this light, the apparent phenomenal and subjective universe contains no "true" objects or events that exist in time. It contains only a great sequence of unique instant objects and unique instant events.

As a matter of nomenclature, all of the sequential instant substantial objects and instant subjective events are, together, existing in the single Instant of the "now"—which is the *apparent* domain of memory. Note that the "now" is described as *apparent* in nature because, as we will soon discover, the "now" is completely empty of information.

> Recall that the information comprising memory is an Experience made up of an iterative sequence of other Experiences. In this context the memory of a duration is syncategorematicly related to the mental event called the "flow of time".

For example: consider someone reading these two pages. Imagine that person sitting in a room for a short period of time. There may be a clock ticking in the background, a pet cat walking past, the curtains moving in the wind, thoughts of being comfortable in the chair and more. According to the ToT, the room and its contents can be thought of as an example of a *sequence of instances*, where each instant constitutes the hypersurface of an instant manifold. Taken together the sequence is a single temporal manifold that manifests as the room existing in time.

The definition of an instant object entails no Experience of movement of any kind. The clock would be stopped, the curtain would be "frozen" in mid-air and the cat would be caught still in mid-stride and the mental event of being comfortable will be a single, instant flash of thought. This example describes the momentary set of Experiences associated with a single instant object or event (a manifold expressing a single point in the time-like dimension).

Now consider the next incident of reality in the sequence, *i.e.* the next instant object or event. It will be slightly different; and the next after that slightly different again, etc., following the sequence.

Now consider all of the elements that make up the sequence. Each of the component instant objects in the sequence is there because its genitive EQ fulfill certain requirements according to their relationships in the Matrix. Those requirements are judged (so to speak) as being acceptable (or not) according to the Anthropic principle.

ANTHROPIC DENIAL

According to the ToT, the past and the presumed future are a sequence of EQ patterns (that resolve to concepts) that play out as Memories. These concepts can be thought of as math objects (manifolds); and with respect to three-dimensional reality these math objects are phenomenal objects laid out against the iterative background fabric of the three "space-like" dimensions around us in V.1.

With respect to phenomenal reality, we humans will accept* only certain math objects. For example, regarding substantial objects, we will only accept* those math objects that do not contain a spike or pit whose surface indicates a rush to infinity; and those math objects that do not portray "holes" in the Experience of reality.

> In terms of the ToT we don't actually "accept" certain concepts—instead they are a pattern that is part of what's called the human condition. In this fashion the term accept is denoted as accept.* Logically it is impossible to imagine what a "hole" in the Experience of reality would look like; because it would be an area of no information or non-existence. In the ToT, a black hole is the result of an area of negative curvature in the 4-manifold whose hypersurface is the cosmos. In contemporary physics wormholes are hypothetical, and if they do exist naturally, Einstein's equations tell us they would be unstable.[97]

It appears that if untenable and/or "dangerous" math objects such as those that resolve to black holes or spatial wormholes exist, but they are not close by. If they were, they might be very destructive and would therefore not "fit" within our reality map according to the Anthropic principle. In the context of the ToT, they would be **anthropically denied**.

> In the ToT, the term "anthropically denied" is used to describe a figurative pattern resident in the information of time-past that has denied certain other time-past Experiences that would be found in memory.
>
> Anthropic denial is an expression of the "weak anthropic principle" that is similar to the principle defined by

Brandon Carter,[D] which states that the universe's ostensible fine tuning is the result of selection bias: i.e., only in a universe capable of eventually supporting life will there be living beings capable of observing any such fine tuning, while a universe less compatible with life will go un-beheld.[98] [This definition fails to define the nature of the beholder, however.]

In the universe as we know it (V.1) potentially deniable objects may exist if they are not close by, because their effects are not a destructive personal Experience—which is a statement of the Anthropic principle.

Recall that, in terms of the ToT, the Anthropic principle states that we see* the world as we remember it to be; and that we exist in the instant of the present. In this way, the present dictates time-past (our history).

Previously, in the first section of the book, our sun was described as being one star among several hundred billion stars that comprise a single galaxy—and that galaxy is one among two hundred billion plus other galaxies physically existing in a four dimensional, folded, spacetime universe that has no natural geometric center. We can now add to that description the idea that the physical universe is exemplified by a 4-manifold whose existing untenable and/or dangerous areas are either: far away from the areas of Experience of the human condition; or are "cut out of reality as we know it" with the process of anthropic denial.

Thus the 3-sphere described by Poincaré does not exclusively describe the substantial aspects of our temporal physical universe. We can and do have Experiences of physical objects that are saddle-shaped (with negative curvature possibly leading to an infinity peak or pit); and we may well have manifolds describing Experiences of reality that are not closed or are not simply connected. However the existence of these Experiences is anthropically denied in V.1 .

[D] Brandon Carter, FRS (born 1942) is an Australian theoretical physicist, best known for his work on the properties of black holes and for being the first to name and employ the anthropic principle in its contemporary form.

2.2 - NAKED SPACE

A fundamental tantra of the Tibetan *Dzogchen* Semde teaching is entitled *Kunjed Gyalpo*.[99] The term translates as "ultimate source". In context it is unequivocally the absolute condition of reality transcending all word and thought... beyond the concept of beyond.

Also found in Tibetan Buddhism is the Sanskrit term *shunyata*. It is often translated as the "Void", but it has different philosophical meanings depending on the school of Buddhism one looks at.

The ToT uses geometric analogs and a concept labeled "**naked space**" to point at a reflection of *Kunjed Gyalpo*, *shunyata*, or the Void; because words and concepts, by definition, must fail. Consequently the idea of naked space refers to something different than the three dimensions of space that surround us in our everyday world.

In the ToT it is naked space upon which patterns of EQ (math objects) are figuratively imbedded as warps; and those patterns resolve to the Experiences of reality. Therefore in terms of the ToT... We are immersed in and (in a sense) a part of naked space. Our reality and who we think we are comprise a set of patterns in naked space. (Interestingly one of the patterns is the concept of the three dimensions of space as we define it in spacetime reality.)

In the ToT:

o Naked space is a concept that is ontologically one step above a pairing of EQ and Awareness. (Thus, in the ToT the latter two are defined as sub-set features of naked space.) Together the three metaphorically describe the absolute condition of Totality.

o EQ are described as resolving to an Experience when figuratively held against the lens of Awareness.

o   An EQ is defined as 1) a distinct warp in naked space, and 2) the single most basic quantum of existence.

o   The EQ, *never* resolve directly to substantial objects. They *always* resolve to Experiences; and those Experiences may be of substantial objects or of mental events. The quanta themselves never become* substantial in any way.

o   There can be no direct Experience of a warp in naked space (an EQ) because the warp itself is the most basic, genitive component of an Experience.

o   Collections of warps resolve to a patterns of information that form the illusion of ongoing reality.

The most basic axiomatic assertions of the ToT are:

1) The existence of naked space,

2) The existence of warps in naked space [EQ] and

3) The existence of Awareness [classed as the essence of naked space.]

It is only these three that have absolute existence according to the ToT. Numbers 2) and 3) together are the philosophically equivalent to the "pure non-duel cognitive potentiality".

According to the Yogācāna School of Buddhist philosophy (the Mind Only School)[100] only "… cognitive potentiality" has absolute existence.

Another school, called *Madhyamika* which is based on the *Prajnaparametia Sutra,* describes the absolute condition [*shunyata*] as transcending all conceptual limits and thus does not even accept the existence of the consciousness as absolute. The ToT, with its pragmatic focus on the relative condition, does not follow this thinking.

SPACE WARPS IN A SPACETIME UNIVERSE

In 1919, an experiment was conducted to measure the amount to which a star's light ray will be deflected as it passes through the warped space closely surrounding our Sun. According to a typical interpretation of Einstein's general theory of relativity, the warping of space is an expression of gravity; and the warp occurs because of the existence of a large massive object such as the sun. The completion of this experiment was seen as proof of the general theory.

The first observation of light deflection (owing to a warp of space) was performed by noting the change in position of stars, as they passed near the Sun on the celestial sphere. The observations were performed by Sir Arthur Eddington and his collaborators in 1919, during a total solar eclipse, so that the stars near the Sun could be observed. Observations were made simultaneously in the cities of Sobral and Ceará in Brazil; as well as in São Tomé and Príncipe on the west coast of Africa. The result was considered spectacular news and made the front page of most major newspapers. It made Einstein and his general theory of relativity world famous.[101]

One of Eddington's photographs of the total solar eclipse of 29 May 1919, presented in his 1920 paper announcing its success, confirming Einstein's theory that light "bends."[102]

As mentioned above, a typical interpretation of Einstein's general theory of relativity states that the warping of space is due to the effect of the gravity associated with the large mass of the sun. In terms of the ToT this is understood differently. An Experience and an Experience-object exist in a coordinated syncategorematic relationship. For example: in Edington's experiment there was the Experience-object of the sun and the Experience-object of the space warps. Using the logic of the ToT we can infer that the sun did not *cause* the warps, instead they both simply existed syncategorematicly in a single instant; and the *space* that was warped was a 'configuration space", not a real element of reality.

Also, recall that there is no "space" (in terms of spacetime) that can be warped. There is only the information describing the Sun and the information describing the beam of light; and they affect* one another in a predictable, interrelated fashion according to a concept called the "laws of physics", as we know them. Those laws are anthropically defined as a feature of the V.1 universe.

Compare the concept Eddington was working with the concept of a warp in naked space. The naked space "warp" is an analog serving to facilitate an understanding of the Void. The nature of the constructed understanding both follows the lead of Buddhist thought; and "works" with the other tenets of the ToT.

For example: consider an EQ and its associated multi-dimensional warps in naked space. In essence, a single EQ *is* the tiny set of dimensional space warps. What is such a warp? What is the EQ? Neither really has a form or position (naked space is non-local); and neither one can affect the other or anything else (naked space is non-temporal, *i.e.* no verbs).

When Awareness figuratively Parses the EQ, information arises… in the relative condition. In terms of the standard terminology of spacetime, it's all quite magical and unexplainable. It's magical like the movement of light, like being consciousness of the "self", like sensing the flow of time or like the awareness of being alive.

How can all of this be? According to the ToT it's all totally an anthropically defined sequence of Experiences; and we exist in a single, instant, parallel, viewing of the entire sequence simultaneously!

THE PRINCIPLE OF TWO REALITIES

When we consider the human condition, or the relative condition in general, we immediately realize that it is made up of many types of Experiences—all the possible things, feelings and realizations that comprise the concept of being alive. According to the ToT they fall into two classes of reality—those classed as phenomenal reality and those classed as mental events, both classes within the relative condition. This bifurcation of apparent reality is a primary feature of the ToT called the **principle of two realities**. This was briefly described earlier.

> In general Buddhist thought describes three (of what the ToT identifies as) versions of reality. In Buddhism they are **body, speech** and **mind**. The three are known as the Three Vajras in Tibetan Buddhism and Bon. In Japanese Buddhism they are called the Three Mysteries. In the *Dzogchen* teaching the three are related to the doctrine of "sound, light and rays" which together point at a being's total identity.
>
> The designation of "speech" is not used in the ToT. In terms of the relative condition, "speech" is a combination of phenomenal reality and mental events. This is done because the ToT is a simplification of esoteric teachings that is essentially not designed as a path to enlightenment.

The separation of the relative condition into two areas has been effectively described by others. Sir Isaac Newton distinguished two classes of reality that parallel what the ToT calls phenomenal objects and mental events. He referred to these classes as **mind-independent** and **mind-dependent**, respectively.

René Descartes famously defended the idea that there are two fundamental kinds of substance: mental and material. His philosophy, often called **Cartesian dualism**, is also known as substance dualism.

> The Philosopher David Chalmers[103] recently developed a thought experiment inspired by the movie *The Matrix* in which substance dualism could be true. Consider a computer simulation in which the bodies of the creatures are controlled by their minds and the minds remain strictly external to the simulation. The creatures can do all the science they want in the world, but they will never be able to figure out where their minds are, for they do not exist in their observable universe.[104]

The thought experiment is also elegantly parallel the ToT's comparison of the relative and the absolute condition of reality, however in the ToT Awareness rests outside of relative condition (the condition of reality that is the venue for both aspects substance dualism). This differs from Chalmers' thought experiment where the "self-awareness" of the individual is the "observer" of reality and rests in the mind—which lays in the brain/body, operates in time and is a feature of the relative condition.

Also, according to the historic underpinnings upon which the ToT based, a Buddhist practitioner can, ultimately, taste a presence of Awareness (beyond the relative condition) that has a view of both the aspects of the dualism expressed in the thought experiment.

In the late 19th century, the German philosopher/educator, Franz Brentano, described our consciousness as divided into two classes: 1) physical phenomena and 2) mental phenomena.[105] He was particularly interested in the mental phenomena.

Generally, a Theory of Everything is an attempt to explain the phenomenal world (phenomenal reality) and typically it does not deal with the subjective reality of the mind (called mental events in the ToT). The ToT incorporates both classes of reality because they equally resolve from EQ and manifest as Experiences; however, there is a marked difference between them.

In the ToT an Experience of phenomenal reality existing in a flow of time is expressed using a math object that is a 4-manifold. Specifically it uses three space-like dimensions and one time-like dimension—that together are described as the hypersurface of the spacetime 4-manifold. Mental events are expressed differently. They use multiple **event-like dimensions** and one time-like dimension that are expressed as the hypersurface of an n-manifold.

> The term "event-like dimension" is a play on words following Minkowski's description of a *time-like dimension etc.* The term is coined to highlight a qualitative similarity between the Experiences of substantial objects and of thoughts, feelings, emotions etc. (mental events) within the ToT.

It's easy to think of event-like dimensions as higher in number; but in essence all dimensions are simply orthogonal to one another and the concept of higher or lower is a matter of perspective. With respect to what a relative self would define as the 4 dimensions of spacetime, mental events are described by higher dimensional manifolds, with each dimension being a Feature of the EQ. Any numbering indicating rank or relative position is simply nomenclature. For example, consider a hypothetical situation where the mental event describing an appreciation of violin music might be described by a set of dimensions labeled 1, 2, 3, 4, 5, 8, 9 and 13. Or, (another example) the Experience of rage that may be described by a set of dimensions labeled 1, 2, 3, 4, 5, 11, 17 and

18. Each of these mental events would be represented by manifolds that have an eight-dimensional hypersurface; but each would be comprised of information resident in different "higher" dimensions.[A]   Each EQ would also have the same four dimensions of spacetime that indicate the physical reality of the apparent "self" in the relative condition of the V.1 universe.

DANGEROUS MATH OBJECTS

With respect to the concept of a single relative self the universe is a *set* of Thoughts or a *collection* of Experiences.   Recall that each Thought is a *group* of Experiences. (The "grouping" terminology is important here. See the Pattern Chart.)

We can also describe a relative self as a collection of n-manifolds which resolve from EQ.   Generally, in our spacetime universe [as we know it] an EQ always contains a set of space-like dimensional Features which resolve to information describing the Experience of the physical body.   This links *all* of the information in the collection of n-manifolds to the physical body of a relative self, because the physical body is almost universally considered to represent the "self" [in spacetime as we know it][B]; and the "self" is the one who is apparently experiencing* the information of reality.   This highlights the idea that the full nature of a relative self is obviously more than just a physical body.   The nature of a relative self is determined by the *total* number and the dimensional expanse of the manifolds needed to describe all the associated information.   This includes possible information resolving to what the ToT calls **dangerous math objects**.

In the lexicon of the ToT a dangerous math object is an area on the hypersurface of an instant manifold that includes the n-dimension equivalent of a black hole and/or a spatial wormhole.   The terms "black hole" and "wormhole" specifically label dangerous math objects that exist as instant 3-manifolds, but in the ToT math objects with this label can describe instant manifolds of any dimension. Dangerous math objects are always instant manifolds because their defining nature is to express a pending state of untenable existence—a shape that is *on the verge* of untenability.   In general this book deals with instant 3-manifolds as a

---

[A] In these examples the "higher" dimension numbers are randomly selected.

[B] The exception to this would be a yogi who has mentally placed his/her mind in a state outside of the physical universe… but still in the relative condition.

representation of substantial reality, because that is the realm of contemporary physics. They are also much easier to talk about.

Recall that the hypersurface of an instant 3-manifold is the possible domain of areas of negative curvature, or of areas of the manifold being not simply connected. Mathematically these phenomena can manifest in any n-manifold; but it's not an issue within the human condition if the problem areas are not extreme or are of sufficient distance away as to pose no danger to the continuing existence of the relative self. For example: we can easily live with cosmic black holes if we don't get to close to them.

If there is a genuine threat, the dangerous math objects will be anthropically denied—if the karmic milieu allows for it.[C]

> The term **"karmic milieu"** is an expression of a linking pattern (in the Matrix) that is associated with a certain relative self.

The concept of dangerous math objects (also called dangerous manifolds) will be revisited in Part III.

The idea of anthropic denial at all dimensional levels is based on work done in the field of mathematics in 1961. In that year Stephen Smale[D] proved what is called the Generalized Poincaré Conjecture for dimensions greater than four.

In 1982 Michael Freedman[E] proved the Poincaré Conjecture in dimension four; and in 2006 Grigori Perelman's proof of the Poincaré Conjecture for dimension three was confirmed.

The ToT generally takes this body of mathematics to mean that anthropic denial of dangerous math objects is repeated at all dimensional levels. This means that the geometric equivalent of a black hole, or a wormhole, may also occur on the surface of a manifold describing a

---

[C] These sentences are written in the context of a relative *self*.

[D] Stephen Smale was on the faculty of the University of California, Berkeley when he did his work on the Generalized Poincaré Conjecture. He received the Fields Medal in 1966. In 2007, Smale was awarded the Wolf Prize in mathematics. He is one of twelve Fields Medalists to win both prizes.

[E] The Poincaré Conjecture for a 4-sphere was proved by Michael Freedman of the University of California, San Diego. In 1986 he received the Fields Medal for this work. This is considered to be an elegant piece of mathematics but also somewhat less of a challenge than the proof for a 3-sphere.

mental event. Such a concept is difficult to imagine, but hopefully, whatever it is, it would be anthropically denied—if the karmic milieu allows for it.

> For example, on a sad personal note, I have met individuals that on emotional level, appear to be so in need of certain fulfillments that they will never be satisfied in a single lifetime. It's as if they were looking into an infinity pit laying in one of the "event-like" dimensions.

AN OVERLAIN EXPERIENCE

Within a relative self *all* individual Experiences are functionally instantaneous. However there are Experiences (such as the flow of time and the action of most verbs) that are conceptually not instantaneous. According to the ToT only the verb "to be" can be seen as truly instantaneous.

We might consider the verb "remember" to be non-temporal in the context of the ToT because it appears that the moment of the Now is comprised of memories of time-past. However these memories are not "remembered" by a *self* that is separate from the memories; instead the memories (nouns) comprise the *self*—they <u>are</u> the *self*. There is no *self* other than the information that is the memories.

How can this be?

The most basic description of an Experience is one that is said to resolve from a single EQ. It is the first of two classes of Experience found in the ToT—it's called a **native Experience** or an **nExperience**. The second class of Experiences resolves from the comparison of multiple EQ. A member of this second class of Experiences is called an **overlain Experience** or an **oExperience**. An oExperience resolves from the comparison of one EQ or group of EQ with another similar EQ or group of EQ. The comparing is done by Awareness.

> The expression ". . . comparison of one group of EQ with another group of EQ . . ." is a semantic tool for describing a pattern of EQ that is made up of a certain combination of the constituent EQ or EQ groups. It can be envisioned as a meta-EQ-group, or a group comprised of a certain number of other EQ-groups.

The Experience of a flow of time, of movement, or of heat is an oExperience. Therefore (in the parlance of the ToT) the Experience of the flow of time does not resolve directly from a single EQ. Instead, it resolves from a pattern of EQ. An analogy that can help explain this is the property of human speech.

The human ability to produce speech may be described as an "overlain ability". In anthropological terms there are no physical organs directly attributable to the process of speech.

> In terms of the relative self, the organs used for speech produce and control the many sounds needed for language. Those organs include: the lips, teeth, tongue, alveolar ridge, nasal cavities, hard palate, velum (soft palate), uvula, glottis, pharynx, larynx, lungs, diaphragm, various musculatures, components of the ear and the brain.

All of the organs of speech exist to facilitate bodily functions that operate at a more basic level than speech. Examples of these more basic functions are breathing, hearing, eating, biting and closing the larynx (to allow the pressurization of the lungs when lifting heavy objects and to make sounds). All of these organs are variously found in animals that do not have the faculty of speech. In this way, the human ability to produce speech is termed to be an "overlain ability". The concept serves as an analogy for an oExperience, such as the overlain Experience of time.

Just as there are no dedicated organs of speech, there is also no single EQ that resolves to oExperiences; such as, for example, the flow of time or a change in location. There are, for example single EQ that are indicative of a given instant in the flow of time or a (relative) location, but they alone will not produce an oExperience of time flow or of movement. The Experience of the flow of time or of movement is always an oExperience.

THE EXPERIENCE OF THE FLOW OF TIME

In terms of the relative self the oExperience of the flow of time is *the memory of a duration*. This is axiomatic in the ToT. It is an oExperience of sequential iterations in the time-like dimension.

Understand that the sequence is not functionally described as unfolding at a certain flow or rate; it is merely a *sequence*, like the buttons on a shirt. There is no time involved. The phenomenal V.1 universe is defined as an Instantaneous and static entity comprised of multiple iterations of instant 3-manifolds laid out across the four-dimensional hypersurface fabric of the relative self. Mental events (emotions etc.) are linked to the three-dimensional body of the being having* the emotion or mental event.

Another way to express successive iterations of three-dimensional reality is with the concept of a series of instantaneous snap shots of static, single-incident "slices" of phenomenal reality within a virtual flow of time. The oExperience of a sequence of the "slices" amounts to an Experience of the flow of time; and the oExperience is Instantaneous.

To understand this, consider a two-dimensional analogy for the oExperience of time flow. Imagine a certain two-dimensional image (call it an "instant image") that is one of multiple images comprising an animation. As the animation proceeds, we see an image that apparently moves and gradually changes shape as time passes (call this a "temporal image"). If the depicted animation were occurring at 24 frames per second, we would actually be looking at twenty four different instant images each second.

In order to see ten seconds of the animation, an expanse of ten seconds of time is necessary. In those ten seconds of time we would see 240 frames of the animation, or 240 different instant images. For the animation to occur we must allow ten seconds of time for viewing. If we wanted to see all of the frames but didn't allow any viewing time, all of the various instant images would occupy the same display window simultaneously—which would produce a blurry mess!

Thus an oExperience of the dancing stick figure described above would be the instant of remembering the movement of the dancing stick figure at any point during the 10 second play.

We can explain the flow of time or movement in an Instantaneous universe in a similar fashion. To do this, envision an iterative sequence of instant 3-manifolds. According to the ToT the oExperience of time flow is a result of the sequence; because without that oExperience, all of the instant 3-manifolds would be "observed" as occupying the same relative position simultaneously—which would produce a moment of reality that would be the blurry mess described above. Instead, because Awareness can Parse (in parallel) the multiple patterns that resolve to an oExperience; the collection of images appears in sequence and appears to "move" (in the context of a relative self.) Thus the appearance of movement is a function of the memory of a duration... where the "duration" is the oExperience of the length of the sequence of information packets.

The Experience of the "self" existing in the flow of time occurs because in our modern world, the concept of the "self" is strongly associated with a being's physical body. The physical body is a part of the phenomenal universe—which is the metaphoric operative domain of the Experience of the flow of time.

MINDMOMENTS

As stated above, every relative self is composed of (what appears to be) previous versions of (what appears to be) the moment in play. Each of these versions of the moment in play is called a **MindMoment** in the lexicon of the ToT. It is denoted with the symbol "Ш" (large format lower case letter "M" turned).

The term MindMoment is an adaption of the term "mind moment" which is a translation of the *Pāli* text word *cittakkana*.[106] The *Pāli* word is found in the Tripitaka, the traditional name for the southern Buddhist canon of scripture called the *Pāli Canon*.

> The *Pāli Canon* is the standard collection of scriptures in the Theravada Buddhist tradition. It was transcribed from oral tradition in the last century BCE. The particular area of knowledge being referenced is called the *Abhidhamma* (a bee dam' ma).

The word *cittakkana* refers to the life span of a *citta*—which is a very small item [but it is not instantaneous!]. The verbal root of *citta* is to "know" or to "have cognizance." The term *citta* may be thought of as consciousness in its most basic context. In the ToT a MindMoment (one word with uppercase "M") is defined as instantaneous and it does *not* represent consciousness; instead it represents information. It's part of the relative condition.

The concept of the mind moment as found in the *Abhidhamma* has been logically negated in Mahayana Buddhist philosophy; but that argument does not apply to a MindMoment because, unlike the mind moment, a MindMoment is instantaneous.

Think of a MindMoment as if it is a package of Thoughts or a package of the Experiences that make up the Thoughts. The Experiences in the package are those that make up a single instant of time-past for a relative self. A group of MindMoments in sequence comprise what is described as the oExperience of memory, or a memory.

THE INSTANT OF THE NOW

In terms of the relative self, a MindMoment is a snapshot of what appears to be a *moment of existence in the past*. It is never a snapshot of the moment of the present... which is called the moment of the **Now**. The Now is always empty of MindMoments. In terms of a relative self the Now serves only as a virtual vantage point that overlooks time-past. It does not overlook time-future because (obviously) a relative self only "knows*" time-past and can only "predict*" time-future with a varying probability of accuracy. What appears to be a confident prediction of time-future, to any degree, even the very shortest reach into time-future, is actually an oExperience of "what is expected to be" based on time-past MindMoments. The Experience of "what is expected to be" does not resolve from time-future MindMoments. It is an oExperience that is a part of the oExperience of memory (i.e. time-past MindMoments).

For example: if you let loose a ceramic cup above a concrete floor you will expect it to shatter when it hits the floor—which is an oExperience found in memory of (for example) a time-past Experiences of fragile objects breaking. Both Mind Moments, together, resolve to the oExperience of an "expectation" of a time-future event, i.e. the cup shattering. Thus an expected future is an oExperience of memory that represents the information in time-past MindMoments.

Each MindMoment resolves to a set of Thoughts that specifically expresses a limited, instant version of the total information in play at some instant in time-past. In this fashion each MindMoment is an instantaneous collection of Experiences that appears to be an instant in a "remembered" past. The Experiences resolving from MindMoments are described using three conditions:

- o A MindMoment describes a single instant in time-past for a certain relative self.,
- o A MindMoment is a package of information describing only a portion of a the relative self, and
- o The Experiences that resolve from multiple MindMoments (groups of Experiences) are resolved as a group—thus becoming oExperiences.

We will discover that in the context of the ToT there are time-future MindMoments, but those MindMoments do not resolve to an Experience of reality in terms of spacetime and are not part of a relative self. To understand this recall that herein the term "spacetime" refers to the physical universe as the sciences describe it; and according to the

ToT, a relative self is the Experiences of reality *in terms of spacetime*; which is a limited view of the relative condition.

Thus a larger view of the relative condition can be had from the vantage of the absolute condition. From this view time-future Mind-Moments are described as part of a ToT-defined entity called an "individuated SELF". This is explained below, but first a bit more about MindMoments.

INTERPRETING THE BUDDHA'S WORDS

Many interpretations of the Buddha's words rest on a background concept of time flow (for example: *karma, cause and effect*). The earlier pages of the book display numerous examples of Buddhist doctrine described in this way. It is difficult to avoid this because often such doctrines arise from comments spoken by the Buddha that occurred in a span of time. We must also remember that the Buddha crafted and extended his teachings to people of all levels of understanding. Many of the practices for ending personal suffering were described in the context an ongoing flow of time in which a practitioner might act in a certain way.

Textual versions of these teachings first showed up at the beginning of the first millennia. Thus many interpretations of the Buddha's words and associated teachings have been transcribed, discussed and interpreted for the last two millennia. We can follow the lead of these interpretations, or we can in some cases find our own interpretation, if it appears more sensible to do such.

Certain records suggest an awareness* of nontemporal conditions of reality. For example: the last four lines of the Diamond Sutra[F] appear to indicate that the phenomenal experience* of the "flow of time" should be considered as illusory because the experience* of it is a conditioned phenomenon—it cannot exist without a past and a future.

[F] A copy of the Chinese version of *Diamond Sutra*, found among the Dunhuang manuscripts in the early 20th century and dated back to 868 CE, is, in the words of the British Library, "the earliest complete survival of a dated printed book." The book was block printed approximately 587 years before the Gutenberg Bible was first printed. The *Diamond Sutra* is from the Prajnaparametia genre, perhaps originally composed as far back as the 1st century CE. See Appendix, Diamond Sutra.

All conditioned phenomena
Are like dreams, illusions, bubbles, or shadows;
Like drops of dew, or flashes of lightning;
Thusly should they be contemplated.

~The Diamond Sutra (excerpt)[107]

The Heart Sutra[G] also appears to negate the existence of the flow of time as a "real" phenomenon. The term *Dharmas* means visions of reality, or in terms of the ToT, a relative self. Notice the denial of the verb-actions (create, extinguish, defile, increase and decrease) in this excerpt:

...all Dharmas are empty of appearances,
are not created, are not extinguished,
are not defiled, are not pure;
do not increase, do not decrease.

~The Heart Sutra (excerpt)

The appendix contains a small analysis of one of the *Yoga Sutras* of Patanjali, an ancient orally transmitted tradition that was first written about two thousand years ago. It describes how Patanjali may have held a non-temporal vision of reality.

In terms of the ToT, these ancient texts indicate a static sequence of MindMoments that is Instantaneous. The sequence does not describe a literal, active flow of time. The Experience of change is manifest as a comparison between iterations within the sequence; which is laid out across a time-like dimension. In this way the flow of time is an oExperience. Each sequence displays the oExperience of a complete universe in terms of a relative self. This vision of the universe is one of many visions that are intertwingled amongst one another because of the proximate Clouds of EQ that resolve to a shared universe comprised of all living beings. Later in the book we will discover that each vision of a shared universe is in sync with all other visions because effectively, they each hold the same value for c (the speed of light).

This communality for the value of c is one of the ways in which the ToT differs from the specific lines of logic found in Buddhism. The concept of a **MindMoment constant** is another.

The universe is not only stranger than we imagine, it is stranger than we *can* imagine.

~Arthur C. Clark, paraphrasing J. B. S. Haldane

[G] The *Heart Sutra* was likely composed in the 1st century CE. See the complete text in the Appendix, Heart Sutra.

THE MINDMOMENT CONSTANT

The *Abhidhamma* states that "...in the time it takes for lightning to flash or for the eyes to blink, billions of mind moments can elapse."[108] The duration of a mind moment changes in accordance with the commentator who is discussing the *Abhidhamma*. The general consensus is that it is very small and the actual number is not an issue. It also appears to me that originally the Buddha described the mind moment as instantaneous—but that would be a large discussion among the scholars. [I say this because for it to have a duration appears to be illogical.]

The dialectic schools of the Nyingma sect of Vajrayana Buddhism have logically negated the idea of a "mind moment" that exists for a very short duration of time. This negation lends credence to presumption that the concept was translated or interpreted wrongly. If this were not the case, either the Buddha would have to have made a logical error or someone intentionally fabricated the information—either situation appearing less likely than some long ago group of monks misinterpreting an extremely complex concept.

. . . .

For me, the first reference to a mind moment that I recall was in a lecture given by Ram Dass in the 70s. He said (I remember the words), "...there are ten trillion (10^{13}) mind-moments during a single eye blink." He apparently gained this information during his time studying with his guru in India. The statement provides the criterion for the stated number of MindMoments associated with a described (apparent) smallest unit of time in the ToT. This becomes what is called the **MindMoment constant,** denoted with the symbol $\tilde{A}$ (upper case "A" with a tilde). The **working value** for this constant is derived from a generalization of the information provided by Ram Dass. The value is effectively axiomatic, because the actual value is unknown in this universe and in all others. As you read on you will discover other constants unique to the lexicon and logic of the ToT. Their values will be a function of the working value of the ToT's primary, axiomatically defined constant—the MindMoment constant.

The working value for the MindMoment constant is derived as follows: If there are 10 trillion (10^{13}) MindMoments occurring during a single blink of an eye, and a blink of the eye is assumed to be 1/10 of one second in duration, then there are 100 trillion (10^{14}) MindMoments needed to produce the Experience of one second passing.

The MindMoment constant:

$$\tilde{A} = 10^{14} \, \text{Ш}/\text{sec}.$$

Where:
- Ш is the symbol for a MindMoment
- Ã the MindMoment constant

TIME ROUTES

Sequences of MindMoments describe an "apparent route of existence across an expanse of apparent time for a relative self". These sequence are called a **time routes** in the ToT lexicon. In terms of the absolute condition a time route resolves from a Cloud. In terms of a relative self an oExperience of an expanse of time flow is the syncategorematic rendition of the information held in a collection of MindMoments laid out across the time-like dimension of an n-manifold.

If we consider only substantial reality aspect of a relative self, a single time route is a sequential array of instant, three-dimensional, math objects with each object being an instant universe. The sequence is described as populating the time-like dimension of a 4-manifold. Each of these instant universes has a single point value on the four-dimensional hypersurface. In this way a time route is a super-set of instant 3-manifolds.

In terms of a contemporary scientific description of reality, every time route is expressed as containing a semblance of spacetime; because its makeup always includes a sequence of MindMoments that describe the three space-like dimensions and one time-like dimension. These are the dimensions of the phenomenal reality addressed by spacetime physics.

Time routes are comprised of a series of MindMoments. According to the description so far (given in terms of a view from the relative self) these are MindMoments only containing information resolving to time-past. However in terms of a view from the absolute condition, where all of the relative condition is evident simultaneously, a time route also contains MindMoments that resolve to time-future Experiences. Thus the full expression of a time route, from the vantage point of the Awareness of the absolute condition, is Experiences of time-past *and* time-future with the moment of the Now at the midpoint of the sequence. However the moment of the Now is always empty.

158

THE INDIVIDUATED SELF AND A SHEAF

Naked space is the seminal "launching pad" for the collection of information that is a time route. However, with respect to the viewpoint of a relative self, beings remember only one flow of time-past and expect only one flow of time-future. This is the nature of V.1. We can easily imagine a person saying: "In my reality, at any instant, the past is as it has transpired and the future can be only one of various multiple possibilities."

Now consider the idea of multiple time routes associated with a single individual existing simultaneously. They obviously can't resolve to a single relative self—that would be chaos. However, according to the ToT they can exist in a (somewhat) parallel fashion; and in so doing, as a group describe the single, grand definition of an individual—called an **Individuated SELF.**

An individuated SELF describes a gathering of time routes. Philosophically the term labels the grandest, most complete expression of an individual. In simple terms, it is the information that describes various, multiple renditions of a relative self, with each rendition laid out across a unique track in the time-like dimension. In this way, an individuated SELF is a gathering of time routes with each time route containing one of multiple possible versions of time-future and of time-past, all of which are associated with the same single individuated SELF at the moment of the Now.

Geometrically the collection is resident on the hypersurface of a temporal 4-manifold that provides the field upon which the various instant 4-manifolds are arrayed, *i.e.* the gathering of time routes.

A temporal 4-manifold is synonymous with a single point on the hypersurface of an instant 5-manifold. Here we are simply saying that a minimum of one extra dimension (number five) is needed to have a view of a temporal 4-manifold—and ultimately look at a gathering of many-dimensional time routes from the vantage point of the absolute condition.

In that context we can think of an individuated SELF as a bundle of sticks with each stick being a time route and with the midpoint of each stick in the bundle (the Now) occupying the same relative position in naked space. Think of the sticks as metaphorically gathered into a bundle called a **time route bundle** or a **Sheaf**; and think of a bundle as tied at the center with each end splayed out like a sheaf of wheat. The tie at the center of the bundle is envisioned as very tight—so tight that

159

the sticks merge together at that point. The tie point represents the nexus of all time route center points, which is the Now or the instantaneous moment of the present. In the lexicon of the ToT the information in a Sheaf resolves to an individuated SELF.

The term "sheaf" is a concept found in geometry. Its special meaning in the ToT is denoted with an uppercase "S".

A time route resolves from a Cloud of EQ. A Sheaf is similar in concept but one dimension larger. In the lexicon of the ToT it resolves from what's called a **meta-Cloud**.

To understand a Sheaf, consider the idea that the future has many possibilities (a concept that often comes to mind). Within the scope of an individuated SELF each possible time-future is represented by a separate and different time route—albeit with an associated separate and different time-past (a concept that seldom comes to mind). Each time route in a Sheaf is unique with a different time-future and a different time-past; but with the exact same moment of the Now.

Image of a sheaf of grain on a plaque.[109]

For the sake of a clear, easy to understand explanation, a Sheaf is being explained as containing a group of four-dimensional time routes.

160

This is reasonable because people generally see the substantial world around them (often their waking body) as the "thing" that is traveling through time. However it's clear that the relative self (which is synonymous with the time-past section of a time route) always contains a wealth of mental event information described by various dimensions other than spacetime. Because of this we should more correctly think of a time route as being represented by a stick with a bunch of hairs on it; and the hairs metaphorically reach into multiple other dimensions, *i.e.* those dimensions that contain information that indicating subjective mental events.

If we describe the constituents of a Sheaf as representing only spacetime reality, then a single time route represents the surface of an instant 4-manifold. When we consider the multiple time routes in a Sheaf, we are working with multiple instant 4-manifolds; or five dimensions of configuration space—which is expressed as the hypersurface of an instant **5-manifold**.

In general the book describes Sheaves as a five-dimensional instant manifold (for ease of description); but in all cases a Sheaf is understood to contain time routes of many dimensions more than four.

A CRYSTAL POLYHEDRON

A Sheaf defines the extent of individuated SELF. To better explain the nature of a Sheaf, imagine a huge assemblage of crystal balls floating in space, with each crystal ball representing the collection of Experiences comprising a unique MindMoment.

If we were to be inside one of the crystal balls, we would have an Experience of many straight-line views across the array of other crystal balls. The view from "our crystal" is analogous to the moment of the present, and all of the other crystals are viewed as if existing in the future or the past at some other apparent moment. Any "line of view" across the array of crystals is a time route; and it is also relative self if we are looking at the time-past section. Every other crystal in the line of view is a MindMoment, *i.e.* a group of Experiences or a package of instant information. Thus the relative self is a "view of time-past information packages."

To take this analogy further, imagine the collection of crystal balls extending in every direction: up, down, forward, back, left and right. Additionally, each crystal ball has been cut and polished such that it has a large number of symmetrical, parallel sides. In terms of geometry, it is no longer a sphere but rather a polyhedron. Its shape can be imagined as something like a light-reflecting mirror ball that is sometimes seen suspended and slowly spinning over a dance floor, throwing moving dots of light on the dancers. However, in this case there are many crystal polyhedrons and they are all transparent. They also float in space in very regular, straight-line patterns—horizontal, vertical and at multiple diagonal angles.

Now continue to imagine that you are inside of one of the polyhedrons and at its exact center. This is your crystal polyhedron. If you look at one of the flat sides and see through to the outside you will have a vision of a straight line-up of many other crystals that make up the neighborhood of floating crystals. Each of the crystals in the line-up that you see will be a slightly different color. Their differences appear to manifest in a progressive fashion because they each represent a different MindMoment in a sequence. The view through any one of the sides of your crystal will be of a different line-up of crystals extending away from your viewing crystal. In terms of the absolute condition you are capable of seeing all of the line-ups simultaneously in both directions—your view extends forward and backward in every direction, as if your eyes can see in all directions simultaneously. Each view of a line-up is analogous to a single time route as if had from the moment of the Now. In terms of a relative self your view is always into time-past, but you have great confidence in time-future extending out behind you, even though you can't really turn and look in that direction to see it.

The consideration of which direction is time-future and which is time-past is a result of anthropic denial (this is explained below).

Remember, none of the crystals are moving in this analog. Instead, you are at the moment of the Now... the center of the universe, capable employing a precise, selective view along any time route. It's a view had from the omnipotent absolute condition (Awareness). This selective viewing allows you to shift your angle of view from within your crystal. When you adopt a slightly different viewing angle your viewpoint will display a different line-up of the crystal polyhedrons for viewing, and thus a different relative self.

Each crystal in a line of crystals is a metaphoric "snapshot" of an instant in time-past, and the complete line-up is the relative self. But remember, this is an analog for an exposition of the ToT, and the ToT is an analog for reality. None of these grand conceptual patterns actually

162

describes the true nature of reality; but they might give us some tools to use.

In terms of a relative self we are able to see only the time-past section of any single lineup of crystals (*i.e.* one half of the total array). To have the Experience of time-future *and* time-past; or of all crystals simultaneously is anthropically denied (either case being undoubtedly confusing). Therefore, we always have an Experience of only the time-past portion of one time route—with respect to a relative self.

A feature of this analogy is that to recognize any crystal as a snapshot of a partial relative self (a MindMoment) we must see the outside of the crystal. This means our own crystal cannot be part of the lineup of crystals. This then describes the concept of the relative self being totally comprised of time-past MindMoments, and accordingly, the moment of the Now or the actual instant of the present is emptiness, or *shunyata*.

THE ARROW OF TIME

According to the ToT the arrow of time is the name of the oExperience of the direction of the flow of time. It reflects a pattern within a time route. It is not, as might be described in terms of a relative self, related to the basic nature of an actual flow of time.

The philosophical concept of the arrow of time arose out of the (seemingly) intuitive nature of entropy. Entropy is a measure of the disorganization in a system. For example, hot water molecules when gathered together (such as in a cup of hot coffee) express a lot of organization, thus the coffee will eventually cool to the surrounding room temperature. A physicist would say that a disorganized arrangement (cold coffee) has high entropy, whereas the ordered arrangement (hot coffee) has low entropy. Simply put: hot things cool.

In a relative self, the time-past portion of a time route, the arrow of time always points toward the moment of the Now. The arrow of time cannot manifest as an oExperience in a reverse direction because the sequence of MindMoments would be anthropically denied—*i.e.* they would not make sense with respect to the concept of causality as we know it. Other than anthropic denial there is no good reason for the direction of the arrow of time to be "forward" or "backward" with respect to a time route.

163

> In the science of physics, the equations used to de-
> scribe the simultaneous motions of large numbers of particles
> are valid regardless of the stated direction of the flow of time.

The arrow of time is a philosophical concept described in terms of a relative self. It is an oExperience of a direction—which is anthropically defined, and thus a feature of memory. However, recall that in the ToT memory is and oExperience and is part of the information package that *is* the relative self; thus the definition of the arrow of time is strongly related to the definition of the (Experience of) "self" and to the definition of the (oExperience of) memory. In the sciences these definitions are given in terms of the relative self and therefore they are, figuratively "held captive" by the framework in which they are embedded.

MORE ABOUT THE STOR

Within the ToT, a single Thought is described as resolving from a group of EQ. As a further classification, a set of Thoughts comprises a relative self—which is synonymous with the time-past portion of a time route. A gathering (or a bundle) of time routes comprises a Sheaf— that is described as resolving from a meta-Cloud.

In terms of the Stor a Sheaf can be thought of as a virtual encyclopedia of all elements of a certain individuated SELF. Recall that the Stor is defined as representing all the "stuff of reality" within the complete relative condition; but every individuated SELF describes a small, unique portion of the Stor. It is that portion that contains all possible Thoughts that resolve from the various collections of MindMoments that make up the multiple time routes in the Sheaf. A Sheaf defines the individuated SELF; and therefore a very small portion of the Stor contains all possible time-past and time-future Experiences that are associated with a each individuated SELF.

The principle of proximity is evident in the Stor. As stated above, proximity is defined according to any one of a variety of different dimensions—with each dimension indicating a different aspect of reality, be it of substantial objects or of subjective mental events.   All of the information in these various dimensions is resident in Stor and can be thought of as resolving from configurations of EQ patterns.

Each of the EQ patterns is in some fashion proximate to neighboring patterns. Some of these indicators of proximity are associated with phenomenal objects and some are associated with mental events.

For example, in terms of a V.1 universe: the emotional baggage associated with a traumatic event in a person's youth may stay with him or her for a lifetime (maybe 100 years in terms of a relative self). He or she may retain the anxiety without an overt memory of the cause of the anxiety. The Experience of the memory of anxiety could always be just one Thought away.

The Stor is also the virtual domain of information representing great lengths of time; however, the oExperience of such information generally does not occur because great lengths of time are not that useful in everyday life. Therefore, what is commonly termed to be the memory of a relative self generally encompasses events only as far back as early childhood.

As a counter point, Buddhism and some other teachings incorporate the concept of reincarnation. According to the ToT, various features of the human condition can be seen as remaining proximate across many life times,[H] even though they may not be "remembered*" well in a "present life."

NO SELF IN BUDDHISM

In Buddhism, there is the idea of "no self." This encompasses the idea that the <u>concept</u> of an "individual *per se*" (or the "self") does <u>not</u> reincarnate; instead the karmic milieu of what constitutes the apparent individual is described as ever-continuing *samsara*. The Buddhist idea of reincarnation, in terms of there being "no self", is evidenced in the ToT with the idea that the Matrix of EQ can ultimately resolve to information describing all lifetimes that have ever existed!

Therefore, in common terms—according to Buddhism—the concept of a "self", which is an Experience set within a flow of time, does not reincarnate. Instead, the "self" is said to create karmic situations that remain as issues with which a subsequent "self" will have to deal; because the (present) "self" is described as an entity that is comprised of, or strongly associated with, the karmic milieu. In this way, the "self", understood as a relative self, may contain an Experience of being a reflection of a previous incarnation. This description, of course, describes the "self" as acting in time in a verb-like fashion; therefore it doesn't fit with the logic of the ToT, where the question of there being a "self" or "no self" is simply not an issue—it's just another Experience.

[H] This assumes that information from multiple "life-times" is included in that portion of the Stor associated with an individuated SELF.

OVERVIEW OF NOMENCLATURE
THE STOR, MINDMOMENTS, SHEAVES, TIME ROUTES, CLOUDS, EQ, AND RELATIVE SELVES

Generally relating to the contents of a single Sheaf—which is a gathering of time routes, where three-dimensional substantial reality is the primary descriptor of reality.

1. The Stor contains all possible time-past and time-future Experiences that comprise the relative condition. In Buddhist terms it is a reflection of *samsara*.

2. A portion of the Stor contains all possible time-past and time-future Experiences that are associated with the bundle of time routes that comprise a certain Sheaf, and thus also with a individuated SELF.

3. A smaller portion of the Stor contains all possible time-past Experiences that are associated with a certain relative self, which is an expression of the time-past portion of a single time route.

4. A time route bundle (a Sheaf) resolves from a gathering of Clouds or a meta-Cloud.

5. A Sheaf is synonymous with a bundle of time routes.

6. A relative self is made up of (what appears to be) an iterative sequence of similar, gradually changing, *snapshots* of partial relative selves laid out in a fashion that yields oExperiences called "the past" and, these Experiences include "expectations of the future."

7. Each *snapshot* is called a MindMoment (denoted by the symbol Ш) and is defined as a package of Thoughts or a group of Experiences.

8. The sequential array of MindMoments from "time-past" to "time-future" is called a time route.

9. A single MindMoment is a virtual image of a single instantaneous point, either in time-past or time-future.

10. A relative self (time-past portion of a time route) contains the oExperience of a duration and a direction, called "the flow of time"—which always flows toward the Now; and can be expressed as the arrow of time.

11. There is no MindMoment that is associated with the moment of the Now—because it does not hold a position in time-past or time-future.

166

12. From the vantage point of the absolute condition the Now is the seat of the relative self and the central focus of the MindMoments comprising a time route.

13. In the ToT lexicon each successive MindMoment extending backward in sequence from the Now (describing "time-past") is denoted with a negative numeric subscript; e.g. $Ш_{-1}$, $Ш_{-2}$, $Ш_{-3}$... etc.; with $Ш_{-1}$ being the most contemporary.

14. Each successive MindMoment extending forward in sequence from the Now (describing "time-future") is denoted with a positive numeric subscript; e.g. $Ш_1$, $Ш_2$, $Ш_3$ ... etc.; and $Ш_1$ is the most contemporary.

15. A MindMoment with the designation of $Ш_0$ (MindMoment zero) is a placeholder indicating the moment of the Now of the relative self. $Ш_0$ is not a true MindMoment. It is empty.

16. The substantial reality portion of the relative self is a sequence of instant 3-manifolds. When the sequence is Parsed by Awareness it becomes a temporal 3-manifold. As this occurs* the complete time route, not just the time-past portion (*i.e.* the relative self) is displayed as a single representation on the hypersurface of an instant 4-manifold. The instant 4-manifold expresses a time-like configuration space.

17. For ease of explanation, the multiple time routes comprising a Sheaf are described only by the information resulting in the substantial reality of spacetime. Thus we see a Sheaf portrayed as multiple instant 4-manifolds on the hypersurface of an instant 5-manifold.

18. The moment of the present, the Now, is a single point where a gathering of time routes (a Sheaf) come together.

19. A Sheaf is the grandest conceptualization of an individuated SELF.

Note that a sequence of a least two consecutive MindMoments is the smallest expression of existence *in the context of a space and time universe*. Thus, if there is to be an Experience of existence in spacetime; then a MindMoment must be part of a sequence. If it isn't the oExperience of time flow, the Experience of location and the oExperience of movement cannot manifest. Recall that all information is relative to other information.

EINSTEIN'S INSTANT

The Instancy Principle states the universe is Instantaneous, and the "flow of time" is an Experience included in that Instant.

The Instancy principle specifically addresses (and stands opposed to) the concept that phenomenal objects are substantial and exist in spacetime. Defining existence as continuous within the flow of time leads to logical problems like Zeno's paradox.

Albert Einstein did not agree with all of what we see today in the field of physics. He did not believe that quantum mechanics constituted a complete theory of physical reality. He understood that quantum mechanics can let us predict outcomes but it cannot tell us why they occur. In this way, Einstein believed that the quantum theory was incomplete and something more needed to be added—a deeper layer needed to be discovered. He spent the latter part of his life looking for a unified theory that would describe that deeper layer, but never found it.

Einstein was obviously correct about quantum theory being incomplete. His conclusions were based in large part on what he called the "spooky" and uncertain aspects of quantum mechanics; but I believe that his failure to complete a unified theory was owed to what I would describe as an incomplete understanding of the "self"—which in the ToT is the individuated SELF.

From my point of view Einstein and in general, Western science, held (and still holds) that the existence of the "self" is fully described by the four dimensions of spacetime. As I see it, Professor-Einstein did not consider that the *complete* uniqueness that was "Albert Einstein" *must also be accounted for* within the unified theory he was attempting to construct. For Einstein, it appears that the relevant existence of a person was defined as one's physical presence within spacetime—where the full breath of a being's physical existence is a small, metaphoric "slice" of spacetime equal to the duration of a person's life. According to the ToT, this definition of existence is simply a statement about the limits of the Sheaf.

Within the ToT (using the same slice metaphor) reality is defined using two concepts of the moment. One called an instant and the other, the Instant.

An instant is the smallest possible (quantum) "slice" of spacetime, which amounts to the breath of one quanta of Experience.

In this context, we could say that an Instant of reality is one where all of the MindMoments in a time route are said to occur simultaneously in the same Instant; and a relative self is said to be Instantaneous

168

because it resolves from a single, "snapshot" view of the time-past section of a time route.

> Question: What time is it?
> Answer: "...you mean now?"
> ~Attributed to Yogi Berra

In the Instant of a V.1 shared universe there are many beings, and thus there are many relative selves and therefore many associated individuated SELVES, and respectively many Sheaves. The duration of a Sheaf containing multiple time routes is Instantaneous.

The timelessness of the absolute condition is also described as the Instant. It encompasses all of the sequential instants of the relative condition. The Instant is the only possible Instant that can occur (will occur, or ever has occurred). It is the timeless Instant of existence of naked space. It is the Instant of existence of the genitive potentiality (space warps) that manifest as EQ (plural) which together resolve to all of the possible relative selves of all beings that can ever appear to exist across *samsara*.

From the viewpoint of the relative condition, the elements of *samsara* occur sequentially in a series of <u>instants</u>. From the viewpoint of the absolute condition, all of *samsara* occurs in a single <u>Instant</u>.

That is all that there is! There is *no* true flow of time whatsoever! Within the one and only Instant of existence there is the incredibly large number of (apparently sequential) instantaneous relative selves, each one of them being a self-contained, solo universe. This is another statement of the Instancy principle.

Imbedded in the Instancy principle is the simple idea that a relative self doesn't need an actual flow of time to exist—it does very well on its own with the illusion of such.

TIME ROUTES ON POINT

Within the ToT there is a certain understanding of the Anthropic principle. Another way to express the nature of this principle is (what I term to be) the **persistence of reality**. It expresses the Experience of "continuing to be" who one thinks one is as the surrounding world continues to exist as he/she remembers it to be.

> The man said: "It's been raining for days. Do you think it will stop?"
> I replied: "Historically it always has."
> ~Attributed to Mark Twain

169

To "see the world as it is remembered to be" is a statement about the nature of the present; and in the moment of that present is the collection of Experiences that comprise a relative self. That collection is made up of the Experiences associated with the MindMoments comprising the time-past portion of one of the time routes that make up a Sheaf. It is also a vision that is intertwingled in various ways with all other visions within the V.1 shared universe. Katy Butler, in her book, *Knocking on Heaven's Door*, nicely applauds humanities interconnectedness with a description of "Indra's Net", a concept found in Buddhism that describes how all phenomena are intimately connected.

Indra's Net is a metaphor used in Buddhist philosophy.[110]

"Indra's Net, [is] an ancient Buddhist metaphor for the interrelatedness of all life. The Net of Indra is a vast, bejeweled matrix spanning and encompassing the whole universe."

"Imagine a multidimensional spider's web in the early morning covered with dew drops. And every dew drop contains the reflection of all the other dew drops. And, in each reflected dew drop, the reflections of all the other dew drops in that reflection. And so on *ad infinitum*. That is the Buddhist conception of the universe in an image."

~Alan Watts[111]

Indra's Net is similar to the view of a shared V.1 universe as seen from the vantage point of a Sheaf. The bundle of time routes that make up a Sheaf is comprised of many individual time routes. However, with respect to a certain relative self, there is only one time route whose constituent EQ resolve to the Experiences of time-past and an implied time-future. This certain time route is called the **time route on point** and the information in the time-past portion of that time route resolves to a solo universe—which is V.1 described only with information contained in a certain relative self. All other time routes are called **alternate time routes** and do not resolve to a set of Experiences in a V.1 solo universe *according to the time route on point.*

> Recall that a solo universe is the information describing the V.1 universe from only the perspective of a single relative self.

Therefore, a time route on point is the one that affords the Experience of being alive *with respect to the associated relative self*—a self-serving definition that will be useful in the pages to come.

With respect to a view of the complete Sheaf, all of the time routes afford the Experience of being alive—from their respective viewpoints.

An alternate time route is analogous to different, unviewed, "lines of sight" through the above-described array of crystal polyhedrons (the dance hall mirror balls). An alternate time route can be thought of as any line-up of crystals not resolving to the Experience of "the past" and "implied future" in the V.1 solo universe in play.

COMPARISON OF RELITIVE CONDITION CONCEPTS:

Four closely related concepts have so far been introduced. They are all within the relative condition; and, in terms of substantial reality, they all represent a configuration space described by the surface of an instant 4-manifold.

o   <u>Time route:</u> whose definition emphasizes a vision of a temporal Universe existing in a flow of time, from time-past into time-future.
o   <u>Relative self:</u> whose definition emphasizes a concept of the individual.
o   <u>Solo Universe:</u> whose definition emphasizes the cosmos and the three dimensional world around a single being.

171

- o   <u>Shared Universe:</u> whose definition emphasizes the cosmos and the three dimensional world that are shared between multiple beings (via resolving from overlapping Clouds of EQ).
- o   <u>Instant Universe:</u> whose definition emphasizes the cosmos and the three-dimensional world in a single instantaneous, shared (or solo) universe.

A SHIFT OF PRESENCE

Sometimes beings have an Experience that is unexpected, as when something (that is apparently) extraordinary suddenly occurs and the world is not ... *as it is remembered to be*. Reality appears to have abruptly changed! In the ToT, this is explained as related to the multitude of time routes associated with a Sheaf.

Consider the following: According to the ToT a shift in the status of a time route between on point and alternate can only occur at the moment of the present within the domain of the Sheaf—which defines multiple time routes (both on point and alternate). However, a Sheaf is Instantaneous and the moment of the present is in the Instant; therefore an action (*i.e.* to "shift*") is disallowed because there is no time in which the action can transpire. How can this be?

For now, you must (for a little while) take it on faith that some sort of *shift** (a verb) between the time routes can logically occur—even though no action is allowed. When a shift does occur, it is called a **Shift** or a **Shift of presence**. The two terms are synonymous. The term indicates a different time route on point—in the context of a Sheaf. It is appropriate to describe it in terms of this view, because from the viewpoint of the relative self, the presence of Awareness is always limited to "the time-past portion of the on point time route".

DOLANGI, A BONPO MONASTERY:

A small travel story may help explain the concept of a Shift. In 1988 I visited *Dolangi*, a Tibetan Bonpo[I] monastery in Northern India. The monks who founded Dolangi were refugees from Tibet following China's Cultural Revolution. They traveled by foot over the Himalayan mountain passes carrying very little other than their books. The Dalai

---

[I] **Bon** is the oldest spiritual tradition of Tibet, predating Buddhism by at least a millennium. Some translations of the word "Bon" describe it as an expression of the unending, forever flowing power of the universe. A Bonpo is a follower of the Bon tradition.

Lama was also a refugee but at a different time. He decided to settle in Dharmsala, India. *Dolangi* is some miles away near the town of Shimla in the Indian state of Himachal Pradesh.

Shimla can be reached by riding a delightful narrow gauge train that winds, climbs and tunnels through the Himalayan foothills. The route is topologically intense. At one point the front of the train crossed a bridge that was directly above rails where the rear end of the train had just traveled.

I visited *Dolangi* for two weeks in order to shoot a small documentary of a celebration. The Bon lineage is older than Buddhism. Present-day Yungdrung Bon is an evolution of the original Bon found in the ancient kingdom of Zhang Zhung; and facets of certain Bon ceremonies are ancient. Part of the celebration was a dance in which the monks wore masks, with each mask representing a deity or entity that was associated with a certain conceptualization or type of energy. Before the dance began, I was shooting in the room where the masks were stored. I remember the abbot of the monastery walking by the door, peeking in and saying: ". . . watch your dreams tonight." My dreams were especially intense that evening.

H.E. Yöngdzin Lopön Tenzin Namdak Rinpoche. Founder of Triten Norbutse Monastery, Kathmandu, Nepal.[112] Lopon Tenzin Namdak is one of the most learned teachers in the Bon tradition.

At another point I shot images of a large, 900-year-old book hand written in gold ink on carbon-blackened paper. It was about three feet long and a foot wide. The wood cover had ¼-inch thick intaglio letters in solid gold. The book was entitled *Zermig*, and it told the life story of Shenrab Miwoche, the traditional founder of the Bon lineage who lived c. 4,000 years ago.

The ceremonies, the books, the dances, the artifacts, etc. are all part of the multi-millennial lineage. The monastery was a place of learning with a dialectic debate school that promoted the traditional Tibetan style of that practice. This debate style is extremely active involving wild, waving arms, lunging bodies, and shouting. Not violent, just very dynamic and designed to develop a certain viewpoint on Awareness. All in all, the monastery schools offered a curriculum that could take a small child through grade school, middle school and on up to, more or less, a Western PhD-equivalent level.

The main teacher at the monastery was the Lopön Tenzin Namdak,. I was pleased to have met him. Once when we were having tea, he casually told me that there were five dimensions surrounding the planet Earth. He was talking about realms of existence in the context of Bon tradition. I thought about this for a long time. Eventually I came to the understanding that he was trying to communicate that it is possible to work with the reality maps that define the world around you and shift or change them at will. However, one must be able to consciously rest in the knowledge of each reality map being the full extent of the world we experience*; while at the same time knowing full well that the reality map is simply a point of view (*i.e.* an illusion).

This understanding was for me a gateway to the process of learning to see the world as an illusory manifestation; and the basis of ToT's assertion that a Shift of presence is closely related to causality.

A Sheaf is essentially a 5-manifold; and when a Shift takes place, it happens within the five dimensional configuration space defined by the Sheaf, at its nexus. [Is this the five-dimensionality which the Lopon was referring to? It could be.] When a Shift does occur, a *new* time route is designated as "on point" within the Sheaf. Note that the term: "*new* time route" is a temporal oxymoron; however the use of the word *new* helps explain the concept. The word is italicized to indicate its special meaning.

In the ToT the concept of a Shift of presence is intrinsically related to the temporal synchronization among all Sheaves within the V.1 shared universe. Call it **reality sync**.

Grammatically, the statement that something is synchronized or is not synchronized in a timeless reality is an oxymoron, because synchronization requires time flow. Within the ToT, the **reality sync** is used with respect to the relative position of the Experiences comprising the MindMoments, not to time being conceptualized as a "real" phenomenon. Reality sync is strongly related to the quantum interspace.

THE QUANTUM INTERSPACE

Recall that in the ToT, the number of MindMoments that provide the Experience of one unit of flowing time is a constant within the V.1 shared universe. It's called the MindMoment constant ($\tilde{A}$).

With this in mind consider the ever present natural feature of the universe—the speed of light. It is denoted by the character "c" (lower case) and it is given a certain value that holds across the V.1 universe in all inertial systems and in all directions. The approximate standard value for c is 3×10^8 meters per second in a vacuum[J]; and it is the maximum possible speed of a phenomenal object in V.1.

The previous paragraph speaks of two interesting concepts; the speed of light and the inertial system; both of which are related to the quantum interspace.

According to special relativity, c (the speed of light) is the maximum speed at which all matter and information in the universe can travel. It is the speed at which all massless particles and changes of the associated fields (including electromagnetic radiation such as light and gravitational waves) travel in vacuum. Such particles and waves travel at c regardless of the motion of the source or the inertial frame of reference [the inertial system] of the observer.[113]

In the physical sciences an **inertial system** is a frame of reference in which a body remains at rest or moves with constant linear velocity unless acted upon by forces. Any frame of reference that moves with constant velocity relative to an inertial system is itself an inertial system.[114]

[J] It's also often expressed as 186,000 miles per second.

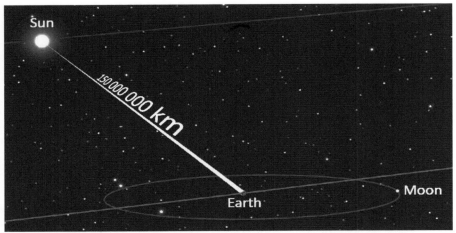

Sunlight takes about 8 minutes 17 seconds to travel the average distance from the surface of the Sun to the Earth.[115]

THE SPEED OF LIGHT IN THE V.1 UNIVERSE.[116]

Exact Values of c

- meters per second   299792458
- Planck length per Planck time   1
  (i.e., Planck units)

Approximate Values of *c*

- meters per second   300,000,000 (3x10⁸)
- kilometers per second   300,000
- miles per second   186,000
- kilometers per hour   1,080,000
- miles per hour   671 million

Approximate Light Signal Travel Times

- one foot   1.0 ns
- one meter   3.3 ns
- from a satellite in Earth orbit   119 ns
  (Geostationary)
- the length of Earth's equator   134 ns
- from Moon to Earth   1.3 seconds
- from Sun to Earth   8.3 minutes
- from nearest star to Sun   4.2 years
- across the Milky Way galaxy   100,000 years

The abbreviation "ns" stands for "nanosecond", one billionth of a second.

In the ToT there is the concept of an absolute minimum change in position. It is called the **quantum interspace,** denoted by the Greek letter Φ (Greek letter phi, upper case). The value for Φ describes the Experience of a change in position between two MindMoments that contain the Experience of an object moving at luminal velocity.

When there is *any* Experience of movement, the distance moved is equal to a quantum interspace (the value of Φ) or there is no movement at all. Thus the quantum interspace is the shortest distance that may be an Experience. It is always an nExperience because it cannot be a composite of shorter distances.

A MindMoment almost always contains multiple phenomenal objects; and the quantum interspace describes the Experience of movement (if any) of one or more of these objects. Thus a single MindMoment may contain EQ that resolve to objects which move* and others which do not move*.

To reiterate, if there is an Experience of a change in position for any of the objects, the change will be a distance equal to the value of Φ, or there will be *no* change in position. The "movement" of a phenomenal object is always with respect to a most recent, time-past MindMoment; and the term "phenomenal object" can refer to objects of very different sizes, from sub-atomic to something larger than a star. The "size" of what moves is according to the scope of the Experience.

The mathematical expression for Φ is:

$$\frac{c}{\tilde{A}} = \Phi$$

Where the units are meters per MindMoment:
- c is the speed of light in a vacuum. (3×10^8 m/sec).
- $\tilde{A}$ is the MindMoment constant (10^{14} Ш/sec).
- Φ is the quantum interspace (3×10^{-6} m/Ш).

The speed of light can be described as the Experience of a change in position equal to 3×10^8 meters during the Experience of 10^{14} MindMoments (where the value for $\tilde{A}$ is the standard value for this rendition of the ToT.)

Thus the value for Φ is:

$$\Phi = \frac{3x10^8 \ meters}{10^{14} \ MindMoments}$$

…which resolves to:

$$\Phi = \frac{3x10^{-6} meters}{MindMoment} = 3x10^{-6} \ meters/MindMoment.$$

A distance of 10^{-6} meters is called a "micron" and it is not a very small distance in the molecular and atomic realms. Thus it is probable that the value for $\tilde{A}$ is much greater than 10^{14} Ш/sec.

It appears the lower limit for Φ is a single Planck length. Current theory suggests that one Planck length is the smallest distance or size about which anything can be known. One Planck length equals approximately $1.62 \ x10^{-35}$ meters.

According to the principle of the quantum interspace, the value for Φ is constant within a V.1 shared universe and is the basis for the lock-step synchronization described by reality sync (for the three space-like dimensions). Therefore if, in the V.1 universe, there is a change in position indicated between two adjacent MindMoments in a time route, the change is equal to the quantum interspace; and the time route bundles of any Sheaf are in reality sync with the time route bundles of all Sheaves in a V.1 shared universe. This includes both the on point time routes and the alternate time routes.

Any change in position is an Experience. Distance, position and time are an Experience.

THE SELF CENTER OF MASS—THE SCM

According to the ToT nothing moves in the absolute condition. There is no time with which to describe a change in position or a velocity (it's non-temporal); and there are no concepts of position (the absolute condition is non-local). The relative condition it is different, it has temporality and locality because of the profusion of information.

The Experience of movement is a major feature of each relative self because the included information package includes a phenomenal body. The ToT axiomatically defines the center of mass of each phenomenal body to be <u>at rest</u>—according to a viewpoint of the associated relative self. Its center of mass is called the **self-center of mass** (the

SCM). In the ToT all Experiences of velocity are accorded to phenomenal objects outside of the SCM. To repeat: the <u>SCM is always at rest</u>.

The SCM is an Overlain Experience that is a virtual concept. It does not functionally represent any substantial object or movement; but it does serve as the figurative axis mundi in V.1 for the position of all objects, any motion they may display and the apparent momentum of their inertial systems. It is the **virtual center point** of a relative self. The SCM sits as a still-point to the Experience of the relativistic flows of time associated with all other objects in a time route expressing different inertial systems. In this way it is instrumental in allowing the ToT to explain time dilation. (More on this below.)

The SCM conceptually rests in the moment of the Now. It is an unusual oExperience that describes the absence of any change and the absence of any movement. It is defined as an oExperience because it is a function of the other MindMoments in a time route in that it expresses what they are not—completely still and devoid of all movement. It is termed an oExperience because it results from a comparison of the information in multiple MindMoments.

The SCM never moves. From the perspective of the relative self everything in the phenomenal universe except the SCM is subject to a change in position. For example, there is almost always some sort of molecular movement that manifests as an Experience of thermal energy. Even at absolute zero (a theoretical limit point) where all thermal energy is removed, there still remains some ground state kinetic energy.[117]

> The detector used on the W.M. Keck telescope at the summit of Mauna Kea in Hawaii is sometimes operated at close to four degrees Kelvin. This is one of the lowest temperatures used in a practical application.
>
> In laboratory experiments at Helsinki University, temperatures reportedly have come within a few billionths of a degree of absolute zero.[118]

SOME CONSTANTS USED IN THE TOT:
- o $\tilde{A} = 10^{14}$ Ш/s, the MindMoment constant, (in MindMoments per second).
- o $\Phi = 3 \times 10^{-6}$ m/Ш, the quantum interspac*e* (meters per Mind-Moment).
- o $c = 3 \times 10^8$ m/s, the speed of light (in meters per second).

Consider the Experience of one second of time for an object moving ten meters per second. In this situation the object moves a distance of 10 meters in one second; or, there is an Experience of a change in position of 10 meters in 10^{14} MindMoments.

However, according to the quantum interspace principle any change in position between MindMoments must be exactly equal to the value for Φ. Therefore a change in position of one meter will amount to 3×10^6 small steps; and a change in position of 10 meters will amount to 3×10^7 small steps.

Accordingly, we find that the distance traveled can be split up into 3×10^7 pieces, with each piece being equal to the value of Φ.

Being that there are 10^{14} MindMoments needed to produce the Experience of one second of time, we can set up a ratio between the number of steps moved and the number of MindMoments in one second.

$$\frac{3x10^7}{3x10^{14}} = 10^{-7}$$

This tells us that for an object moving at 10 m/s, approximately one in every 10^7 (that's one in 10 million) MindMoments will include the Experience of a position shift equal to the value of Φ. (*None* of the other intermediate MindMoments will manifest a position shift.)

At the other extreme, if humans could have the Experience of the movement of a photon traveling at the speed of light for one second, the position shift would equal the value of Φ for every MindMoment.

For example: if you are standing beside a road and have an Experience of an automobile traveling past at a speed of 65 miles per hour (about 30 meters per second) only a small portion of the MindMoments comprising the oExperience (relating to the auto) will resolve to an Experience of a position shift.

If you are standing on earth and have an Experience of a space ship passing by at 80 percent of the speed of light, a large portion of the MindMoments comprising the oExperience (of the spaceship) will include an Experience of a position shift (the associated relativistic time dilation is discussed below.)

If you have an Experience of a rock resting in the landscape of a still, windless night in the Antarctic winter, only a very small portion of the MindMoments comprising the oExperience (relating to the rock) will include a position shift.   If the temperature of rock were even colder—close to absolute zero—very few of the MindMoments comprising the oExperience would include an Experience of a position shift—not to mention the requirement for extremely sensitive equipment.

In all cases the change in position relates to the moving object, not to the SCM. The Experience of movement never applies to the SCM. The quantum interspace essentially describes the quantification of the Experience of position. We can employ this principle to solve an old puzzle.

> In c. 450 BCE, Zeno of Elea posed a paradoxical assertion (which has come to be called "Zeno's Paradox"). The essence of Zeno's assertion is that logically an object must always move one half of the distance to its destination in a subsequent interval of time, and thus it can never arrive at its destination because the object will always be in a position that is one half of the distance to the finish line.
>
> Yet moving objects do reach their destinations—a paradox! This paradox holds if a change in position (or the Experience of it) is not quantum in nature. If the Experience is quantum in nature, Zeno's description will hold true until the length to be traversed is reduced to an amount equal to Φ (the quantum interspace). At that point the Experience of the moving object will change position one final interval in an amount equal to the value of Φ, and thus cross the finish line.

The quantum interspace principle is associated with the principle of reality sync—which explains how we all together have the Experience of synchronous movement in the phenomenal world. The quantum interspace (Φ) is based on the velocity of light; therefore, because all of us together measure and agree on that velocity, we are in reality sync.

Velocity is defined as distance divided by time. Definitions of a span of time are environmentally based (as a function of phenomenal reality) since they develop according to some mutual sequential Experience in the V.1 universe. For example, with respect to the planet earth, time is described in terms of the diurnal cycle (one day equals 24 hours).

Definitions of distance are also generally environmentally based. They develop according to some mutual Experience of a describable phenomenal object. For example, the length of a meter was originally defined as $\frac{1}{10,000,000}$ of the length of the meridian through Paris between the Earth's North pole and the equator. In 1983, after the speed of light was accurately measured, it was re-defined as the distance travelled by light in a vacuum in $\frac{1}{299,792,458}$ second.

THE EXPERIENCE OF SHAPE

The Features of the EQ patterns in the space-like dimensions of a Cloud resolve to information that comprises the three-dimensional reality, the shape, of the V.1 universe. These Features do not resolve to information that is the Experience of the mass of the object.

The mass of a black hole, for example, may be equal to a star but the size and shape of the star is something much different (larger!) than the black hole. The Experience of a stellar object resolves from a group of EQ. The shape, size, color, mass etc. of a stellar object all resolve form different Features of the associated EQ, with each of these features representing different dimensions in the EQ and in the resulting n-manifold of the relative condition. This explanation of course holds for all phenomenal objects, not just stellar objects.

> Recall that there is always the possibility of information being contained in the various higher dimensions of an n-manifold. Each of these dimensions are orthogonal (at ninety degrees) to all other dimensions describing the manifold. Because of this, the information in each of the levels is successively unique and can resolve to many and various aspects of an Experience (such as the mass of a stellar object.)

PARALLEL UNIVERSES

An unusual and profound feature of the ToT is the axiomatic assertion that there are an indefinitely large number of different, **parallel universes** figuratively laid upon naked space, and that all of them hold the same value for the MindMoment constant, Ã. Together these universes form a single **multiverse**.

In terms of the relative condition this is a statement that the number of "instances of reality" per "unit of time" is the same for every universe in the multiverse. The phrase "instance of reality" is a single MindMoment.

Call each parallel universe a **V.n universe**, or a simply **V.n.** Each V.n universe differs one from another by their value for the quantum interspace, Φ. It is axiomatic within the ToT that there may exist an indefinitely large (maybe infinite) number of V.n universes each with a unique value for the quantum interspace. Thus each V.n universe has a

182

different value for Φ, and consequently a different value for c. Whether Φ is quantum in nature, or whether there is a range of "habitable" values for Φ is a matter of conjecture.

In this way the ToT describes multiple, mutually exclusive parallel universes, each with its own V.n classification—like V.1, V.2, V.3, etc. where each of these classifications has an exclusive value for Φ; and each is *not* in reality sync with *any* other universe. These Universes comprise the multiverse, a combination of all possible universes.

Imagine the EQ patterns that comprise coherent Clouds in V.1. An EQ that resolve to a substantial Experience-object in spacetime will have a Feature that resolves to a value for Φ. Imagine that the value for that feature is on a gradient populated by a number of other values. This could result in large number individuated SELVES identical in every way except for their value of Φ.

From this comes an array of perfectly, identical images of the V.1 universe across the multiverse V.n universes. Substantial elements of these doppelgangers cannot resolve to an Experience in the V.1 universe because they have different values for Φ, and thus no lock-step reality sync.

An analogy that describes the "out of sync" situation between parallel universes can be seen when we compare the Fahrenheit and Celsius temperature scales. At -40°, the two scales measure the same temperature. This is the only point at which the numbers on the two thermometers are in sync; but the slightest deviation from that point and they will be out of sync.

The increments on the Fahrenheit scale are larger than on the Celsius scale. For example if we heat a piece of -40° ice to its melting point the Celsius scale rises 40 degrees (to 0°C) and the Fahrenheit scale rises 72 degrees (to 32°F). A similar discrepancy in scales occurs as we take heat out of the system. If we freeze a piece of ice to -100 degrees Celsius the Fahrenheit thermometer will read -148 degrees. There is only one point (-40°) where the two temperature systems are in sync; and that point is analogous to the instantaneous moment of the present in the two parallel universes.

The concept of parallel universes is similar to certain facets of holistic Eastern philosophy that hold that all of reality is to be found in the instantaneous moment of the present. In the ToT this moment may also include a doorway into parallel universes; but that is an extensive discussion not dealt with in this writing.

There are meditative practices that lead to a quasi-awareness* of such a point of presence; but maintaining* it is a tricky thing to do during meditation because it touches deeply on the five-dimensional nature of the individuated SELF, a decidedly ephemeral state of existence that is *non-personal* in nature. It is a state of being that is best described as "tasting" Awareness in the moment of the present—a fleeting concept.

To further the discussion of reality sync: Consider two *parallel* universes called: V.1 and V.2. Every being (every relative self) in the V.1 universe is in sync because the value of Φ associated with every time route is equal. The same is true in V.2, but since the value for Φ in V.1 does not equal the value in V.2 nothing in V.1 will be in sync with V.2.

Reality sync in any universe applies only to those Experiences containing the spacetime dimensions. This is because reality sync is ultimately related to the Experience of movement—which is a function of an Experience of a change in position (equal to the value of Φ) between MindMoments. The Experience of movement is related to the physical body—which is usually considered to be the "self", in terms of the relative self. The synchronization of the Experiences not defined by the spacetime dimensions is based on a different principle.

REALITY SYNC AND MENTAL EVENTS

Every Sheaf is made up of a collection of Experiences that fall into one of two classifications: those that are phenomenal reality or those that are mental events. Experiences that are mental events are those in the domain of emotion or personal spirit such as: feeling good, feeling bad, enjoying a pleasant fragrance, reacting to music, appreciating art, feeling fear, feeling hope, falling in love, anger, etc.

The reason both classifications of Experience are in reality sync is because those Experiences containing the spacetime dimensions define the shape and limits of the physical body of a being, as well as the oExperience of the flow of time. These features of the phenomenal universe are crucial because, with respect to the present planet-wide karmic vision, there is an almost universally recognized concept of a "self" that is one-in-the-same with a being's physical body. The concept of "self" is considered to be the perceiver of all Experiences; including the Experiences of mental events. In this way, all Experiences are seen to be a function of a being's physical body, which is defined by the spacetime dimensions.

184

> Through the power of habit I have come to view an insignif-
> icant sperm and egg as myself.
>
> ~ Shantideva[K]

The following example is in the context of a relative self where a "self" is a person who experiences* something in time.

Consider two people sitting quietly looking at a tree whose limbs are swaying in the wind. During some short period of time, both people will have a simultaneous experience* of the tree limbs bending. However, they will likely have completely different experiences* of mental events—*i.e.* private thoughts that could be about anything (there is little likelihood that the two people will be thinking the same private thoughts). All of their thoughts, however, will be in sync.

Rephrasing this to employ terms found in the ToT it becomes: Consider two relative selves that contain the Experiences of sitting quietly looking at a certain tree with its limbs swaying in the wind. At some instant both relative selves will contain a synchronized Experience of the tree limbs bending. However, both relative selves will likely also contain Experiences that are completely different mental events—*i.e.* private thoughts. In this fashion, because substantial objects are in sync, their bodies are in sync, and all of their Thoughts are also in sync.

All Thoughts are in reality sync because the groups of EQ that have levels of information resolving to Experiences of mental events also define some Experience of a physical object (defined by the spacetime dimensions). The physical object is usually the physical body—unless the being is dreaming.

DREAM STATES

The ToT posits a fairly simple description of the **dream state**. During the dream state there are exceptions to the synchronization of Experiences, whether they are of mental events or of physical objects.[L] During certain stages of the dream state the Experiences that comprise the relative self are not always associated with the phenomenal body because the Experiences relating to the physical senses are intermittent or

---

[K] Shantideva (c.685-763CE) was an 8th-century Indian Buddhist scholar at Nalanda University and an adherent of the Madhyamaka philosophy of Nagarjuna.
[L] Exceptions to synchronization may also result if a person is under the influence of what's termed a "mind-altering drug" or a disease. However, this writing of the ToT does not deal with these categories.

missing. In this description the physical senses are: sight, hearing, taste, touch and smell.

In the Tibetan culture there is the recognition of another sense called the "mind". In terms of the ToT, this is the sense that is associated with an Experience that is a mental event; and it is also the sense overwhelmingly responsible for the Experience of the continuity of being during the dream state. During the waking state this Experience is related to the physical body.

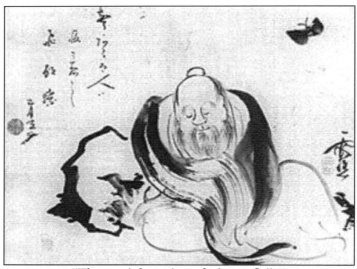

"Zhuangzi dreaming of a butterfly"[119]
Zhuangzi was a Chinese philosopher, c. 4th century BCE. When asleep he was dreaming of a butterfly. When he awakened he asked: "am I awake or am I a butterfly dreaming of a man?"

The result of this is that in the dream state, the Experiences that are associated with a certain relative self are usually not in reality sync with the Experiences of other relative selves in V.1 because an Experience of the physical body is not always in play—in other words, the space-like dimensions are not an issue in the Experience which is the concept of the "self".

Recall that the: the *persistence of reality* expresses the Experience of "continuing to be" who one thinks one is as the surrounding world continues to exist as it is remembered.

A break in the persistence of reality means that the on point time route is seemingly divided into a random sequence of disjointed sections made up of groupings of MindMoments from various sections of the time route. One or more of these groupings of MindMoments can resolve to an Experience that is a time-past or a time-future event—with respect to the karmic milieu of the dreamer.[M]

> In terms of the relative condition, it appears that the Experience of a memory (of a time-past event) is what Freud identified as the source of dream instigation. Whereas according to the ToT, the Experience of a memory *is the dream*.
>
> The *analysis* (that Freud is famous for) is a systematic understanding of a person's most probable karmic milieu which is indicated by the Experience of the dream.

The random sequence of disjointed groupings of MindMoments is also considered to be the basis of a premonition or a precognition—which are often a part of the dream state. Such Experiences are what allows information to apparently "move backwards in time" with respect to the arrow of time.

This mixture of what appears to be time-past and time-future Experiences is the nature of the relative self during a dream state. A dream state is where disjointed iterative collections of Experiences comprise the time route that is responsible for the Experience of a relative self. Call this sequence of disjointed Experiences a **pseudo time route**. In such a situation, some of the Experiences may resolve from EQ patterns resident in a variety of time routes contained in the being's Sheaf. The oExperience that is the flow of time (according to the pseudo time route) describes various, sometimes intermingled time-futures and time-pasts. The determination of which is which is left to the individual when they awaken. The *kahunas* (priests) of ancient Hawaii had a similar problem.

> In pre-contact Hawaii (before 1778) the *heiaus* (temples) often included an oracle tower, called an *anu'u* in Hawaiian. It was a place where a *kahuna* could speak with the spirits and gain information about time-future events. A *kahuna* was trained in recognizing which information was time-future versus time-past. In that culture, to dream was to visit another realm of reality.[120]

[M] This is stated with respect to the persistence of reality of the "awake" relative *self*.

With respect to a waking "self" a pseudo time route is often a somewhat confusing section of memory. In the ToT the concept of being asleep is described as a relative self comprised of various EQ groups resolving to Experiences that are not necessarily contiguous. This is expressed in a time route comprised of Experiences that appear to intermittently drift away from a focus on the physical body—most likely because there is no clear oExperience of the flow of time, because the Experiences of the physical senses are missing during sleep.

Common wisdom and scientific research tells us there are different stages of sleep. Dream researchers give them labels such as: beta, alpha, theta, delta, REM, hypnagogia, hypnopompia, etc. These stages may be explained in terms of the ToT with the possibility of them involving different senses in varying amounts.

Düsum Khyenpa, 1st Karmapa Lama, 1110-1193 CE
Master of Tibetan dream yoga.[121]

The Tibetan culture also identifies different stages of sleep. There is a stage of the dream state where most people have no memorable awareness* ("it is like going through a dark tunnel").[122]   According to the ToT this is a part of the dream state where there is no Experience of phenomenal reality in terms of the spacetime dimensions—hence there is no Persistence of reality. As I understand it, only the most skilled meditation master can maintain awareness* during this condition of existence. In terms of the ToT, it is described as a state of existence because the relative self can contain the Experience of a memory of coming out of this condition.

When there is a lack of Experiences containing the spacetime dimensions, the relative self does not necessarily relate to the physical body (*i.e.* there is intermittent reality sync and intermittent persistence of reality.) This brings about a unique situation related to the state of being "asleep." The situation is best understood in terms of being "awake" just before or just *after* being in a dream state. In terms of the ToT the dream state can be described in two fashions:

1) *With respect to reality sync being intermittent while a person is dreaming:*

The neighboring groups of EQ describing a pseudo time route may represent disjointed Experiences—hence comes the above described disjointed groupings of Mind-Moments that are not in *proper* temporal order. Thus the Experience can be from the "past" or the "future", and there is no reference for determining which it is—while a person is dreaming. When the person awakens his/her physical body comes back into reality sync and what is past and what is future is defined. Consider an Experience that is part of a MindMoment resident in the pseudo time route of a dream. Upon awakening that Experience may be recognized as 1) a premonition; or 2) an instigation of the dream from a past event.

2) *With respect to the persistence of reality being intermittent while a person is dreaming:*

Within the Matrix, the neighborhood of a Cloud may contain groups of EQ that belong to the Cloud associated with "another person." The term "another person" refers to the EQ resolving to a "self" other than the dreamer. The term "self" (or the "I") is an Experience strongly associated with the phenomenal body (in terms of being awake with the persistence of reality in effect). This would be a problem (and anthropically denied) if an Experience of one's physical body were in play—but the physical body often is not an issue. Therefore, in a dream state a person may have an Experience of existing as a different person or being, and have no problem with the situation.

189

In the Tibetan tradition there is a general consideration that the more introspection, contemplation and/or meditation a person engages in; the more likely clarity will increase.   Greater clarity can give one the vision to maintain awareness* in the various stages of the dream state. According to the ToT, such clarity means that the Experience of the continuity of being, normally the concept of the "self", is defined less and less by the spacetime dimensions. As a person enters the dream state there is a loosening of the grip on worldly desires (with respect to the physical body). What comes about is a presence of Awareness that is not personal.

Tibetan Buddhism offers specific techniques to increase clarity during the dream state, one of which is "dream training."[123] Buddhism typically describes dying as being similar to entering the dream state.

The next chapter deals with how a person may have the Experience of "free will" in a timeless universe.

2.3 - A DIFFERENT REALITY

The full meaning of the term "individuated SELF" is unique and complex. Yet in common terms, it is who we generally describe ourselves to be.

PERSPECTIVES

Logically, in order to have a complete view of a system, the perspective must be outside of the system being viewed. How then can we discuss Totality?

A ToE (Theory of Every*thing*) typically fails to provide a valid viewpoint. With a ToE the system is limited to all things; and the "cognizance" or "intelligence" which is describing the system is not considered to be a thing. Thus the consciousness of the individual that is describing the system appears to be resting within the individual when there is a description of the "self", and to be apart from the individual when there is a discussion of the phenomenal stuff of reality. In general, within a ToE, the nature of the existence of consciousness is not addressed. There is no discussion of where it resides.

The issue is different with the ToT because the ToT also includes the concept of the individuated SELF as the grandest conception of an individual. The SELF is also specifically denied the role of doing the logical analysis of the system; and is specifically included in the system that is being analyzed (the figurative analysis being performed by Awareness, which is part of the absolute condition.)

This explanation works well for the individuated SELF but; how can one have a vantage point for a discussion of Totality? Totality encompasses all things, all concepts, and all Thoughts. It also includes all existence and all Awareness of what is being analyzed!

To address this issue the ToT employs a fabricated tool of logic entitled **virtual omnipotence**. **Virtual omnipotence** provides a vantage point for a perspective on Totality that is axiomatically placed outside of Totality. It is something like the square root of -1, it's useful but by its own definition, it *cannot* exist. It is a concept that has a vantage point on *all* concepts except itself, and in this way provides a perspective on Totality.

An Analog for the Absolute Condition

The concept of virtual omnipotence is a necessity when describing the absolute condition. It's called *virtual* because it is not possible to truly conceptualize the absolute condition in terms of the universe …*as we believe it to be*.[A] Virtual omnipotence is analogous in function to certain described states of existence found in Buddhism. You will need a special teacher to experience* these states of being.

The projection of concepts (such as those labeled "EQ", "Clouds," etc.) onto the absolute condition allows for it to be described in terms of the relative condition. Remember that the absolute condition is specifically defined as being comprised of the basic "stuff" out of which concepts resolve. Ontologically then, there is no viewpoint from which to produce a concept. The nature of the absolute condition can't be expressed in terms of a concept. This leads to the conundrum: all things and all mental events within the relative condition are a concept—so then how can we talk about the nature of a concept?

The answer: apply projected (or virtual) concepts that describe the absolute condition in terms of its functional relationship to the relative condition, using terms from the relative condition. This is what the ToT attempts to do. For example: the absolute condition is (expressed as) a pattern of sub-patterns that describe an array of EQ. The array subtends certain multi-dimensional **virtual hyper-volumes** of naked space.

[A] The possible exception to this categorical statement is pure mathematics; but in that case it appears that we don't have all of the necessary tools. Mathematics is continually evolving and this is not a sure bet—it may be beyond the bounds of any math, now or in time-future.

The absolute condition is also described as timeless or non-temporal. According to the described nature of the absolute condition, the concepts of "time" or "timeless" are moot because these relative concepts do not intrinsically apply in the absolute condition; yet the term helps us talk about the nature of the absolute condition.

As an analogy, consider a baker making cookies using a cookie-press (or a pastry bag).[124] When the baker squeezes the cookie-press, an un-baked cookie of a certain, predictable shape emerges from the end of the device onto a cookie sheet.   The shape of the cookie is determined by the template used. The template could be in the shape of a star, a flower, an animal, etc.

If we imagine our point of view as being inside the cookie-press, we would see that there are no specific cookie shapes implicit in the dough and that there is an enormous amount of cookie dough (it is a very large cookie-press).

However, if we imagine ourselves as resting on the cookie sheet and looking upward through the template and into the cookie dough, we might say: " . . . there is obviously is a certain (limited) amount of dough that will comprise a single cookie."

The view from within the cookie-press is analogous to the absolute condition. The view from the cookie sheet is analogous to the relative condition. The "limited amount of dough," a description from the vantage point of the cookie sheet, is analogous to a description of the EQ patterns that comprise a Cloud.

In this way the inside of the cookie-press (the absolute condition) is described in terms of the view from the outside, *i.e.* from the cookie sheet—which is what we are doing with our analogies.   The cookie, after it hits the cookie sheet, is like an individuated SELF; and from the viewpoint of the relative condition, a portion of Awareness may be described as associated with a certain relative self.

The Finite Nature of the Stor

Recall that the Stor (the "stuff of reality") consists of both phenomenal reality and mental events, the second of which includes the flow of time. The Stor can be seen as more or less, the illusion of *samsara*. By definition the Stor includes *all* possible expositions of relative condition reality. This includes all possible universes (all V.n) across the entire (apparent) expanse of time; but it does not include the absolute condition.

Buddhist philosophy stipulates that the absolute condition is beyond any possible conceptuality. By analogy, in order to include it into a definition of Totality, the ToT describes the absolute condition as being naked space that is infinitely dimensional and Euclidian-like in that it extends infinitely in all directions... beyond all bound.

The ToT describes the relative condition as indefinitely large but not beyond all bound. The relative condition is a finite, non-Euclidian configuration space described by a geometry laid onto an indefinite number of dimensions of naked space. In this way, the relative condition may be characterized as a finite set of geometric manifolds that describe the nature of all relative selves; while naked space remains infinite.

The Stor is really, really big, but it is not infinite; and from a certain perspective it may even be described as repeating itself endlessly as a set of patterns laid out on the hypersurface of a very large, grossly multi-dimensional n-manifold.

> Recall the ideas set forth by the mathematician Sir Roger Penrose, where the end of one eon merges with next at the moment of a big bang. Perhaps the far future is linked with the far past?

The array of MindMoments within a time route produces the oExperience of the flow of time. A primary feature of that Experience is the related oExperience of *a belief that a being is able to perform actions in the phenomenal universe.* This lies at the heart of the illusion of the Stor.

> In all instances the described *illusory* nature of the Stor is not meant to suggest a hallucination, instead it simply states that the Stor is not a true depiction of the nature of reality.
> Whenever a being believes they are "doing something in time," they are perpetuating *samsara*—that is, they are continuing the illusion (unless they are aware of their situation).

In general, the idea that a being can *willfully cause a change* within the universe is called free will, which is a part of the larger concept of *causality.*

NONTEMPORAL CAUSALITY

In the ToT causality is in always nontemporal in nature. There are two ways to express it. One way is within a relative self; where there is an apparent oExperience of a relationship between one event (called cause) and its consequence (called effect). In this case we could say that it is the oExperience of a relationship between one MindMoment and another within a sequence of MindMoments comprising a time route. Within the ToT, this type of causality is known as **sequential causality**.

Another variety, **hyper-causality**, involves an Experience of the actual concept of **free will**, not the illusion of what appears to be free will, as it is portrayed in a relative self (the time-past portion of a time route).

SEQUENTIAL CAUSALITY

Sequential causality is described as a simple karmic relationship within the Matrix. It is not a true example of free will on the part of an individuated SELF. A good example of sequential causality occurs in the plants. The Experience of a plant as it appears to change over time is an example of sequential causality. Consider a plant that is fertilized. It will be seen to grow bigger than another plant without fertilizer. Chemical reactions and mechanical events are also good examples of sequential causality. For example: when a dish falls on the floor it breaks. Sequential causality often relates to elements in the phenomenal universe.

Remember that, according to the ToT, sequential causality indicates a relationship (in the Matrix) between overlapping Clouds of EQ. The overlap resolves to a measure of proximity; and ultimately in terms of the relative condition, an exposition of karma, which *appears* to be a causal relationship.

In the ToT, an act of free will cannot actually occur within a relative self because there is no agent within the relative self that can act to make a choice; it has no awareness. There is also no "opportunity" within its structure for a change to occur; because it's simply a static, unchangeable, sequential, collection of information.

HYPER-CAUSALITY

The concept of true free will is expressed with hyper-causality.

True free will happens when the verb-like action of a choice occurs within the Instantaneous condition associated with the nexus of a Sheaf. It is the oExperience of actually having made a choice, an *act of free will*, on the level of the individuated SELF. A choice made in this fashion is an example of hyper-causality, a reflection of a Shift in the presence of Awareness from one time route to another, within the domain of a single Sheaf. Recall that this is called a Shift of presence or, simply, a Shift.

The question is: if the domain of a time route is timeless, how can the functional domain of the verb-like Shifting of a presence of Awareness from one time route to another occur? This question came up earlier when the concept of a Shift in presence was first introduced.

To answer this question the ToT axiomatically employs a concept that is outside of the normal realm of perceived reality. It is best described as a **quasi-concept**, which is what generically describes the verb-like Shift of presence of Awareness.

QUASI-CONCEPTS

Buddhist philosophy states that there is no conceptualization possible outside of the relative condition. In terms of the ToT this would be phrased similarly but it could also be described as there being no conceptualization possible outside of the Stor—where all conceptualizations are defined as elements of the Stor. With respect to Buddhism witness the words of the final lines of the Heart Sutra which appear to describe an ontological shift in the nature of existence beyond the relative condition, suggesting the condition of reality of an enlightened being.

> *Gate, gate,*
> *paragate,*
> *parasamgate,*
> *bodhi svaha . . .* [B]

Loosely translated, the mantra means:

> Gone, gone,
> Gone beyond,
> Gone beyond even the concept of beyond . . .
> Wow![C]

The ToT provides a slightly different view. It identifies certain concepts that partially describe such things as "beyond the concept of beyond" labeling them as quasi-concepts. The true nature of a quasi-

---

[B] These words are Sanskrit. the complete Heart Sutra can be found in the Appendix.
[C] Translation from Ram Dass.

concept cannot resolve to an Experience-object that is *fully* describable in terms of the relative condition.

Examples of quasi-concepts are associated with the (explained) nature of naked space. In general, a quasi-concept describes the *functional* nature of a concept from the perspective of the relative self; however the concept points at something outside of the domain of the relative self using terms such as: infinitely multidimensional, Enlightenment,[D] nontemporal, Totality, Experience Quanta or Awareness.

Other examples of quasi-concepts are ideas such as warped space, nonlocal space, spatial wormholes and timeless reality. Bernard Riemann, Henri Poincaré, Albert Einstein and David Hilbert are a few of the modern Western thinkers to describe some of these concepts using mathematics.

The meaning of the statement: "…beyond the concept of beyond" is a quasi-concept. The concept of Totality is a quasi-concept that cannot be an Experience-object described in terms of the relative condition. However there are a number of quasi-concepts with associated Experience-objects in a relative self, however the essential nature of these quasi-concepts is not a direct Experience in a relative self because it lies outside of the concept of a single time route.

SOME QUASI-CONCEPTS AND THEIR EXPERIENCES:
o   The Experience-object of the flow of time is associated with the quasi-concept of a time route.
o   The Experience-object of light existing simultaneously as a particle and as a wave is a quasi-concept associated with the quasi-concept of MindMoments.
o   The Experience-object of velocity is a concept associated with the quasi-concept of the "self-center of mass" and the Mind-Moment constant.
o   The Experience-objects of precognition, remote viewing, etc. are associated with the quasi-concept of ESP (see below).

The essence of a quasi-concept is not available as an Experience in a relative self; but its mathematical analog and the feelings (the Experiences that are mental events) associated with it are sometimes available. Thus the relative self can contain no Experience-object that *completely* exemplifies a quasi-concept. However there are pieces of the puzzle that

---

[D] The term "Enlightenment" is used in the classic spiritual sense.

198

indicate its nature; and some of those pieces are evident in the quasi-concepts associated with a Shift.

4ᵀᴴ TIME

A Shift is a quasi-concept; it's different than a shift [lower case]. Typically, for any kind of shift (or change) to occur, time is required. This is the normal way we understand a concept that is "an action described by a verb." However, in terms of a time route a Shift is instantaneous. It occurs in the moment of the present—it can do this, it's a quasi-concept.

This highlights the idea of a Shift not being a part of the relative self—which in common terms means it is not a function of the "self".

Chögyal Namkhai Norbu, 1988, Tibet.[125]

The axiomatic genesis of a Shift is based on another, seldom mentioned idea from Tibet. It's a pseudo-temporal concept found in esoteric Tibetan Buddhist thought called **4ᵗʰ time**. In terms of the ToT 4ᵗʰ time is a quasi-concept.

4th time is like normal time… but it's different.

~Chōgyal Namkhai Norbu

It has been difficult for me to find a clear conceptualization of 4th time within the Buddhist tradition. I have talked with several lamas about this. They are aware of the concept but they often have little to say. It appears that its nature is something that must be discovered via one's own endeavors.

For example, some years ago I attended a lecture given by Lama Wangdor Rinpoche—a Tibetan scholar and master of the *Dzogchen* teaching who has spent many years in solitude meditating (much of the time in a cave, I am told.)   After the lecture I asked the Lama to tell me about 4th time. (We communicated through an interpreter.) The Lama explained that ". . . there are the first three types of time: the past, the future and the present (he pointed at his fingers) and then there is whatever is left over that's not part of the first three. That is 4th time." Then he laughed and went on to someone else's question.

My conversations with lamas leads me to believe that there is some sort of an Experience-object that resolves from 4th time that can be empirically verified (in terms of the relative condition) by the corroborated reports of those accomplished at meditating.

The quasi-concept of 4th time is associated with **nonconceptual meditation.** Meditation is often described as focused on some concept, such as an object, the breath, the void, compassion, a certain deity, the suffering of humanity, etc. All of these are worthy concepts; but the act of nonconceptual meditation requires no such focus. For me this means that it is also without the concept of the flow of time—*i.e.* it is a *timeless* state of being, but that is a tricky thing to let happen.[E] Logically, when a person does this sort of meditation they need some sort of temporal "elbowroom" in which to accomplish it . . . hence 4th time. The tricky bit is that 4th time has no duration in spacetime.

As best I can determine, the Buddhist understanding of 4th time describes the Experience associated with it as *conditionally* being a part of the relative condition. It is *conditional* because it has no measurable temporal characteristics; but aspects of it may on occasion resolve to an oExperience during certain types of meditation. That Experience appears to be the remembrance of an Instantaneous vision of the play of

---

[E] You will need a teacher to show you how to do this.

200

great arrays of time, space, and/or mental events. The description appears to explain an episode I had in the cave beside Lake Manasarovar while in Tibet. [Note that this description is according to the relative condition where the term "experience*" exists in time.]

In 1988, on the trip to Mount Kailash (in Eastern Tibet) I had the opportunity to sit in meditation in a unique place. It was a small cave located at the top of a rocky, pyramid-shaped hill that lies between the two great lakes named *Manasarovar* (lake of the sun) and *Rakshastal* (lake of the moon). These Himalayan lakes are the highest on the planet.[F] Very near the cave, at the top of the hill, is the small *Chiu Gompa* Monastery that has only a few rooms carved into and built up from the rock.

Chiu Gompa and Mount Kailash[126]

The cave is small and once inside I could not stand up straight. The local monk called it Padmasambhava's cave in honor of the great teacher who had brought Tantric Buddhism to Tibet at the beginning of the 9th century AD. But the use of the cave is even more ancient. The cave is said to be the dwelling place of many Bon masters dating back thousands of years to the old kingdom of Zhang Zhung before the time of the Tibetan kingdom. "Bon" is the old, pre-Buddhist religion of the land now called Tibet. The location of the cave obviously made it a very

---

[F] Lake Manasarovar sits at 15,042 ft. (4058 m.) altitude, Google Earth.

special place; and various histories describe many notable occupants and visitors. Mount Kailash was central to the old kingdom.

I sat in the cave for about an hour. It was a very peaceful place after the trials of the month-plus-long journey that brought me there. The ambiance was amazing. It was so easy to settle my mind and bring the process of thinking into focus, letting it then rest in the moment. I had done this meditation many times before, but here is just happened as if by itself.

In the cave, my meditation was unusual. It seemed that the more I was able to focus on being in the moment, the more "images" would come rolling past my mind's eye. However, the images were distinctly devoid of substance. It was like watching a fast-paced dream while knowing you are dreaming. I saw <u>everything</u> as an illusion with the exception of the one small solid spot where I was sitting cross-legged. The more I relaxed my effort to control things, the faster the images would churn and roll by.

It appeared that the closer I came to being in the single instant of the present, the faster the images would stream past. I remember thinking it was like being very close to a fast moving freight train roaring past. It was a feeling of enormous energy—I wanted to "do" everything that could be done on planet earth! There was a background desire to taste all possible experiences*. I continued as best I could to remain calm (without trying to be calm). I was aware of some kind of paradox pulling on me (that was obvious). I could almost perceive* a space between the thoughts, but when it was over I couldn't remember what was there... and then I could stay no longer. It was as if a bubble had burst! I suddenly fell out of the meditation. There was no way to continue. It was all too fast and I was left in a mental rush of energy. It was a state of intense, totally alert energy, completely incapable of again slowing down my mind enough to go back into the meditative state. I was so full of energy I had to leave the cave. I wanted to move!

I thought about this in retrospect and I came up with the idea that I was somehow experiencing multiple viewpoints associated with a single "self"—which sounded silly at the time, however in terms of the ToT I can now see this conceptualization as the basis for an explanation for a logical grouping of relative selves (in the formation of the multiple time routes of a Sheaf). I was beginning to have a view from 4th time, and I was trying to force the view to be seen with normal spacetime glasses.

The Experience of 4th time can sometimes be thought of as a doorway. The term "doorway" came up during a meeting with the late Jean Klein. Jean Klein was a lecturer and author who traveled in Europe and the United States offering seminars. The content of his teachings seemed to parallel the teachings of the Indian saint Ramana Maharshi.

> Effortless and choice-less awareness is our real nature.
> ~Ramana Maharshi

Jean Klein's teaching style was to invite questions and then respond. I once asked him: "what does the true self feel like?" He explained that a person can't remember what it is like in terms that can be communicated in words, however a person can sometimes remember going in or coming out, as if through a doorway.

My idea is that with respect to the illusion of being alive in the relative condition, we can envision an experience* of 4th time only as a **doorway Experience**. One may have the experience* of a memory of coming out of a door, but there can be no true experience* of the reality of being on the other side of the door; because that reality is five-dimensional, one where multiple experiences* of the moment of the present occur simultaneously. As such, it is a state of being that is beyond the normal Experience of memory—in terms of spacetime. Sometimes there is a feeling of being extremely blissful, and associated with this the experience of foggy idea that there may be the memory of a doorway Experience, but you are not sure. This lingering feeling of bliss can be associated with the presumption of being "on the other side of the door," if you will. The Experience of such a memory can last for several days or more.

A doorway Experience is a quasi-concept. Only a portion of it is part of the information comprising a relative self. However, it sometimes turns out that the experience* of having come out of the doorway contains a glimpse of the other side of the doorway; as if one has a foot on both sides of the portal.

The experience* of that glimpse in terms of the relative condition is unique. The experience* can be an incredibly expansive *feeling* (in an emotional sense); or it may be a personal experience* expressing the physical enormity of the universe. It is something that is "almost" beyond conceptualization.

When such an experience* is set within the context of the relative condition (for me) there was an immediate pullback from the doorway. One is left with a memory of something that can't quite be fully conceptualized. Another way to say this is: if you try to conceptualize or explain the simultaneity of reality (as depicted in the doorway or on the other side in terms of the relative condition), it will be extremely difficult (if not impossible) and in a flash it will be gone.

In essence the quasi-concept of 4th time can never be expressed as a part of a relative self. This is because there is no Experience-object to which it may resolve.

For example: the concept of "happiness" or the concept of a "tree" essentially can be expressed as an Experience-object that is part of a relative self. However the concept of "multiple, simultaneous time routes that constitute a single individuated SELF" can never be essentially expressed as Experience-objects which are described in terms of a relative self. We can talk about such a situation but a relative self can never fully incorporate the experience* of it into its information package because it is in a form that is anthropically unacceptable.

For instance: try to gain the experience* of imagining the look and/or feel of several hundred thousand simultaneous, unique, parallel streams of reality where a single moment of existence in each of those realities is a focal point of what appears to be an enormous array of events that extends inconceivably far into time-past and time-future; and where the total content of all of those Instantaneous, simultaneously occurring reality streams, when considered together, is a full definition of who you may possibly think you are as an individual at that single Instant of the Now. This is obviously impossible for any human to do—in terms of a relative self... where such a concept would be chaos. According to the ToT, it is a quasi-concept that describes an individuated SELF.

On the other hand consider that at some moment of reality you exist at a position in space; are having a certain subjective mental experience*; and time appears to be flowing along a single track from what is called "the past" into what is called "the apparent future." This is easy to do! It's life on earth as a relative self; and it's a concept. In contrast, the previous paragraph describes the perspective of a Sheaf—which is the realm of a quasi-concept.

A Shift occurs in the configuration space defined by the hypersurface of the 5-manifold. It occurs between the time routes comprising

204

the Sheaf. Functionally, the Shift occurs between one time route and another… occurring at the nexus of the bundle making up the Sheaf… at the tie point… at the moment of the Now. We can think of this point as the domain of 4th time, the **temporal elbowroom** in which a Shift occurs.

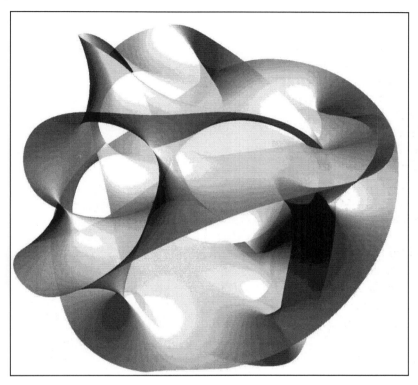

Shown is an image of a two-dimensional hypersurface of the quintic, six-dimensional, Calabi-Yau three-fold. A Calabi-Yau three-fold is "…a special type of manifold that shows up in certain branches of mathematics such as algebraic geometry, as well as in theoretical physics. Particularly in superstring theory, the extra dimensions of spacetime are sometimes conjectured to take the form of [this] manifold." [127]

Recall that a Sheaf is laid out on a five-dimensional hypersurface. Perhaps a Calabi-Yau manifold describes a nice group of Sheafs comprising a six-dimensional section of an n-dimensional multiverse.

SPACETIME-TIME AND A SHIFT

With respect to the relative self, a Shift has no measurable temporal characteristics.   It may occur instantaneously or it may take an eternity. The two interludes are functionally synonymous and meaningless. A Shift changes the status of a time route from "alternate" to "on point" (in terms of the on point) however it has no effect on the reality sync of the Sheaf. This means that all Shifts in the V.1 are transparent to any and all beings within the V.1 universe. We can also say that all Shifts occur simultaneously. This may stagger the imagination, but it is the condition in a reality defined as timeless.

A Shift occurs within the fabric of the configuration space of the hypersurface of a 5-manifold that expresses three space-like dimensions, one time-like dimension and one 4th time-like dimension. Together they form what the ToT calls **spacetime-time**.

There are other, higher dimensions that are each orthogonal to the spacetime-time package of dimensions. They contain information resolving to mental events. Within the ToT a Shift is commonly described as occurring according to the configuration space of the 5-manifold describing spacetime-time,[G] but it could conceivably occur according to the information in any dimension.

The concept of something occurring with zero time duration is difficult or impossible to imagine. So, how does such an "action" take place?

Earlier we learned that the oExperience of the flow of time is a feature of Awareness parsing multiple MindMoments in the same Instant. If we are to discuss this from the vantage of virtual omnipotence we could say that Awareness has the quality of parsing a Cloud, or parsing a collection of EQ (*i.e.* multiple, simultaneous MindMoments). It does this in a fashion that makes the components appear as if they are each examples of an iterative sequence of moments of reality extending from the moment of the present into time-past and time-future. The limited scope of the relative self of course contains only time-past Mind-Moments. Prosaically we could say that Awareness "looks at" a certain time route in its entirety and makes it appear as a flow of time on either

---

[G] A Shift is commonly described as defining spacetime-time because this is the domain most closely associated with standard spacetime physics.

206

side of its center point. As it does this it's "using" only the spacetime dimensions to come up with the Experience of the flow of time.

Recall that Awareness has a universal presence. It is by nature everywhere, thus with respect to the static nature of the V.1 universe, nothing has to move during a Shift of presence. Awareness already occupies the new position for Parsing the *new* time route, *i.e.* the one designated as "on point." To help understand a Shift without movement, do the following exercise:

> Look at the group of characters and simultaneously consider all three.

X O Z

> Fix your gaze firmly on the "O" and do not move it. While gazing in this fashion put your attention on the "X", hold it for a few seconds and then shift your attention to the "Z". Do this without altering the fixity of your gaze on the "O".

The exercise is *analogous* to a Shift; it is *not* an example of a Shift. It affords some idea of the quasi-concept set forth by the ToT—in the sense that nothing moves, yet presence Shifts and the designated time route on point gains a different designation. When this occurs a *new* relative self comes into play; however the *new* relative self does not include a memory of the old one. Because of this, the oExperience of a Shift does not resolve to part of a relative self and therefore does not appear to exist.

Functionally, a Shift must be instantaneous. This is why it is described as occurring at the nexus of time routes within a bundle comprising a Sheaf. The nexus is the moment of the present (denoted with $Ш_0$).

The nature of a Shift can be understood according to three different perspectives (or streams of logic).

1--In terms of a perspective of virtual omnipotence and a view from the vantage point of the absolute condition: all of the time routes in a Sheaf are equal, and they each, individually *and* simultaneously contain the information sequences that Instantly resolve to a version of apparent reality (*i.e.* "being* alive"). All time routes in a Sheaf are *simultaneously* expressing the information of "being*alive". There is no on point time route or *concept* of a Shift.

207

2--In terms of a perspective of spacetime, looking at a single time route—there is an oExperience of multiple MindMoments in a sequence resolving to an Experience-object of the flow of time in a single time route. That single time route appears to be the only one that exists. It resolves to an oExperience of being* "alive" in V.1. In these terms it is on point and a Shift is generally unrecognized.

3--In terms of a perspective of spacetime-time—there is the quasi-concept of a *choice among time routes* for the designation of "on point." Thus the quasi-concept of an "on point" vs. "alternate" time route is logically valid only from the perspective of spacetime-time. In that context a Shift is described as an example of hyper-causality.

Therefore, in terms of a relative self, to be alive is simply a view of spacetime reality as we know it (the time-past portion of a single time route). In terms of looking at a Sheaf (multiple time routes) a certain time route is designated as the one on point. However, from the virtual omnipotent perspective of the absolute condition there is no on point time route; *or* all time routes are "on point" simultaneously.

There is an obvious conundrum here. First, from the perspective of the virtual omnipotence of the absolute condition, there is no possible designation of on point (vs. alternate) for a time route because, existentially, there is no difference between any time routes. All patterns of EQ are all nascent information that resolves to the Experience of being* alive. Second, from the viewpoint of the relative self there is also no possible designation of on point (vs. alternate) for a time route because, existentially, there is only one time route. Third, it is only from the perspective of spacetime-time that there is the distinction between on point and alternative time routes and the quasi-concept of a Shift.

The conundrum exists because the description of a Shift ultimately speaks to the definition of the individual, which is different depending on the perspective taken. With respect to the relative self, the individual is generally defined in terms of contemporary concepts of the "viewer of reality", which could be the ego, the I, the "self", a single being, etc.—all spacetime concepts. Conversely, with respect to a perspective of spacetime-time, the individual is defined as the individuated SELF, and its corresponding geometry, the Sheaf, is comprised of time routes.

In either case there is no independent point of reference that designates "on point." To say it differently, there is no location where the "on point" designation resides. This statement prompts the question: can the oExperience of a Shift truly occur within the context of the ToT's definition?

The answer: It does occur; and it doesn't occur, depending on your viewpoint. In the overall scheme of the ToT, both viewpoints are equally an illusion, equally part of the relative condition, and equally valid ways to construe reality.

You may question this premise on the basis that it states that there is no specific (or permanent) entity that identifies an individual. This implies that there is nothing outside of the relative self or the Individuated SELF that makes the individual unique (such as a soul or self awareness). This is also a statement of the nature of Buddhism.

> The scholar Durgacharan Chatterji noted that: ". . . all the schools of Brahmanic[H] philosophy have posited some permanent entity, *i.e.* soul as the cognizer to which cognition is variously related. The Buddhists have, however, denied the existence of any such permanent entity.[128]

> The Theravada Buddhist monk Thanissaro Bhikkhu explains, ". . . (when) the Buddha was asked point-blank whether or not there was a self, he refused to answer. When later asked why, he said that to hold either that there is a self or that there is no self is to fall into extreme forms of wrong view that make the path of Buddhist practice impossible." [129]

The puzzling statement by the Buddha highlights the difficulty of describing the nature of reality in terms of space and time. In spirit, the statement also appears to be similar to the Zen *koan*: "What is the sound of one hand clapping?"[I] It can't be understood with common logic.

There is no way to directly tell if a Shift occurs in terms of a relative self; because *after* a shift the associated syncategorematic Experience-objects will appear to have associations with different (apparently causal) predicate Experiences; or they will have no relationship at all. This happens because the Experience-objects within the *new* time route are part of the package that is the *new* time route on point.

[H] Buddhism arose out of a culture of milieu of Brahmanic philosophy.
[I] A Zen Buddhist koan is a puzzling, usually paradoxical statement or question that appears to often incorporate concepts describing a five-dimensional view of reality.

However it might sometimes be possible to answer questions (in terms of spacetime) about the occurrence of a Shift from the subtle viewpoint of spacetime-time. This viewpoint may be had from within deep, meditative absorption (see below); and from the recognition of visions afforded by a presumed natural ability associated with hyper-causality.

THE CUSP BETWEEN CAUSALITIES

The distinction between hyper-causality and sequential causality emphasizes the importance of the perspective associated with the quasi-concept of spacetime-time. By definition hyper-causality lies within the spacetime-time domain of a Sheaf.

Some of the Experience-objects that resolve from a Shift are an example of hyper-causality. Whereas the Experience-objects that exemplify sequential causality are an exposition of karma—which resolves from relationships existing within a single time route.

Prosaically, a relative self contains the figurative "innate equipment" for an Experience-object associated with an Experience of spacetime-time, but it doesn't have the means to "display" it as such in the spacetime world we know. Because of this, when a Shift occurs, it "looks like" sequential causality because the apparent result is described in terms of a relative self.

For example, (in terms of a relative self where the flow of time is an oExperience): consider a tennis ball set on an outdoor picnic table with a seated person calmly watching the ball. The ball is at rest (unmoving). If a strong breeze comes along, it may blow the ball and cause it to roll off the edge of the table (event 1). On the other hand, if the person pushes the ball, it might also roll off the edge of the table (event 2). In both cases, the functional mechanics of the situation within the relative self appear to be similar; *i.e.* a force pushes the ball. However, the first case (event 1) resolves from sequential causality and the second case (event 2) resolves from hyper-causality. In both cases, classical mechanics is used to describe the initiation of the ball's movement.

In event 1 the person is passive within the flow of time while in event 2 the person makes a free will decision to push the ball. Or, we could also say: in event 1 the term "sequential causality" identifies the Experience associated with the initiation of the ball's movement (the wind moving the ball) and in event 2 the term "hyper-causality" identifies the Experience associated with the initiation (the person's hand moving the ball).

210

In event 1, all was predetermined because the action—the person passively watching, the wind, the ball's movement, and the ball's eventual fall—occurred within a certain single time route. In event 2, the initiation of the ball's movement lies within a (*new*) time route that is different from the one displaying the ball's beginning, at-rest condition. The *new* time route resolves to a relative self that includes the Experience-object that is a mental event called "the choice to act in the flow of time", or "an act of free will." It also includes the Experience of pushing the ball. The Experience-object that is generically classed as "an act of free will" resolves from a Shift.

> Recall that the term "Experience" is often used to simultaneously refer to the Experience and the Experience-object that is associated with it. This is done as a matter of textual expediency when both members of the pair are in the perspective of spacetime.

The obvious logical question is: what initiates* a Shift? Such a question is, of course, framed as within the context of the flow of time. Thus, a better question is: what is at the cusp between the concepts of sequential causality and hyper-causality? Or, what unique batch of information is associated with the Shift? It is the Experience-object called an **Intension** (w/ upper case "I").

INTENSION AND A SHIFT OF PRESENCE

The Experience of an Intension occurs just prior to the instant of the present, at Ш_{-1}, which is the first MindMoment in the time-past array of a relative self, i.e. the most contemporary MindMoment in a relative self. An Intension is an nExperience and it is the only true expression of free will resident in a relative self.

It's important to understand that the nExperience of an Intention is a true expression of free will. The memory of the "verb-like" *actuation** of free will is generically just another Experience in a sequence of MindMoments and are an expression of sequential causality unfolding—they do not indicate a Shift. The Intension however (resting at Ш_{-1}) indicates an Experience-object that resolves from a Shift, and is thus described as an example of hyper-causality—but the nature of this special Experience-object is usually not evident within a relative self.

In the ToT a Shift *per se* is described as resolving to a phenomenal object that is the person's physical body because functionally, a Shift

211

occurs on the spacetime-time hypersurface of a 5-manifold where each of various time routes resolve to the spacetime substantial reality aspect of various relative selves.

The *new* relative self brought on point by the Shift also includes higher dimensional mental events. The nExperience of an Intension is one of these higher dimensional mental events; but often, a failure in our presence of Awareness leads to the subtle uniqueness of these special nExperiences not being included in the common relative self. Such a lapse in Awareness has been the topic of many traditional discourses.

Mahasiddha Naropa[130] [J] (956–1041)

Naropa was an Indian Buddhist yogi, mystic and monk. He was the disciple and brother of Tilopa. Naropa was the main teacher of Marpa[K], the founder of the Kagyu school of Tibetan Buddhism. As an Indian tantric Buddhist, he has a place in Vajrayana Buddhism as a whole, but he is particularly renowned in Tibetan Buddhism, his name being attached to the six yogas of Naropa, a suite of advanced yogic practices for the attainment of skills relevant to the completion stage of Anuttarayogatantra.

[J] A first hand descriptive vignette of **Naropa** can be found in the Appendix.
[K] **Marpa Lotsawa** (1012–1097), known commonly as **Marpa the Translator**, was a Tibetan Buddhist teacher credited with the transmission of many Vajrayana teachings from India, including the teachings and lineages of Mahamudra.

For more than two millennia we find a tradition of logical argument within the schools of Buddhism. The segment you have just read may in some ways have paralleled what the Indian Buddhist monk Naropa described approximately 1000 years ago. He described a set of practices [called the six yogas of Naropa] that allowed a person to realize the psychophysical nature of what (I am assuming) was the "taste" of a Shift in Awareness.

Naropa is particularly renowned in Tibetan Buddhism because of his full realization of the advanced *Mahamudra* teaching.

Follows is a translation of the first stanza of a set of verses he wrote referencing this. Notice how he describes the mind as a movement of attention.

> *Verses of Mahamudra:*
> Homage to the state of great bliss!
> Concerning what is called *Mahamudra*
> All things are your own mind.
> Seeing objects as external is a mistaken concept;
> Like a dream, they are empty of concreteness.
> This mind, as well, is a mere movement of attention
> That has no self-nature, being merely a gust of wind.
> Empty of identity, like space.
> All things, like space, are equal…
>
> ~Naropa[131]

CHANGE AND ATTACHMENT

The concept of change is intimately linked to free will.

When reflecting on compassion, Ram Dass said that with great awareness* all of the pain and suffering in the world will instantly change.[132] The ToT states that with a Shift a certain version of reality will cease to exist (with respect to a relative self) and be replaced with another—but there will be no memory of what it was like before the change. (What fun is that, if one desires or is attached to having made a change?)

This obviates the need to detach from the outcome of an intension* [cum-Intension]. If we are attached we will automatically disallow any change that excludes the satisfaction that comes from a "before" and "after" comparison, and that would have to be explained, of course, in terms of the before—which is often completely impossible for really big changes (such as a paradigm shift in reality). If one demands to have the memory of a "before" with respect to such changes, the changes may

213

have to be conceptually packaged as some kind of magic or miracle; and that could be an asset or a problem.[L]

> The problem is not enjoyment;
> the problem is attachment.
>
> ~Tilopa

FREE WILL AND CAUSALITY

In the first decade of the 21st century, I lived on the island of Hawaii, in the town of Hilo. This is the location of the data processing centers associated with most of the large, state-of-the-art telescopes atop Mauna Kea, the almost 14,000 foot high mountain that overlooks the town. Because of the smooth, laminar flow of air across the Pacific Ocean, Mauna Kea is a premier location on the planet for the construction of large, ground-based telescopes.

During my stay in Hilo, every so often, at a dinner party or such, I had opportunities to talk with some of the researchers operating the telescopes. Some time ago (before I composed this section of the ToT) I recall describing some of my ideas to one astronomer who was obviously conversant with most (if not all) scientific theories concerning the nature of the universe. He said he had heard of other ideas similar to what I was working on, but he felt that none of them dealt with free will.

The concept of free will has long been a focus of discourse as it relates to human nature and the human condition. Within the ToT, the Experience of an apparent act of free will simply resolves from a Thought resident in a time-past MindMoment. It is like many other Experiences of the phenomenal world—nothing special. In the ToT it does not indicate causality in and of itself.

The physical sciences and our vision of the world around us continue to remind us that we exist in spacetime. In this context, the concept of the "self" is portrayed as the viewer of a single time route—which implies that free will comes into play at a single point in a linear flow of time.

This topic of free will is not an easy one to address. For me, it was a challenge until I became familiar with the concept of 4th time; and the ideas of the Sheaf and spacetime-time came forth. Out of this came the concept of an Intention being the specific indication of free will.

[L] The term "…to be attached" and the comparison of the concepts of "before" and "after" obviously place this discussion in the context of the relative condition.

INTENSION AND FREE WILL

In the lexicon of the ToT the nExperience of an Intention indicates an act of true free will. It is always essentially a mental event. For Example: the Intension to lift a cup of coffee and the Intension to compare the taste of different varieties of coffee are both mental events. On the other hand, the associated Experience of sequential causality that unfolds after the Intension may be either a physical action or a mental event. The subsequent Experience-object could be lifting* a cup of coffee or it could be comparing* the taste of one variety of coffee to the memory of the taste of another variety.

An alternate time route becomes an on point time route with a Shift. Functionally a Shift sets the (apparent) V.1 universe onto a *new* time route, or we could say that a Shift brings a *new* time route into play. Either one is correct. The *new* time route contains the memory of an Intension to perform (what appears to be) an act of free will. The *new* time route also contains a certain unique personal history that is in concert with the "act of free will"; but it does not contain a memory of the *old* time-route.

This could be described in terms of karma and *samsara* as well. For example; in the context of certain Buddhist concepts regarding action*, whenever one acts* to do something in the flow of time he/she creates more karma and continues to be enmeshed in *samsara*. This statement interprets karma in terms of cause and effect that places it in the context of the flow of time.

In contrast, recall that the ToT (and some esoteric forms of Buddhism) describes karma as the linking feature of the Matrix. This understanding is in concert with another Buddhist conception that to create strong karma one must: 1) be aware* of an intention to do something; 2) do the act with awareness*; and 3) be satisfied* after the act has been accomplished. These conditions would describe a time route containing many associated links within the Matrix. The first item obviously is associated with a time route that contains MindMoments that resolve to an Experience that is an Intension. The second item expresses the Experience-object that is a memory of an apparent act* of free will; and, the third item indicates an awareness* of continuing *samsara*.

With respect to a relative self the Experience-object of an Intension is part of a MindMoment (Ш_{-1}) that figuratively heralds a *new* on point time route. The tricky thing to mentally "swallow" is that the *new* time route resides in the same instant as the old time route.

The apparent consequences of an Intension may range in nature from very subtle to profound. For example: as you read this sentence, try holding your breath for three seconds, and then continue reading; or don't do it. You make the choice.

1--   2--   3--

The Intension to hold your breath (and then holding it) brought a different time route into play. The new on point time route was (most likely) almost identical to the alternate time route in which you did not hold your breath.

Another example: Consider the pilot of the plane that flew into one of the twin towers on 9-11. His Intension, presumably realized in the W_{-1} MindMoment just before he was vaporized, resulted in a profoundly different on point time route than the one in which the pilot did not hit the tower.

These are two extremely different examples of Intension. The commonality between them is that they both were (apparently) executed with the idea that the flow of time is real. In this way, they both perpetuate *samsara* for the being having the Experience-object of free will, albeit in greatly differing in quality and quantity.[M]

> The key to understanding the nature of an Intension is realizing that its originating Shift functionally occurs in the timeless domain of the configuration space of the Sheaf—but the associated Experience-object functionally occurs in the configuration space of the time route.

THE CAUSALITY CONE

In the relative condition, causality is typically perceived as a function of the arrow of time. In the ToT, this is also the case, but in a different way. The concept of a **causality cone**[N] is a useful pattern for understanding this. The causality cone is defined as the time-past portion of a time route bundle. The time-future portion lies on the "other

---

[M] This assumes the pilot had some sort of Experience of "accomplishing the act" before he died.

[N] In terms of quantum mechanics the causality cone might be seen as similar to the "light cone" predicate to an event occurring in the moment of the present. However, in the ToT the cone is made up of time routes, not rays of light.

side" of the moment of the Now. It defines what is called the **future cone**. Both of these cones can be a source of information for a relative self, but the mechanism is not well accepted by spacetime physics.

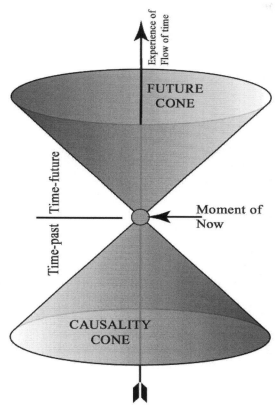

Causality Cone and Future Cone.[133]
A thematic rendition of the configuration space defined by the five-dimensional manifold describing a Sheaf. The cones as pictured are empty. More correctly they would be shown filled with time routes.

Causality is an Experience relative to the moment of the Now. Sequential causality is always described in terms of time-past; and hyper-causality is always described in terms of the Now, *i.e.* its essence is functionally non-temporal.

Sequential causality is always given in terms of a relative self. It is represented by the causality cone, indicating the time-past portion of a Sheaf. Sequential causality is evident only in a single time route.

Hyper-causality is involved with both the time-future and time-past portions of a Sheaf, depicted as both the causality cone and the future cone. Hyper-causality necessarily involves multiple time routes, an on-point and an alternate. A *new* on point time route entails a *new* version of time-future and *new* version of time-past.

> It is not the past that defines the moment of the present and the probable time-future. Instead, it is the moment of the present that the nexus of multiple versions of time-past within the causality cone and multiple versions of time-future within the future cone. Prosaically, the Now defines the past and the future.

5-SPACE VISIONS, A BASIC HUMAN ABILITY

An Experience of a quasi-concept does not always indicate a Shift of presence. It can also be an Experience resolving from time-future MindMoments in the on point time route; or it can be an Experience resolving from MindMoments (time-past or time-future) in various alternate time routes. These Experiences result in an Experience-object called a 5-space vision, if they are not anthropically denied.

According to the ToT 5-space visions are often a source of information within a relative self. They resolve from the Experience of bits and pieces of multiple time routes. Such content, when described in terms of a single relative self, amounts to an Experience-object (a 5-space vision) of fleeting realizations that often appear as out of place in the normal scheme of things. They are usually dismissed as random unrelated Thoughts, flashes of intuition, premonitions, or possibly paranormal events—all of which are mental events.

It is axiomatic in the ToT that all humans, and maybe some animals, incorporate Experience-objects that resolve to 5-space visions.[°] In terms of spacetime physics, the experience* of a 5-space vision is a vaguely understood natural ability.

My wife's dog (named Roxanne) was a small mutt that appeared to be a cross between a Dachshund and a German Shepherd [interesting, eh?]. Roxanne was very bright and was much attached to my wife. Often, for ten to fifteen minutes before my wife arrived home the dog would be sitting in the driveway intently watching the road. Normally,

---

[°] I can imagine that there may be some very basic organisms (microbes like bacteria, amoeba, etc.) where the ability does not come into play.

when my wife was away from the house, the dog seldom sat anywhere near the road—Roxanne appeared to dislike the traffic. [This incident is a personal observation and likely much biased because of my attachment to Roxanne; but it gives you an idea of what I am talking about.] It calls to mind Rupert Sheldrake's work.

In terms of the ToT it appears that certain holistic cultures find versions of 5-space visions to be a part of "normal" reality.[P] A good example of this is evident in a quote from Grandfather Semu found on a Web site[134] dedicated to him:

> My Mother knew when we were going to have company. (It was common knowledge that a lot of people knew this type of thing in those days) . . .
>
> My mother also knew when the phone was going to ring and when she would receive a letter. She'd say, "Go answer the phone because so-and-so's going to call." The phone would ring and it was that person. Or, she'd say, "Go wait for the postman!" It didn't matter that she couldn't read or write! Sure enough, the postman would ride up in his buggy with a letter for her.
>
> Primitive people had mental telepathy because they needed to depend on this kind of other knowledge. They could sense danger or if there was going to be a raid. They used to know everything ahead of time, so they were prepared. That's the way we were raised. Everybody was born with natural talent.
>
> ~ Semu Huaute

Herb Kane, the Hawaiian artist and historian, also told me that in the culture of ancient Hawaii, "people had premonitions *all of the time.*" It was very common; however, it was considered that: "...if you tried to figure it out, you would go crazy." Old Hawaii was a Neolithic, holistic culture that ended c. 1800 CE. [He told me this story with a wry smile when I explained the thesis of the book.]

In terms of the ToT a 5-space vision may appear as a memory of an Experience that spontaneously occurred a few moments ago; however it's one that "doesn't fit" into the normal way of things. There appears to be no associated reason for its occurrence. Its origin is the

---

[P] Some Tibetan, Hawaiian and Native American sub-cultures appear to still value 5-space visions. Also some modern intentional communities, such as those focused on Buddhist thought, appear to hold this view.

configuration space of the time-future portion of the on point time route; or it could be the configuration space of any portion of an alternate time route.

The problem is that to an overwhelming degree, the contemporary scientific paradigm gives us no reasonable method for including information from multiple time routes (or from time-future) into the on point time route, and thus the information is anthropically denied. This problem can be addressed with an understanding of the concept of a 5-space vision

TRUE FREE WILL

A Shift of presence functionally occurs within a Sheaf, which is essentially beyond the ken of normal reality—the relative self. The configuration space of the Sheaf is the hypersurface of the 5-manifold where time route bundles exist. Believing that we are performing an action in time is not free will—it's just the after-the-fact Experience of karma unfolding, an example of sequential causality.

True free will is the choosing of time routes that are "available" within the Sheaf. An awareness* of their "availability" is a 5-space vision; but the Experience of such is very subtle and likely will not fit well with the rest of the Experiences in a relative self.

With respect to the relative self an example of true free will is difficult to explain. In those terms, it involves conducting one's daily existence with a continuous awareness of being. The mind's attention may wander from its focus. Softly let if drift back. Continue to be aware, as if you always have another, simultaneous background point of view that is watching what the mind is doing—like the act of driving a car without thinking about it while being engrossed in a conversation. This promotes a natural openness that entails watching the mind as it considers a certain intension; and then, without trying, allowing it to become an Intension—and the subsequent (apparent) act of free will that follows. This is done in the context of assuming a subliminal presence of 5-space visions. It is something we all do naturally; however being more aware of it may provide opportunities for better choices in one's life.

Be sensitive to 5-space visions. Learn to trust them. There are subtle, subliminal fashions in which one can manage to (what might be called) "promote a predisposition" for managing a change. The Experience of this has the qualities of being confident that you will be able to "see or feel the future." It mentally "tastes like" existing within a Sheaf,

220

instead of a time route. [You may need a good teacher to show you how to do this.]

Another way to say it is that if something "feels right," go for it. To be aware of it "feeling right" you must be continually aware of your mind and completely conversant with all aspects the Experience of "it feeling right" and its opposition, "wanting it to feel right".

> Jean Klein elegantly described this in his book: *I Am*.[Q]
>
> "The only way out is to simply observe. This allows us to take note of our physical reactions, our mental attitudes and patterns in our motivations at the exact moment they appear. [Observing them] involves no evaluation [and] no analysis which is based on memory" . . .
>
> "It is only through silent awareness* that our physical and mental nature can change. This change is completely spontaneous. Make an effort to change and we do no more than shift our attention from one level to another, remaining in the vicious circle. This only transfers energy from one point to another. It still leaves us oscillating between suffering and pleasure, each leading inevitably back to the other. . .
>
> "You must distinguish between passive letting go and active letting go. [With] active letting go [you] remain totally present, clear-sighted, uninvolved and actively alert."

A direct Experience of the perspective of spacetime-time is not possible within the perspective of the relative self. However, a 5-space vision provides some bits and pieces of an Experience of a quasi-concept, such as "going into" or "coming out of" the domain of a Sheaf.

As I see it, the Experience of "going into" the domain of a Sheaf represents the instantaneous moment of the present. This is a difficult Experience-object to incorporate into a relative self because it's very quick (in terms of spacetime.) Only those who have extensive practice watching the many processes of Thought (*i.e.* a highly skilled mediator) can recognize it.

The *Abhidhamma* describes a protocol for navigating the landscape of consciousness where mind moments can be individually identified. The description involves the figurative awareness* of mind moments coming into the field of awareness*, abiding, and then passing

---

[Q] Jean Klein, *I Am*, (United Kingdom, Non-Duality Press). Copyright: Emma Edwards & Non-Duality Press 1989, 2006 & 2007. Emma, a friend of mine, compiled and edited the book.

away.[135] At base this is conceptually different than the ToT, where the MindMoments are instantaneous, but it provides an idea of what's being said.

In the ToT a single MindMoment will resolve to an nExperience. The nExperience of "coming out" of the domain of a Sheaf is different than "going into" it. "Coming out" is something very common. It is usually the unrecognized moment of the initiation of an Intension, followed by unfolding of karma that resolves to an oExperience of sequential casualty. This is the unfolding of the consequences of an act of free will. With just a little bit of practice it can be more than this. The practice amounts to allowing your mind to "slow down" the rate of presenting images of time-past Experiences. It is a basic meditation technique and it is Jean Klein's description of "active letting go."

It is a matter of ultimately learning to see reality as bounded by a 5-manifold—not a 4-manifold; or learning to see reality according to the perspective of a Sheaf—not a time route.

In terms of the lexicon of the ToT, the Experience-object that is the "coming out of the domain of a Sheaf" is a 5-space vision.

A 5-space vision comes into existence instantly (of course!) but it's always associated with certain memories that spread over an expanse of an apparent flow of time—this is the attendant sequential causality. Look closely at your remembered dreams. Sometimes you may be aware of the immediacy of their initiation—which is an example of a certain memory. From this you may begin to see the detailed nature of a memory that includes information from "other than on point" time routes.

A 5-space vision may be comprised of different sorts of Experiences, such as a memory of a possible time-future event—which amounts to the memory of a "future" portion of a time route. Such a memory can be something wonderful or something ominous. It may be of a phenomenal object or a mental event. For example: when some people see a crow (a substantial object) they may infer an ill omen.[R]

An Experience-object that specifically exemplifies a Shift cannot be had within the context of a relative self (because a Shift is a quasi-concept). Yet according to the ToT, Shifts do occur. In prosaic terms, all of the decisions in our lives have already been made. It just doesn't appear to play out that way because the relative self is defined as being generally in charge "as time goes by."

[R] Such relationships may be karmicly or anthropically generated.

222

In Buddhist philosophy this is the principle of "karma, cause and effect"—which is often stressed as a primary feature of the nature of mind. This is a teaching that is generally understood in terms of spacetime. In this context a Buddhist might say that we cannot get away from the karma that is a result of our actions. However, according to the ToT this is an explanation according to the relative self. An explanation in terms of the timeless condition of a Sheaf would be different, because the idea of a *cause* and a subsequent *effect* requires a flow of time, which is understood to be an illusion with zero duration.

To understand this better we revisit a description of the Instancy Principal.

THE INSTANCY PRINCIPLE REVISITED

A full description of the Instancy principle includes the total expanse of conceivable time (the indefinitely far time-past to the indefinitely far time-future) for all possible sentient beings. Within the ToT this concept takes the form of a "great meta-instant" that contains all of the lesser, single instants of existence (lower case "I"). In terms of a relative self the moment of the Now (designated by the placeholder Ш_0) is one of the lesser instants. The great meta-instant is called an Instant (upper case "I").

An Instantaneous collection of instants may be a difficult concept to initially accept; and it is made even more difficult when you recall that each instant contains a full collection of all beings (relative selves) that are alive in that instant. This viewpoint, of course mandates that existence be defined as simply "in the moment"; and the moment must be defined as with zero time duration[5]—i.e. existence is ultimately non-temporal in nature.

The really difficult thing to envision is that there is no "*flow* of instants" that makes up the Instant. In terms of a relative self, the moment of the Now (Ш_0) is *all that exists!*... and, that moment is *empty* of information *per se*; but it is the vantage point of the view of all of the rest of reality.

> Like it or not, if you look at your own mind you will discover that it is void and groundless; as insubstantial as empty space.
>
> ~ Padmasambhava

---

[5] This is a fine example of Ockham's razor.

The ToT, with axiomatic pragmatism, describes existence in this way.

So concludes a philosophical description of the ToT, including all of the created bits and pieces along with the axioms upon which they are based. The next chapter deals with how physics may be interpreted in terms of the ToT.

PART III

INSTANT PHYSICS
Surveying a Timeless Universe

A radical new paradigm of physics based on
conjoining geometry and ancient wisdom.

3.1 - A NEW VIEW OF OLD SCIENCE

To understand the new paradigm of physics based on the ToT we need a background vision of contemporary physics described in terms of the ToT. The vision paints a framework for an operative map of a different way of looking at the nature of reality. At the core of this framework is a discussion of simultaneity where, in the context of the ToT, all "events" truly occur in a single Instant.

THE RELATIVITY OF SIMULTANEITY

According to the physical sciences, the term "simultaneity" is in relation to the inertial reference system of the observer.

An inertial frame of reference is where physical laws hold in their simplest form. According to the first postulate of special relativity, all physical laws take their simplest form in an inertial frame, and there exist multiple inertial frames interrelated by uniform translation. [136]

In special relativity, an observer in inertial (*i.e.*, nonaccelerating) motion has a well-defined means of determining what events occur simultaneously with a given event. A second inertial observer, however, who is in relative motion with respect to the first, will disagree with him regarding which events are simultaneous. (Neither observer is wrong in his determination; rather, their disagreement merely reflects the fact that simultaneity is an observer-dependent notion in special relativity.)

A concept of simultaneity is required in order to compare the clocks carried by the two observers. If the observers are in different inertial systems the first observer will discover that the second observer's clock runs slower by [an amount equal to] the **Lorentz factor**. Similarly, the second observer, according to his concept of simultaneity, will find that the first observer's clock runs slower by the same amount. Thus each inertial observer discovers that all clocks in motion relative to his own run slower. The "slowing down" of a clock is called **time dilation**.

Hendrik Antoon Lorentz (1853-1928)[137]
He received Nobel Prize in Physics in 1902

The Lorentz factor: $$\gamma = \frac{1}{\sqrt{1-\frac{v^2}{c^2}}}$$

Where:

- γ is the Lorentz factor,
- v is the relative velocity of the observer,
- c equals 300,000km (186,000miles) per second—*i.e.* the speed of light.

Albert Einstein (1879-1955)[138]
The recipient of the Nobel Prize in Physics in 1921.

Einstein is credited with saying that ". . . no two events can occur at the same time. . ." He said this within the context of the flow of time being relative to the inertial systems associated with each event and observer. In the context of the ToT, the term "event" refers to an Experience-object.

According to the special theory of relativity, it is impossible to say in an absolute sense whether two events occur at the same time (simultaneously) if those events are separated in space.

A popular picture for understanding [the relativity of simultaneity] is provided by a thought experiment consisting of one observer midway inside a speeding train car and another observer standing on a platform as the train moves past. It is similar to thought experiments suggested by Daniel Frost Comstock in 1910 and Einstein in 1917.[139]

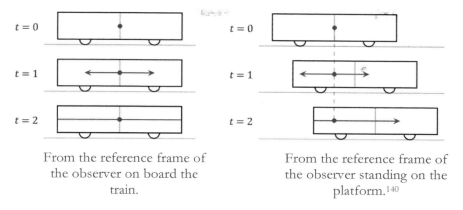

From the reference frame of the observer on board the train.

From the reference frame of the observer standing on the platform.[140]

A flash of light is given off at the center of the train car just as the two observers pass each other. The observer onboard the train sees the front and back of the train car at fixed distances from the source of light and as such, according to this observer, the light will reach the front and back of the train car at the same time.

The observer standing on the platform, on the other hand, sees the rear of the train car moving (catching up) to the point of the flash and the front of the train car moving away from it. As the speed of light is finite and the same in all directions for all observers, the light headed for the back of the train will have less distance to cover than the light headed for the front. Thus, the flashes of light will strike the ends of the train car at different times.

In terms of the ToT an analysis of this thought experiment must include a discussion of the nature of existence, which is different depending on your point of view. When viewed from a position within the apparent reality of a relative self, the experiment clearly describes the relativity of simultaneity. When viewed from a position of virtual omnipotence (a nontemporal and non-local condition of reality) a completely different scenario arises.

EXISTENCE IN TERMS OF A RELATIVE SELF

For a relative self the concept of existence includes a not-clearly-defined "self" that is the perceiver* of reality. The nature of space and time are also necessary to the definition of existence for a relative self (*i.e.* all beings and substantial objects are considered to exist in spacetime.) In this context the point of awareness* of both observers are subject to the relativistic qualities of spacetime and therefore to the inertial systems in which each of them exist. So, for each inertial observer, all clocks in relative motion[A] run slower.

However there is a problem with this analysis. If the observer on the platform says: "for me time is flowing at its normal rate but time on the train has slowed down," then the observer must first have some *reference* to establish that time is flowing at its normal rate. This critique is the same for the observer on the train.

How can such a *reference* be established?

Logically, for either observer, any *reference* that their clock is actually running can only be a view from the instant of the Now—otherwise we would have to define another type of time, and then face the problem of defining that. In terms of the world as we know it the view must also be a memory of a time-past event indicating a duration—because we don't see the future. Such Experiences of duration could take the form of the memory of the hands of a clock being in a different position, or memories of more subtle queues, such as quiet ambient sounds or the soft awareness* of internal processes like the beat of one's heart or, the most intriguing, the subliminal sequencing of Thoughts.

In terms of a relative self existing in spacetime, this soft awareness* of time flow appears to translate into the observer unquestionably relying on a background, subliminal predisposition that "time is naturally flowing at its normal rate" and that this is the way of things in terms of the nature of existence. Thus, the relative self subjectively needs no *reference* to determine that time is flowing at its normal rate.

> The overt concept that the only moment of existence is the Now, and that the flow of time is an illusory experience arising from the memory of a duration, requires a *reference* point outside of spacetime. This would be difficult for the typical relative self because within spacetime there is no available *extra* dimension (5th) in which awareness* could "overlook" the time-like dimension of spacetime.

In terms of physics we could also say that the "perceived" slowing down of the other's clock can be verified by visually recording the differences during a side-by-side comparison of each other's clock images—the result being that the "other's clock" will always appear as running slower. According to the stated terms of the experiment, this dis-

---

[A] That is: relative constant motion between two points of reference within spacetime.

played difference would be attributed to the impossibility of simultaneity, as described by Einstein. However this argument still rests on the ability of the observers to state that the clocks actually move—which is a statement that speaks to the essence of the ToT.

EXISTENCE AS SEEN FROM BEYOND SPACETIME

In the context of the ToT, the tenets of the thought experiment must include the assumption that both the observer on the platform and the observer on the train have a point of Awareness that is not within the framework of spacetime, because both observers are able to objectively evaluate features of space and time.

This overview leads to a deeper analysis of the *reference* for establishing the movement of any clock. This is done by recognizing that the point-of-Awareness of any event [Experience-object] is in the Now; and that such Awareness must have a grander viewpoint in order to hold this perspective. In the ToT, this viewpoint lies in the absolute condition and is able to view the five dimensions of the Sheaf..

Recall that the Now is symbolized with MindMoment zero (Ш_0); which is devoid of information *per se*. The term Ш_0 identifies a placeholder from which extends the time-past and time-future MindMoment sequence within a time route. It indicates zero duration, as opposed to all other MindMoments which indicate a duration equal to one time quanta (see below).

Also recall that all time routes in a Sheaf are coincident in the moment of the Now; and the "tie points" of *all* Sheafs in V.1 are coincident in the moment of the Now—according to the Instancy principal. Therefore all events in V.1 exist simultaneously in the moment of the Now; and the point of *reference* for any movement is the moment of the Now. The Awareness of the Now is non-personal and is axiomatically described as resting in the non-local and nontemporal absolute condition of reality (figuratively in the virtual omnipotence of the ToT).

In terms of a historical overview all of this based on a logic following the philosophical lead developed out of 2000+ years of debate emanating from the ancient cultures of the East and pointed at by other traditional cultures.

By contrast, in the science of physics, the point of *reference* for movement is resting firmly within spacetime [*i.e.* three-dimensional objects (including beings) exist in space and time]. In the sciences, when

233

judgments are made about comparative flows of time, the point of awareness of the "self" is axiomatically described as unquestioningly being under of the umbrella of the relativity of spacetime. In fact the location of the point of awareness is core to the very nature of relativity— which is that there is *no unique, still point of existence.*

However, in a logically contrary fashion, when the *reference* for establishing the flow of time is addressed the criterion (the point of awareness*) for such flow appears to be ascribed to a *prima facie,* background, aether-like fabric that somehow stands apart from spacetime. It manifests as a personal "feeling" that time is flowing, and it serves as the unquestioned and unanalyzed ground from which to judge the generic constancy of time flow.

SIMULTANEITY IN THE TOT

For the contemporary physicist, substantial existence within spacetime appears to be accepted *a priori*; and the requirement for a criterion outside of spacetime (from which to judge a change in location in time) appears to receive a blind eye. Perhaps it is not discussed because the laws of classical physics apply only within spacetime, which brings us back to the question of whether two events can occur simultaneously. According to the ToT:

o   *They cannot when the point of view of the system under scrutiny rests within the system (i.e. in spacetime.)* Such a point of view is a relative self and it's ultimately a function of the observer's inertial reference frame.

o   *They can when the point of view of the system under scrutiny rests outside of the system.* Such a point of view is described as being from the vantage of virtual omnipotence, where an individuated SELF (a five-dimensional Sheaf) can be viewed in its entirety. This is a point of view beyond any reference frame within spacetime.

Within the context of the second classification all events exist simultaneously because of the Instancy principle. From this viewpoint we can identify two types of simultaneity:

1-*EXPERIENTIAL SIMULTANEITY:*
Two or more *events* are termed to be experientially simultaneous when their EQ are contained in the same time-past MindMoment (*i.e.* $\coprod_{-n}$).

2-TRUE SIMULTANEITY:

All events in all time routes (in all Sheafs) are termed to be truly **Simultaneous**. (The upper case "S" indicates *true Simultaneity*.) The concept of **Simultaneity** is with respect to Instancy. Simultaneity entails a point of view from the vantage of virtual omnipotence.

A discussion of Simultaneity and the nature of the individuated SELF touches on core issues in modern physics.

EXISTENCE AND THE "SELF"

For most beings the concept of the "self" is characterized in the context of a certain package of information, that the ToT calls the *relative self*. The package is strongly related to a concept of existence in spacetime—with the overwhelming emphasis on the time-past portion.

The term "individuated SELF" is different. It describes the boundaries of the existence of the complete individual. It includes MindMoments in time-past, in time-future and in the multiple time routes bundled as a Sheaf. The individuated SELF *per se* is seldom an Experience. A vastly adept yogi might experientially* might realize the existence of his or her individuality in this fashion; but it would require a very sophisticated 5-space vision.

If existence is defined in terms of a Sheaf it must be based on multiple time routes that include multiple time-futures and multiple time-pasts. Such a reality map would provide an answer to some obvious problems that have turned up in physics: Schrödinger's cat, for example (see below).

Recall that in the ToT the moment of the present defines a large number of time-past situations (in the causality cone). It is not, as we might normally think, that the past defines the moment of the present. This is an important premise in that it allows for a different view in the field of quantum mechanics—*i.e.* sub-atomic, super small particles such as electrons. For example: according to the Copenhagen interpretation[B] before an observation, the stated position of an electron cannot be known and is described as a *smear*—which is called a **Ψ** function (*psi*

[B] The **Copenhagen interpretation** is one of the earliest and most commonly taught interpretations of quantum mechanics. The essential concepts of the interpretation were devised by Niels Bohr, Werner Heisenberg, and others in the years 1924–27.

function).   After the observation, the Ψ function is said to have collapsed, and the observer can then know the position of the electron at the instant of observation.   What comes into play is the consideration of whether the particle can be said to truly exist in the form of a smear.

According to the ToT, we would envision the moment of the collapse as the moment of the present, and the time-past portion of the causality cone as representing the Ψ function.   When we do this the causality cone is not seen as a *smear* of doubtful existence; instead it describes a finite number of specific time routes that, in the context of the Sheaf, clearly exist in time-past.   This sounds a bit like the "many-worlds interpretation."

THE MANY-WORLDS INTERPRETATION

The many-worlds interpretation (MWI)[C] of quantum mechanics is similar to the ToT in that neither one has an observation triggered Ψ function collapse, which is a main point of the Copenhagen interpretation.[141]

There are multiple variations of the MWI with the **many-minds interpretation**[D] being the closest to the ToT.   Some of them include an understanding that the "mind" should be separate from the "body" to make the system work; but none of them even approach making a definitive attempt at describing the "mind" as it relates to the quantum world.   As best I can determine, they all see the essence of the "self" (that which makes decisions about reality) as resident within the spacetime—that, of course, is a big mistake.

The ToT specifically places the seat of Awareness outside of spacetime and the illusion of the relative condition.   The ToT also clearly describes the collapsed and noncollapsed states of being represented by multiple time routes within a Sheaf.

SCHRÖDINGER'S CAT

In November of 1935, the physicist Erwin Schrödinger[E] published a paper that supported an earlier paper published by Einstein and two other physicists.   Einstein's paper addressed current discussions in quantum mechanics that described the wave functions and probabilities

---

[C] The **MWI** was originally proposed by Hugh Everett in 1957.
[D] This interpretation was suggested by Zeh in 1995.
[E] Erwin Schrödinger is famous for a wave equation that describes how the quantum state of a physical system changes in time.   This is called the psi-function.

of particles that have no definite positions until they are observed. Einstein argued that such definitions failed his test of completeness. By this he was saying that using probabilities did not completely describe a system. This viewpoint is in concert with his famous quote: "God doesn't play dice with the universe."

Erwin Rudolf Josef Alexander Schrödinger (1887-1961)
He received the Nobel Prize in Physics in 1933.

Walter Isaacson describes the Schrödinger/Einstein interaction very well in his book, *Einstein, His Life and Universe:*

> [Schrödinger's] paper poked at a core concept in quantum mechanics, namely that the timing of the emission of a particle from a decaying nucleus is indeterminate until it is actually observed. In the quantum world, a nucleus is in a "superposition," meaning it exists simultaneously as being decayed and undecayed until it is observed, at which point its wave function collapses and it becomes either one or the other.

237

This may be conceivable for the microscopic quantum realm, but it is baffling when one imagines the intersection between the quantum realm and our observable everyday world. So, Schrödinger asked in his thought experiment, when does the system stop being in a superposition incorporating both states and snap into being one reality.[142]

The classic answer to this question in quantum mechanics is that it stops being in a superposition when it is observed; but this is silly! Who observes it, the physicist doing the experiment? A lab technician, who doesn't know what they are looking at? A fly on the wall? Can it be observed remotely via technology? And, the most ungainly quarry: Can Schrödinger's cat observe it?

In 1935 Schrödinger highlighted the ridiculous nature of situation in his paper when he described the following thought experiment concerning the fate of a now famous imaginary cat.

> One can even set up quite ridiculous cases. A cat is penned up in a steel chamber, along with the following device (which must be secured against direct interference by the cat): in a Geiger counter there is a tiny bit of radioactive substance, *so* small, that *perhaps* in the course of the hour one of the atoms decays, but also, with equal probability, perhaps none; if it happens, the counter tube discharges and through a relay releases a hammer which shatters a small flask of hydrocyanic acid. If one has left this entire system to itself for an hour, one would say that the cat still lives *if* meanwhile no atom has decayed. The psi-function of the entire system would express this by having in it the living and dead cat (pardon the expression) mixed or smeared out.[143]

Einstein happily agreed with Schrödinger and wrote back to him:
> Your cat shows that we are in complete agreement concerning our assessment of the character of the current theory…A psi-function that contains the living as well as the dead cat just cannot be taken as a description of a real state of affairs.[144]

This is well said if existence is defined as resident in a single example of spacetime, but that is not the context of the ToT.

If existence is defined as reflected in a Sheaf, Schrödinger's cat exists (as a phenomenal object) very well being both alive and dead; because a live cat and a dead cat may occupy different, simultaneous time routes. In this fashion Einstein's completeness principle is fulfilled because the psi-function for a system (quantum or real world) does not describe an array of possible locations for the existence of reality; instead it describes an array of existences. Thus the psi-function is not related to causality in terms of spacetime, *i.e.* existence is the same for every location before and after the psi function collapses.

Schrödinger's Cat[145]

With this, Einstein and quantum theory are both correct; however outwardly they remain in conflict because they are both based on an incomplete description of the reality of the observer, the "self." In the ToT, substantial reality is expressed as a five-dimensional Sheaf, not as the time-past portion of a single time route (four-dimensional spacetime). When existence is expressed as a Sheaf, the use of a psi-function to describe the state of Schrödinger's cat correctly and completely describes the animal's condition.

Additionally, if existence is defined as resident in a Sheaf, it might also be said that God, in truth, does *not play* dice with the existence of the universe. Instead, he has *already played* (past tense) with the dice—not to decide what will exist but rather to decide the nature of the multitude of sequences that display what's already in existence. In this context, the psi-function is a statement that describes what has already been created by God and how it is distributed about the "landscape" of a time route bundle.

WAVE-LIKE VS. PARTICLE-LIKE EXPERIENCES

Erwin Schrödinger is also famous for what's called his "wave equation." It arose out of the wave-particle duality presented by quantum particles. The nature of a beam of light is a good example of this duality. The beam can be described (and measured) as a series of individual particles (photons) or as a continuous wave of a certain frequency (like for example: pure red or pure blue light). The ToT provides a different understanding.

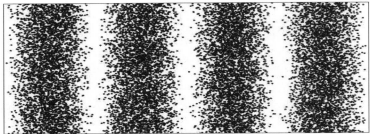

Particle impacts make visible the interference pattern of waves.[146]

Recall that with respect to Experiences described using the dimensions of space and time, an nExperience resolves from a single 3-manifold, and an oExperience resolves from a sequence of 3-manifolds occupying the hypersurface of a 4-manifold.

Consider the native and overlain Experiences that are associated with the Experience-objects of the phenomenal world. The distinction between these two types of Experience implies a simple way of viewing the wave-particle duality concept. An nExperience will necessarily exhibit particle-like properties because such an Experience is a representation of information from only one MindMoment, *i.e.* no sequence of EQ is involved in the specific Experience. It is basically an instantaneous view; whereas an oExperience represents information from multiple MindMoments and therefore always resolves to a sequence that includes an oExperience of the "flow of time."

Every EQ has a Feature that can resolves to a quantum unit of time (see below). It is an Experience that reflects the time-like dimension of spacetime in a relative self. An oExperience that includes this information resolves to the wave-like characteristics that can be associated with matter or energy because the concept of a wave needs time to transpire. An nExperience will portray particle-like characteristics because it is instantaneous.

240

Therefore the Experience of the wave-like aspect of a beam of light should change to an Experience of a particle-like aspect when it passes through a shutter operating faster than the value of the shortest time interval indicated by the MindMoment constant—10^{-14} seconds.[F]

EXISTENCE AND POSITION

In terms of the physical sciences and an understanding of spacetime, two issues are very clear: 1) the existence of a phenomenal object (or event) in a remote position is unknown until a "signal" indicating its existence is received* by the observer; and 2) such a signal can move* no faster than the speed of light.

Contrastingly, the ToT's Instancy principle says that an SCM (self-center of mass) is at rest in spacetime and is truly Simultaneous with all MindMoments in all time routes comprising all Sheaves. There is no "true signal" that needs to (or can) pass between an event and an SCM with respect to the occurrence of an event. This becomes clearer when we remember that the shape or position of a phenomenal object is solely an Experience and has no true physical dimensions or position. Shape and position is an nExperience resolving from information contained in an EQ resident in a single associated MindMoment.

Information about position is always with respect to two issues: 1) the centers of mass of the objects involved; and 2) the SCM of the relative self that contains the Experience of position.

The Experience of a phenomenal object in a remote position (relative to the SCM) is not a part of the relative self unless it is contained in a time-past MindMoment ($ɰ_{-n}$). Thus, for a certain relative self, an event (or an object) is not defined as existing if it is not in the time-past section of the associated time route. According to the Instancy principle, any relative change in position of an object must also be seen to occur in the time-past portion of a relative self.

A CHANGE IN POSITION

Within the ToT, the position of a substantial object is always relative to the reference frame of the SCM of the relative self containing the Experience of the substantial object. The SCM never moves, and any position or change in position is always with respect to the still point

---

[F] Note that this is the standard value for this rendition of the ToT.

of the SCM. In other words, it is the world and reality that is moving—the SCM is always motionless.

> Recall that an Experience of a position or a change in position is quantum in nature. The value of a single quantum of position change is denoted by the symbol "Φ" that stands for "quantum interspace". The value of Φ is 3×10^{-6} meters in V.1.
>
> An nExperience of movement is equal to the value of Φ, or there is no movement at all.

In a relative self, a change in position (movement) is described within successive iterations of the three space-like dimensions and one time-like dimension in the time past portion of a time route. This means that because of the quantum nature of Φ, only certain points on the hypersurface of a related 3-manifold will hold information describing the movement.

It's notable that the Experience of position or movement is completely separate from naked space. There is no possible position or movement in naked space, because any Experience of position or movement is information (described as a math object) overlaying naked space.

Naked space is homogeneous, but the geometry of a time route's 4-manifold is not. It is divided up into quantum MindMoments. The logic of the ToT states that the size of the quantum interspace (Φ) is anthropic in nature. There are perhaps an infinite number of different values for Φ [one for every V.n universe] however the Instancy principle provides an Experience of there being the only one value that exists [in terms of a relative self]—and that one value appears to define a complete universe that extends across all available space and all of time in V.1.

The oExperience of movement resolves from the information contained in EQ that resolve to a series of MindMoments in the time-past portion of a time route. Those MindMoments contain information representing changes in position in amounts equal to the value of the quantum interspace (Φ). Therefore, an Experience of a movement represents a whole number multiple of the value of Φ.

In the lexicon of the ToT, the stipulation that an EQ "contains an Φ" tells us that it has a Feature indicating a quantum change in position (equal to Φ). The change is always with respect to the information in the EQ immediately preceding it.

By definition, an EQ has only one Feature that holds information about an Φ. Thus the EQ may contain only one expression of a change in position equal to the value of Φ—or it can express no change at all. Either case expresses the quantum condition of Φ. Most EQ do not resolve to information describing a change in position…hence these EQ are not identified as "containing an Φ," instead they are identified as being "free of an Φ." This results in the following nomenclature.

NOMENCLATURE:
- o   An EQ containing an Φ is termed to be a "Φ_{con}EQ".
- o   All EQ between consecutive Φ_{con}EQ are termed to be "Φ_{free}EQ".

Movement is always with respect to the SCM. The Φ_{con}EQ that describe the distance that an object moved are equally distributed across the sequence of EQ that define the "inertial system" associated with the object moving. This equal distribution is axiomatic within the ToT and it is called the **quantum distribution principle**.

When we speak of the movement of an object we are specifically talking about the change in position of the **center of mass** of the object (the **CM**).

Nontemporal Velocity

In physics, movement is defined as a change in position. Velocity is a change in position over some duration of time. In the ToT, the oExperience of velocity similarly includes an apparent duration of the movement. For example: a car passes by your position on a street corner. In terms of a relative self the apparent duration of the movement of the car is equal to the time period of your awareness* of the car—which is related to the Experience called "the velocity of the car." An Experience of a value for the velocity can be determined from the associated Experiences of positions and elapsed time.

In the ToT velocity is an oExperience, and like all Experiences is Instantaneous and nontemporal in nature. From this comes the term **nontemporal velocity**—denoted with the symbol "ϋ" (lower case Greek letter upsilon with a dialytika).

Nontemporal velocity describes uniform velocity, which also indicates a certain **inertial system**. Within the ToT an inertial system is denoted with the symbol "I_n", where the subscript is a positive whole number identifying the inertial system of an object other than the SCM.

The inertial system of the SCM is always considered to be at rest and is denoted with the symbol "I_0". Nontemporal velocities are always with respect to the SCM, thus every value for ü other than zero is positive, and every value indicates an inertial system denoted by I_n.

Every EQ in a given inertial system has a Feature that resolves to an Experience of information in the time-like dimension. The time-like information is an oExperience of the flow of time for that object, which resolves from multiple nExperiences of **time quanta, "ŧ"** (small letter t with a stroke). An EQ containing a **time quantum** is called a "**ŧ_{con}EQ**". Every nExperience in a given inertial system has an associated time quantum; unless the EQ resolve to a substantial object in relativistic motion. Then it *may* or *may not* contain a time quantum. If it does not, the EQ is called a "**ŧ_{free}EQ**" (see below).

The value of a time quantum, in terms of duration, is equal to the reciprocal of the MindMoment constant. A single time quantum resolves to the nExperience of a duration equal to the value of ŧ (very quick); and multiple time quanta resolve to the oExperience of the flow of time.

$$\text{ŧ} = \frac{1}{\tilde{A}} = 10^{-14} \text{ second.}$$

A single MindMoment that is, for example, the package containing the Thoughts describing a group of substantial (instant) objects, serves as a purveyor of an nExperience of a single beat of time for the objects. The duration of the beat is equal to the value of a single time quantum. A sequence of MindMoments purveys the oExperience of the objects (as temporal objects) existing in a flow of time—because the nExperience of each instant object includes a time quanta.

Nontemporal velocity describes both a change in position and a duration. The duration is determined with respect to the total number of MindMoments in the sequence describing the nontemporal velocity. This is called the **duration of the event** of interest within a relative self, identified with the symbol "**Đ**" (capitol D with stroke).

For example, consider a person watching a car drive past. The person watches for two seconds and the car moves 88 ft. If we were to ask: What is the value of ü for the Experience the car moving 88 feet in two seconds? The oExperience of movement is part of a relative self and thus the total number of MindMoments being considered must express the oExperience of two seconds of time flow for that relative self. The total number of ŧ_{con}EQ would of course be equal to the total number

244

of MindMoments, Đ. An oExperience of two seconds of time flow would require 2×10^{14} t_{con}EQ, one for each MindMoment in the sequence. Each MindMoment in the two second sequence would contain:

1) An EQ that resolves to: the Experience of the substantial object that is the car, and an Experience of a single time quanta associated with the car.
2) An EQ that resolves to: the Experience of the physical body of the person watching the car move, (i.e. the SCM), and an Experience of a single time quanta associated with the SCM.

In the above thought experiment the nontemporal velocity (ü) of the car, with respect to the SCM of the relative self, is 30 mph (44 feet per second). In terms of relative self the SCM is, more or less, the Experience of the substantial object called a physical body; and it is strongly associated with a concept of a "self." In this vain it is denoted with the term **body-self**. Every waking relative self contains a body-self (as well as many other substantial objects.) If we discount the movement of arms, legs etc. the body-self can be thought of as basically never moving, just like the SCM.

In this thought experiment, the number of EQ that resolve to the moving object (the car) is equal to the number of MindMoments in the duration of the event of interest in relative self (Đ); but the EQ resolving to the car are not all Φ_{con}EQ. Some are Φ_{free}EQ.

Nontemporal velocity is described by the ratio between the number of Φ_{con}EQ in play and the total number of MindMoments that describe a duration of interest (Đ). Thus the sequence describing the car contains both Φ_{con}EQ and Φ_{free}EQ.

As a matter of nomenclature: the sequence of EQ describing a moving object (*i.e.* an object that is separate from the body-self) is called the **mo-sequence**; and the sequence of EQ describing a body-self is called the **bs-sequence**. The elements of these sequences may variously occupy (and share) the same MindMoments.

The number of t_{con}EQ in any sequence is denoted with the symbol "Ŧ" (capitol "T" with a stroke).

In the bs-sequence Ŧ is always equal to the value of "Đ", the duration of the MindMoment sequence.

In any mo-sequence Ŧ is equal to the value of "Đ" if the moving object is not in relativistic motion (see below).

245

The number of $\Phi_{con}EQ$ in the mo-sequence is denoted with the symbol "p" (lower case.)

$$\ddot{\upsilon} = \frac{p\Phi}{Đ} = \text{meters/MindMoment.}$$

Where:

- $\ddot{\upsilon}$ = is nontemporal velocity.
- p is the number of $\Phi_{con}EQ$ in the mo-sequence.
- $Đ$ is the number of MindMoments in the bs-sequence.
- Φ is the quantum interspace ($\Phi = 3 \times 10^{-6}$ meters).
- $Ã$ is the MindMoment constant ($Ã = 10^{14}$ MindMoments/sec).

Multiplying the result by the MindMoment constant ($Ã$) gives an answer in meters per second.

$$\ddot{\upsilon} = \frac{p\Phi \, Ã}{Đ} = \text{meters/sec.}$$

EXAMPLES OF NONTEMPORAL VELOCITY:

The following four scenarios describe different examples of non-temporal velocity. They are all described as occurring within the time-past portion of a time route and within the duration of one second (10^{14} MindMoments). All of these instances are examples of constant velocity calculated with respect to inertial system of the body-self, I_0 (*i.e.* the SCM.)

1) If there is an Experience of no movement there is no velocity involved, and none of the EQ in the mo-sequence contain a Φ_{con}. There are only $\Phi_{free}EQ$ involved in the time route.

2) If there is an Experience of the smallest possible movement [a distance equal to Φ] there is a very small associated velocity. The velocity ($\ddot{\upsilon}$) will be 3×10^{-6} meters per second; and there will be $10^{14} - 1$ (ten to the fourteenth minus one) $\Phi_{free}EQ$ in the mo-sequence.

3) If there is an Experience of a movement of one meter, the velocity ($\ddot{\upsilon}$) will be one meter per second. The mo-sequence ($Đ = 10^{14}$) will contain 3×10^{6} EQ that are Φ_{con}, and a remainder of EQ that are Φ_{free}.

This amounts to 3×10^6 $\Phi_{con}EQ$ and 99,999,997,000,000 $\Phi_{free}EQ$ (this number is 10^{14} minus 3×10^6; or one hundred trillion minus three million). According to the Quantum distribution principle, the $\Phi_{con}EQ$ will be equally distributed throughout the sequence—which means there will be 99,999,997 $\Phi_{free}EQ$ between each of the $\Phi_{con}EQ$. This also means that there will be a maximum of 99,999,997 $\Phi_{free}EQ$ between the $Ш_0$ and the $\Phi_{con}EQ$ that is most recent time-past.

4) If there is (somehow) an Experience of the movement of a photon traveling in a vacuum the velocity will be the speed of light, there will be no $\Phi_{free}EQ$ in the mo-sequence; every Mind-Moment contains information resolving from a $\Phi_{con}EQ$. The photon is moving at the maximum possible velocity that may be an Experience in V.1. [There will also be no $t_{con}EQ$ (*i.e.* no time quanta) because this is the ultimate relativistic velocity. More on this below.]

In each of these examples:
- We are looking at two EQ sequences, the moving object and the body-self;
- The EQ that resolve to an Experience of movement [the $\Phi_{con}EQ$] are resident in the EQ sequence that resolves to the moving object, *i.e.* the mo-sequence;
- The EQ that resolve to an Experience of body-self are part of the bs-sequence. The sequence contains only $\Phi_{free}EQ$ and it resolve to the SCM, which never moves.
- The two EQ sequences reside coincidently and in parallel within the single sequence of MindMoments comprising a time route; and
- The duration of the sequence of MindMoments is equal to Đ, the duration of the relative self.

All of the above Examples describe uniform, constant velocity. If any of the examples were describing an average velocity, the Φ_{con} might not be evenly distributed. In such a situation there could also be various oExperiences of acceleration within the sequence—which, in an automobile, would feel like a jerky ride, as if the engine was occasionally misfiring.

The intermittent changes in velocity would resolve to an oExperience of acceleration—which can be either positive or negative. Within the ToT, acceleration has a different explanation than that found in the physical sciences.

NONTEMPORAL ACCELERATION

Common knowledge tells us that acceleration is a change in velocity. In the physical sciences acceleration is associated with: 1) a change in velocity, 2) a change in direction, or 3) due to the nature of gravity.

In relativistic physics the term "proper acceleration" is the physical acceleration (*i.e.* measurable acceleration as by an accelerometer) experienced* by an object. According to the ToT this makes sense only in the fashion that all objects are contained in a relative self. An object alone cannot have an Experience.

Within the ToT all of these types of acceleration are functionally the same oExperience, differing only in the relative direction and value of a predicate inertial system (I_n) compared to a subsequent inertial system (I_{n+1})—all with respect to the ever unmoving inertial system of the SCM (I_0).

Much more can be said about **nontemporal acceleration**; but it is beyond the scope of this book and it would take us off on a tangent, away from the next topic—the nature of a universal constant.

TIME DILATION & SEQUENCE DILATION

Time dilation is a scientific principle described in Albert Einstein's theory of special relativity. **Time dilation** is discussed in the context of constant velocity, *i.e.* without acceleration of any kind, and involves the observed "slowing down" of a clock positioned in a different inertial system than that of the observer. It becomes evident at relativistic speeds (more than 10% the speed of light). If a person standing on earth were to observe a clock positioned on board a spaceship traveling past Earth at one half the speed of light, that person would observe the space ship clock as moving slower than a similar clock sitting on Earth. Einstein used this principle to help explain the nature of reality according to his theories.

A parallel concept in the ToT is called **sequence dilation.** It describes the Experience of the "slowing down" of a clock on a moving physical object in some inertial system (I_n) other than the inertial system (I_0) of the SCM.

248

A REVIEW OF BASIC CONCEPTS:

Recall that a relative self (the time past portion of a time route) consists of a set of MindMoments in sequence, and each of these Mind-Moments is made up of a group of EQ. These groups are repeated, gradually changing in an iterative fashion, from MindMoment to Mind-Moment across the sequence of MindMoments comprising the relative self. In this way there are various parallel sequences of EQ existing synchronously within the containing MindMoment sequence that is the relative self.

These sequences of EQ resolve to different, continuing oExperiences "within the flow of time", because iterations of the particular EQ repeat in succession within the sequence. Geometrically the sequences are expressed as information extending in the time-like dimension of spacetime. Thus, for example, the oExperience a *single* substantial object appears to exist in the flow of time, as a temporal object, because it resolves from a sequence of EQ.

In the process of sequence dilation we are interested in those temporal objects that move and in the one temporal object that does not move (the body-self). Each of these objects resolves from a different sequence of EQ and represents a different inertial system. For example the Experience of a moving object is said to resolve from a sequence of EQ called the moving-object sequence (the mo-sequence); and the Experience of the body-self, the only non-moving object is said to resolve from the body-self sequence (the bs-sequence). The inertial system of each sequence is, labeled respectively I_n and I_0. The moving object is represented by its center of mass (the CM), and the body-self is represented by the self center of mass (the SCM) which is always unmoving.

Each of the repeating EQ in a sequence holds various Features that contain information that may change as the sequence progresses. For example, a single Feature may indicate a change in position or no change in position. For example, it could do this with information describing a quantum interspace or the lack of a quantum interspace. The same single EQ could also hold other information in a different Feature, such as an indication of a time quanta or the lack of a time quanta.

THE NATURE OF EQ SEQUENCES:
1. There is always the same number of EQ in the mo-sequence, as there is in the bs-sequence; and this number always equals Đ. The value of Đ is the number of MindMoments in the duration of the event of interest within the relative self

2. All of the EQ in the bs-sequence are always Φ_{free}EQ, because the SCM never moves.
3. The EQ in the mo-sequence are a combination of Φ_{con}EQ and Φ_{free}EQ; and their total number always equals the value of Đ. The combination may range from a single Φ_{con}EQ and the rest Φ_{free}EQ [very cold]; to all Φ_{con}EQ [which indicates light speed].
4. All of the EQ in the bs-sequence are always t_{con}EQ, because the SCM acts as the criterion for the Experience of time flow.
5. The EQ in the mo-sequence may be t_{con}EQ or t_{free}EQ; and their total number always equals the value of Đ. The combination may range from all t_{con}EQ [non-relativistic velocities]; to no t_{con}EQ and all t_{free}EQ [which indicates light speed]. At relativistic speeds the EQ are a combination of both types.

Sequence dilation describes the quantum dilation of a series of time quanta in the mo-sequence of EQ expressing the inertial system (I_n) of an object other than the body-self. The number of time quanta in the mo-sequence is denoted by the symbol " $Ŧ'$ " ("$Ŧ$" with a prime designation).

> Recall that the number of time quanta in the bs-sequence is denoted by $Ŧ$ (not prime). When the mo-sequence does not indicate relativistic motion $Ŧ$ equals $Ŧ'$. The number of time quanta in the bs-sequence ($Ŧ$) always equals Đ, the duration of the event of interest within the relative self.
> A single time quanta is denoted by the symbol "$ŧ$"; and its value is 10^{-14} second.

At nonrelativistic speeds (less than 10% of the speed of light) we seldom consider a difference in time flow between moving objects and the body-self. This is because, at such velocities there is no significant difference between time flow in I_n and I_0. That is to say: …there is no significant difference between the value of $Ŧ$ in I_n and $Ŧ'$ in I_0.

At greater velocities there is a difference that can be expressed with *sequence dilation*.

A relative self is comprised of many different sequences of EQ making up the single sequence of MindMoments of its time route. Many of the EQ resolve to the oExperience of moving objects, such as: other

250

beings, trees, buildings, mountains, airplanes, clouds, planets, stars, galaxies, photons etc., each having its own unique inertial system (I_n) and unique center of mass. When any of these objects moves with a non-temporal velocity greater than 10% of the speed of light, sequence dilation comes into play.

EXAMPLES OF TIME AND SEQUENCE DILATION:

NO TIME DILATION—in terms of the physical sciences: Consider a car moving at about 45 mph and being observed for 2 seconds by a person standing on the side of the road. Both the car's clock and the observer's clock are in sync at the end of 2 seconds because the car is moving at a non-relativistic speed.

NO SEQUENCE DILATION—in terms of the ToT: Consider the time route that resolves to a relative self which includes the oExperience of an automobile driving past the body-self. It's moving at constant nontemporal velocity of 20 meters per second (about 45 mph). In this example the moment of the present, the Now, for the relative self is coincident with an apparent point in the flow of time that is two seconds after the observer (the body-self) first notices the automobile, thus the duration of the event of interest (Đ) is 2 seconds and the value for Đ is 2×10^{14} MindMoments. The relative self contains the following Experiences:

1) The Experience of the car having changed position in the amount of 40 meters—which is equivalent to 1.33×10^7 $\Phi_{con}EQ$ in the mo-sequence resolving to the car. The remainder of the EQ in the mo-sequence is $\Phi_{free}EQ$ for a total of 2×10^{14} EQ in the complete sequence. Thus at a speed of 20 m./sec a very small percentage of the EQ are $\Phi_{con}EQ$.

2) The Experience of a view of the clock on the dashboard of the car exhibiting time flow that resolves from the $t_{con}EQ$ in the mo-sequence. Because the car is moving far slower than a relativistic speed, effectively every EQ in the mo-sequence is a $t_{con}EQ$; and the value of $\mathcal{T}$ equals the value of $\mathcal{T}'$.

3) The Experience of the body-self, which has not moved, and thus has only $\Phi_{free}EQ$ in its bs-sequence.

4) The Experience of a watch on the wrist of the body-self that is indicating the oExperience of two seconds of elapse time since the car was first noticed. This oExperience resolves

from all of the EQ in the bs-sequence being t_{con}EQ. Thus Ŧ equals Đ.

WITH TIME DIALTION—in terms of the physical sciences: Consider a spaceship traveling past an observer on Earth at one half the speed of light. The velocity of light is given as $3x10^8$ meters per second. There are identical clocks on the spaceship and on Earth. Call them the "Earth clock" and the "spaceship clock." The moment of the present for an observer on Earth is coincident with an apparent point in the flow of time that is two seconds after the observer first notices the spaceship. With respect to the observer on Earth, in the two seconds following the first observance of the spaceship, the spaceship clock changed position by an amount equal to $3x10^8$ meters (a distance associated with a velocity of one half light speed for two seconds).

The Earth clock shows an elapsed time of two seconds while the spaceship clock shows less than two seconds; and that amount is in accord with the Lorentz transformation.

WITH SEQUENCE DIALTION—in terms of the ToT: The observer is the body-self standing on Earth. The nontemporal velocity of light is $3x10^8$ meters in 10^{14} MindMoments; or, $3x10^{-6}$ m/Ш. At the moment of the Now (two seconds after the spaceship was first noticed) the relative self contains two sequences of EQ (among others) which resolve to the oExperiences of:

1) The body-self (the SCM) which is not moving.
2) The spaceship having changed position by $3x10^8$ meters (according to the SCM of the body-self). The Experience resolves from the mo-sequence of EQ which contains 10^{14} Φ_{con}EQ.
3) A wrist watch on the body-self that indicates an oExperience of 2 seconds resolving from the number of t_{con}EQ in the bs-sequence of EQ, which is equal to the value of Đ.
4) The spaceship clock showing a lapse of time of *less than* 2 seconds. This is an Experience that resolves from the number of t_{con}EQ in the mo-sequence of EQ. The number indicates the value of Ŧ′ which is a function of the Lorentz transformation. Thus Ŧ′ is less than Ŧ, the number of t_{con}EQ in the bs-sequence.

The 4th example prompts the question: What does the spaceship clock and the Earth clock look like from opposite viewpoints?

In terms of time dilation: a view of the spaceship clock from Earth shows it slowed; but a view of the spaceship clock, from the spaceship, shows it running at normal rate.

In terms of sequence dilation: a view of the spaceship clock from Earth shows it slowed; and a view of the spaceship clock from the spaceship will be a view had by a different relative self (a different SCM) so it's irrelevant in a discussion of an Earth bound relative self. The spaceship relative self is part of the same shared universe and thus shares the same value for c (light speed) but its view of the relative motion of an earthbound clock will be described as a function of a different SCM.

Simply put: the flow of time for any substantial moving object resolves from the number of time quanta associated with the object's EQ sequence (the mo-sequence). If the inertial system of the object indicates movement that is greater than 10% of the speed of light, the principle of sequence dilation comes into play to explain the "slowing down" of the object's clock. Thus the number of time quanta ($\mathcal{F}'$) associated with the oExperience of the flow of time for an object moving at relativistic speed is less than the number of time quanta associated with the body-self ($\mathcal{F}$). The difference between $\mathcal{F}'$ and $\mathcal{F}$ is given by the Lorentz transformation.

THE QUALITY OF SPACE REFERRED TO AS "c"

According to the physical sciences there is a unique quality, labeled "c", that is a feature of space in general. The value of c indicates the velocity of light in a vacuum and the maximum speed at which a signal can travel between two locations. It is a constant in our universe, measured to be approximately 3×10^8 meters per second.

Time dilation (as described by Einstein) is an expression of the relatively asymmetric contraction of one of the dimensional reference frames in a four-dimensional geometry. In terms of physics, the asymmetry occurs because the observed value for the speed of light is a constant regardless of the observer or the inertial system of reference.

. . . .

In contrast the quality of c is described differently in the ToT—there is no signal that "travels*" between moving objects and the "observer", regardless of their position. In the ToT, the Experience of c resolves from a quality of naked space that serves as a relational constant within the static V.1 universe where oExperiences of multiple, unique moving* objects express different inertial systems.

Sequence dilation is an expression of the continuation of reality sync across all inertial systems. Unlike time dilation, it is quantum in nature—it's a function of a whole-number quantity of time quanta.

The amount of sequence dilation is in accordance with the Lorentz transformation. As the relative nontemporal velocity of an object increases, the number of $t_{con}EQ$ decrease, while the number of $\Phi_{con}EQ$ increase, within a mo-sequence. This asymmetry continues as velocity increases toward the limit point, the speed of light. The gradual lessening of the number of $t_{con}EQ$ in the associated EQ Feature is a natural quality of the relative condition; because the ongoing balance between these two items of information ($t_{con}EQ$ and $\Phi_{con}EQ$) results in the speed of light being constant for all inertial systems. Thus the constant value for c describes the continuing relationship between substantial objects (and therefore between relative selves) in a shared V.n universe, regardless of the inertial systems of the various objects.

In this way c is figuratively the glue that holds us all together; and in terms of the ToT it is analogous to the Experience of compassion— i.e. the intertwingled nature of all elements of the Matrix.

MATHEMATICS OF TIME AND SEQUENCE DILATION

Mathematics is a very good tool for showing the relationships between concepts. Consider the following.

TIME DILATION IN SPECIAL RELATIVITY:

Time dilation is a concept that explains features of special relativity. Speeds of approximately 1/10 light speed and above are where time dilation becomes important. This equation deals with uniform relative motion that is hypothetically far from all gravitational mass. [In a gravitational field the situation is more complex and not addressed in this writing.]

$$\Delta t' = \gamma \Delta t = \frac{\Delta t}{\sqrt{1 - \frac{v^2}{c^2}}}$$

Where:
- v is the relative velocity between two events.
- c is the speed of light.

- Δt is the time between two events happening in the same place for an observer in some inertial frame (e.g. ticks on a clock). This is known as *proper time*.
- $\Delta t'$ is the time interval between those same events, as measured by another observer, moving with velocity v relative to the former observer. This is known as *coordinate time*.
- γ is the Lorentz factor: $\gamma = \dfrac{1}{\sqrt{1-\dfrac{v^2}{c^2}}}$

SEQUENCE DILATION OWING TO UNIFORM RELATIVE MOTION

The formula for sequence dilation is derived by employing the Lorentz factor in the same fashion as is done in the special relativity equation. When The ToT system of measurement is used, the "v" in the special relativity equation is replaced with ʊ, and the Δt is replaced with Ŧ. The equation becomes:

$$\text{Ŧ}' = \gamma\,\text{Ŧ} = \frac{\text{Ŧ}}{\sqrt{1-\dfrac{\text{ʊ}^2}{c^2}}}$$

Where:
- ʊ is the nontemporal velocity of the moving object with respect to the SCM.
- c is the speed of light in V.1 .
- Ŧ is the total number of $t_{con}EQ$ in the bs-sequence (the body-self). The value of Ŧ is equal to Đ, the duration of the event of interest in MindMoments. The bs-sequence contains only $t_{con}EQ$. This is the correlate to *proper time* in the time dilation equation.
- Ŧ′ is the total number of $t_{con}EQ$ in the mo-sequence (the moving object). The sequence length is equal to Đ, but the mo-sequence also contains $t_{free}EQ$. Ŧ′ is the correlate to *coordinate time* in the time dilation equation.
- γ is the Lorentz factor.

This is simple mathematics but it provides an idea of the relationship. The answers should be rounded up to the next whole number because Đ′ is quantum in nature.

AN EXPERIMENTAL TEST OF Ã

According to the logic of the ToT, it is impossible for a shutter to operate at a rate greater than the MindMoment constant (Ã), because such an Experience would have no quantum position in which to exist. With this in mind there may be an experiment that could verify the concept of the quantum interspace—a function of the MindMoment constant.

THE EXPERIMENT:

Imagine a rotating mirror set up in association with a good telescope and a powerful laser, the idea being to project a sweeping swath of laser light across the surface of the moon—a dark, new moon.

If the mirror were rotating at one revolution per second (one rps) we would see a sweep of laser light appear on the surface of the moon once every second. This can be calculated...the following numbers are rounded:

Mean distance of earth to moon:
3.85×10^8 meters

If we describe the mean distance between the earth and moon as the radius of sweep of the laser beam, then:

The circumference of the laser sweep will be:
$2(\pi)(r) = (2)\pi(3.85 \times 10^8) = 24.2 \times 10^8$ m,
or roughly 25×10^8 meters.
The reflecting mirror is spinning at one rps, thus the apparent speed of the moving laser spot will be:
2.5×10^9 mps (meters/second)

The spot appears to be moving at a velocity almost ten times greater than the V.1 value for the speed of light—which is 3×10^8 mps. This can happen because nothing is really moving, it's simply a spot of light sequentially illuminating successive, discrete locations (if the illumination is quantum in nature).

If the mirror were spinning at 2000rps (120,000rpm) the laser spot would appear to travel at 5×10^{12} mps, or 5×10^{14} centimeters per second. Therefore a single centimeter of travel would require only 5×10^{-14} second.

If we set up a shutter that allowed us to detect a single sweep of the 2000rps experiment (less than 1/2000 of a second) we could create a window for viewing one transition of the laser beam across a one centimeter-wide target.

Physics tells us that if our detector recognized a single sweep of the "moving" spot of light crossing a one centimeter target on the moon's surface, it would appear as a continuous line of light because the projected spot of light at any position on the target would overlap the position next to it and all of the spots would appear as a single line of light. However, according to the ToT we would see something different.

Recall that the working value of the MindMoment constant in V.1 is: $\tilde{A} = 10^{14} \, \text{Ш/sec}$.

We have established that a centimeter of "travel" for the laser beam would require 5×10^{-14} second. Thus there would be five Mind-Moments in the time it takes the beam to "traverse" one centimeter; or we could say, the oExperience of the spot of laser light "crossing" the target would be comprised of five MindMoments. This means there could be no Experience of a spot of light in the spaces between the five MindMoments. Therefore, if $\tilde{A} = 10^{14}\text{Ш/sec}$, we would not detect a *continuous line of light* on the target, *i.e.* we would not have an oExperience—instead we would have an nExperience of five spots of laser light on the one centimeter target.

Hypothetically, in terms of the ToT, this experiment is providing a high-resolution look into the detailed contents of a time route. There is no light actually traveling to the moon—because nothing moves in an Instant universe. In this experiment the spinning laser, the telescope, the beam of light and the moon are all understood to be elements in a package of instantaneous concepts that exist in relation to another concept, which is the display across the detector. The detector effectively provides the view of an array of MindMoments laid out in the time-past portion of a time route.

It appears obvious that the value for $\tilde{A}$ in the V.1 universe should be considerably higher, closer to a value derived from a Planck time. There is really no way to calculate it. It must be determined experimentally. The constant would have a naturally occurring value in the V.1 universe; and like the speed of light, it simply must be measured. A search for higher values could entail raising the rps of the mirror, increasing the resolution of the detector and/or extending the sweep radius of the laser beam, any of which might be difficult if a laser is used; but there may be other options.

One possible variation of the experiment would involve a pulsar. "Pulsar" is a portmanteau word from *pulsating star*. It is believed that pulsars are rotating neutron stars that produce a very bright beam of electromagnetic energy that sweeps across the sky at a regular rate. For example, a pulsar that might be useful in this experiment is the pulsar named *PSR J1748-2446ad*.[147]

This is a "millisecond pulsar" rotating at high speed (716 rps). Its rotation rate is approximately 1.4×10^{-3} revolutions per second and it is approximately 18,000 light years from Earth. This distance makes its effective sweep radius 18,000 light years or 1.7×10^{20} meters, which translates into a total sweep circumference of about 10^{21} meters. If we divide the circumference by the rotation rate we will see a "sweep velocity" on Earth of about 7×10^{23} m/sec. There may be a problem constructing a detector if this pulsar is used.

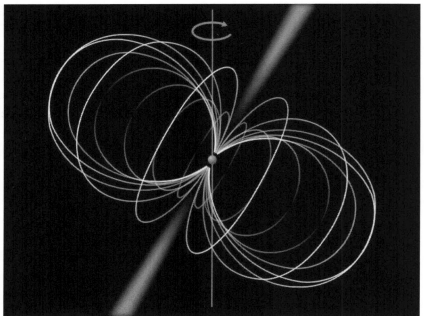

Schematic view of a pulsar. The sphere in the middle represents the neutron star, the curves indicate the magnetic field lines, the protruding cones represent the emission beams and the vertical line represents the axis on which the star rotates.[148]

258

It should be understood that the experiment hypothesizes that there is no information between the spots on the detector, it does not say that there is no existence. This statement is made in terms of the absolute condition indicating existence without the concept of information.

THE TOT SYSTEM OF SYMBOLS AND MEASUREMENT

The metric system of measurement has largely taken precedent on the planet. In time-past there were many different systems that were defined locally—such as the length of the king's foot; the amount of liquid held in a sack made from the stomach of a certain animal; or the weight of a certain stone.

In the ToT there is the unique concept of the MindMoment constant (Ã) that is defined as holding true across all universes in the multiverse. Other than that all values are locally defined according to the areas, planets and universes they are associated with.

For example: there is the quantum interspace (Φ) a Feature of an EQ that is unique for each universe. The value for the speed of light in a given universe (V.n) arises out of a comparison between Φ and Ã, and thus it is also unique to each universe.

The following definitions and constants describe a system of natural quantum units found in the ToT. In the ToT system all of the units are described as quantum nature. They logically define the various sequences that resolve to the Experiences of reality within the flow of time.

DEFINITIONS AND CONSTANTS IN THE ToT:
- Ã is the "MindMoment constant" $\tilde{A} = 10^{14}$ Ш/sec.
- Ш is the symbol for MindMoment.
- t is the symbol for a time quanta. It is an Experience that resolves from the information in a single Feature of an EQ. It is locally defined in each universe. The value of t is the reciprocal of Ã. The oExperience of one second resolves from 10^{14} time quanta.
- A **time route** is a sequence of MindMoments that resolve to the oExperience of time-past and time-future reality for a relative Self.
- $Ш_{-n}$ is a MindMoment in the time-past portion of a time route. "n" is a whole number.
- $Ш_{+n}$ is a MindMoment in the time-future portion of a time route. "n" is a whole number.

259

o III_0 is a placeholder representing the moment of the Now. It is not a MindMoment.

o   A **relative self** is the oExperience of reality in terms of space and time as it is typically defined by the sciences. It resolves from all the information in the time-past section of a single time-route.

o   A **Sheaf** is a bundle of time routes crossing at the tie-point nexus that is the moment of the Now.

o   An **individuated SELF** is the information resident in a Sheaf. It is the most extensive display of an individual that is possible. Beyond a Sheaf Awareness of reality becomes non-personal.

o   A **body-self** describes the three-dimensional object that is the physical body contained in a relative self. The body-self is often thought of as the "self" in terms of the relative condition.

o Φ is a quantum interspace. It is the information in a Feature of a single EQ; and it is the smallest possible change in position that may be an Experience. It is quantum in nature and is derived from the measured speed of light and Å. $\Phi = c/\text{Å} = 3\text{x}10^{-6}$ meters.

o c is the symbol for the speed of light in a vacuum, about $3\text{x}10^{8}$ m/sec; or in the ToT system $10^{14}\,\Phi$/sec.

o $\Phi_{con}\text{EQ}$ designates an EQ with a Feature that contains information that resolves to an Experience of a quantum interspace.

o $\Phi_{free}\text{EQ}$ designates an EQ with a Feature that does not contain information that resolves to an Experience of a quantum interspace.

o   A **mo-sequence** designates a sequence of EQ in the time past portion of a time route resolves to the oExperience of a moving three-dimensional object in a relative self. This sequence always represents an I_n inertial system.

o   A **bs-sequence** designates a sequence of EQ in the time past portion of a time route resolves to the oExperience of a body-self in a relative self. Except for local movements (*i.e.* changes in position of arms, legs, organs etc.) the body-self can be equated to the SCM, which never moves in the universe. This sequence always represents the I_0 inertial system.

260

- The **SCM** is the "self-center of mass" within a relative self, considered to be always at-rest.
- The **CM** is the center of mass of any moving* object in a relative self.
- I_0 is the inertial system of SCM of the body-self—always associated with the bs-sequence of EQ.
- I_n is the inertial system of CM of an object—always associated with the mo-sequence of EQ.
- **Đ** is the number of MindMoments in the duration of an event of interest within a relative self. Đ comes into play when determining nontemporal velocity.
- **ʊ** is nontemporal velocity of a phenomenal object in inertial system I_n. It is movement relative to the SCM.
- **p** is the number of $\Phi_{con}EQ$ in the EQ mo-sequence (*i.e.* an object other than the body-self). p comes into play when determining nontemporal velocity.
- **d** is distance, a concept reflecting a change in position within the relative self.
- **t** is time, a concept reflecting the flow of time within a relative self.
- **v** is temporal velocity, a concept reflecting a change in position in time within a relative self.
- **t_{con}EQ** is the symbol for an EQ containing a Feature whose information resolves to the Experience of a single time quantum.
- **t_{free}EQ** is the symbol for an EQ containing a Feature whose information does not resolve to the Experience of a time quantum.
- **Ŧ** is the total number of $t_{con}EQ$ in the bs-sequence (the body-self). The value of Đ is equal to đ, the duration of the relative self in MindMoments. The bs-sequence contains only $t_{con}EQ$. This is the correlate to *proper time* in the time dilation equation
- **Ŧ′** is the total number of $t_{con}EQ$ in the mo-sequence (the moving object). The sequence length is equal to Đ, the duration of the event of interest within a relative self. The mo-sequence also contains $t_{free}EQ$. This is the correlate to *coordinate time* in the time dilation equation
- **γ** is the Lorentz factor.

EQUATIONS:

Velocity:
$$v = \frac{d}{t}$$

Nontemporal velocity:
$$\ddot{\upsilon} = \frac{p\Phi}{Đ}$$

Quantum interspace:
$$\Phi = \frac{c}{\tilde{A}}$$

Time quanta:
$$\mathfrak{t} = \frac{1}{\tilde{A}}$$

Lorentz factor:
$$\gamma = \frac{1}{\sqrt{1-\frac{v^2}{c^2}}}$$

Time dilation:
$$\Delta t' = \gamma \Delta t = \frac{\Delta t}{\sqrt{1-\frac{v^2}{c^2}}}$$

Sequence dilation:
$$\mathfrak{F}' = \gamma \mathfrak{F} = \frac{\mathfrak{F}}{\sqrt{1-\frac{\ddot{\upsilon}^2}{c^2}}}$$

3.2 - A NEW REALITY MAP

What you have read so far basically describes contemporary physics in terms of the ToT. Based on that description, this chapter pictures what might be in store for us, as a people, if we begin to see realty according to a different, broader, more inclusive reality map.

If you were able to get your mind around all or some of the material in this book to this point, you may have experienced* what appear to be ideas you've never encountered before. Some Buddhists would describe such and experience* a special *awareness*. Whenever one learns something new, something like this special *awareness* may occur.

> The term *awareness*, as it is used here, is difficult to define. It is obviously in the context of the relative condition but it has the connotation of possibly being understood as a taste of the Awareness which is part of the absolute condition.

What's written here may have struck you as unusual, and you had to stretch your thought processes a bit to get a handle on it. When you did this, the continuing concept of the self may have dropped out (a little bit). For example, consider carefully the letters that make up the word GOOGLE. If you look with keen acuity, you will notice that the space comprising the inside of the "O" is slightly smaller than the space comprising the inside of the "G" (if it were closed).

Now think back. At the moment you made this observation there was probably no specific awareness* of "self" involved *while the observation was occurring*. There was just acuity and focus coupled with an awareness* of looking at the "O" and the "G." Likely, there were no other concepts comprising the set of Experiences, such as "who you thought you were" at the moment of observation. Try it again, carefully.

Every time you do this sort of thing, or learn about unusual new concepts, it's likely that you taste a little bit of the special "non-personal Awareness" that's found in Buddhism. In the ToT it's Awareness with an upper case "A". Now you can maybe exercise more of that special Awareness by considering "dangerous manifolds".

DANGEROUS MANIFOLDS

According to the ToT an interpretation of Poincaré's work is: "A simply connected, finite, temporal, 3-manifold with positive curvature is the only one that may *continue* to exist." In the ToT such a temporal manifold is made up of a sequence of instant manifolds, called **proper manifolds.** With respect to a relative self—if the conditions of Poincaré's description are not met, then the Experience of the surrounding reality could manifest as a hole in space, an infinitely deep pit or some other equally unpleasant situation over the course of the apparent flow of time. In the ToT the instant manifolds in the sequence that resolve to the unpleasant situation are called a **dangerous manifolds**. Dangerous manifolds are always instant manifolds.

Simulated view of a black hole in front of the Large Magellanic Cloud.[149]

In simple terms, the ToT tells us that a time route is comprised of an iterative sequence of instant 3-manifolds, and the sequence will **self-terminate** if one of those iterations is a dangerous manifold which is close enough to the SCM to cause problems. The words "close enough" mean that the time route describes a clear, unavoidable sequence leading to an existential threat. If this occurs, a 5-space vision will cause a Shift of awareness (if such is possible within the given karmic milieu) and the **self-terminating time route** will be anthropically denied with a Shift causing the relative self to instead resolve from an alternate time route incorporating a proper manifold.

> Note that in terms of this discussion a sequence of instant 3-manifolds is synonymous with: a temporal 3-manifold, an instant 4-manifold, and a time route.

The ToT does *not* state that a temporal manifold that is not simply connected, or not of positive curvature, cannot exist at some instant; or that it cannot exist in a limited sequence. But, it does say that such a limited sequence may at some point be denied (with a Shift) as part of a relative self from an anthropic standpoint.

For example, we could postulate that for some short sequence of MindMoments there may be an oExperience leading to an existential anomaly in the three-dimensional configuration space of a substantial object; or it might be something like a nearby infinite pit, or a small black hole in the vicinity of the SCM. In the cosmos it could be a wormhole or a large black hole. What is the nature of such an Experience? I don't know. These are not concepts that fit well within the bounds of the human condition, which is why they are anthropically denied.

> The feature film "Interstellar"[150] has wonderful images of a black hole up close. These images were mathematically described by the physicist Kip Thorne and then were rendered in ultra-high resolution for IMAX projection. Anyone at all interested in the phenomena should see this movie.

These Experiences can be seen as resolving from two types of dangerous 3-manifolds; one with areas of *negative curvature*, or another that is *not simply connected*.

It's notable that the concept of time route bundle doesn't flourish on a 5-manifold that contains areas of infinitely tall peaks or infinitely deep pits (possibly those manifolds that are not simply connected); or

266

that have areas with holes in which to "get stuck" (possibly those manifolds that are tori).

In the ToT these situations do not appear as important issues because the Anthropic principle will cull and deny untenable situations. Therefore, an untenable time route will not be "chosen" when a Shift occurs... more on this below.

MANIFOLDS—NOT SIMPLY CONNECTED

Consider a manifold that is not simply connected, such as a 3-torus. This could be a dangerous manifold. It is not easy to envisioned a 3-toris, to allow discussion we'll drop down one dimension and think of a 2-torus, like a standard doughnut.

Within a relative self portions of a dangerous manifold may appear to be normal; for example the rounded outside area of the torus, not the part next to the hole. If the information constituting a relative self is limited to this outer area there would be no problem—no possible holes in space. In this area the geometry of the spacetime universe will appear as normal, provided our time route on point does not depict a sequence that **wanders** into the destructive area of the doughnut hole. The operative term *to wander* indicates the pathway of a single time route on the surface of an instant 5-manifold (a Sheaf).

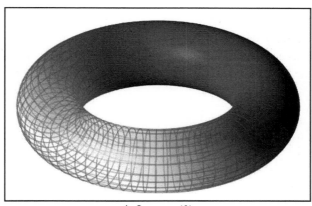

A 2-torus.[151]

Prosaically this is similar to an overview of a layman's vision of the surface of our planet in pre-renaissance Europe—"If we don't sail too far from the shoreline... the area we know and believe in, there will be no danger of sailing off the edge of the world. Beware!"

Thus, if the information comprising the time route does not express the wormhole areas, the time route would appear as if it is a proper temporal 3-manifold and there would be no problem with the spacetime nature of the world as they know it.

If, on the other hand, the time-past portion of the time route included an Experience of coming disaster (perhaps a 5-space vision) then the apparent time-future may appear as very dark. An analogy might be something like the assumption of a time-future as seen by the crew on board a space ship that is about to plunge into an unknown spatial wormhole.

A relative self (the time-past section of a time route) that includes an Experience of such destruction, may contain a subliminal 5-space vision of something other than the destruction. In addition it may also contain an Intension that bodes a Shift of presence to an alternate time route. If this were the case, the Sheaf would contain an alternate time route that extends beyond the point of termination because the alternate does not contain a time-future which ventures into the figurative abyss. In terms of the described wormhole, it would skirt the hole and zoom past it into a safe area.

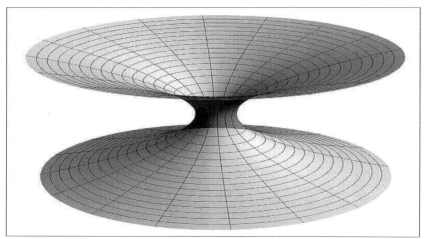

A 2-space diagram of a Schwarzschild wormhole[152]
This could be the cutout of the central area of a torus.

Thus two relative selves, one with a bright and positive future and one heading for apparent annihilation may exist quite well as time routes next to each other in a Sheaf. The difference between the two is their relationship to the karmic milieu; and a 5-space vision in the one that avoids destruction. In terms of mathematical objects this difference shows up as different locations on the hypersurface of the Sheaf.

Recall that with respect to spacetime-time a Sheaf is clearly defined as an instant 5-manifold, or a gathering of instant 4-manifolds. A single time route is defined as an instant 4-manifold.

We call instant 4-manifolds that are not simply connected as those that contain **wormhole areas**.

MANIFOLDS—WITH NEGATIVE CURVATURE

Another type of dangerous manifold is one that contains areas of severe negative curvature that figuratively "rush to infinity" (it's an instant manifold so there is really no possible "rushing movement" involved.) Call these areas **infinity pits**, be they negative (a peak) or positive (a pit). Such deep pits or high peaks may appear as black holes or some other phenomena that are good to avoid up close; but they can also belie a condition that makes the associated Experience-objects unique and interesting.

Artist's conception of a supermassive black hole. These are enormously dense objects buried at the hearts of galaxies.[153]

Imagine a time route that contains MindMoments expressing various parts of the surface of a near spherical temporal 3-manifold (de-

269

scribing a time route.) Assume that in one area this manifold also contains a limited sequence of instant manifolds that hold infinitely deep pits (placing them in the dangerous class). As long as the relative self does not include a MindMoment containing a phenomenal object that reflects the pit "close by," it may continue to exist. "Close by" effectively results in anthropic denial.

For example: a space ship, which is part of the information comprising the surface of a dangerous manifold, could exist as part of a time route that resolves to flying a safe distance from a black hole viewing it and gathering data. As long as the time route does not include the space ship diving into the black hole, the time route is not terminated.

According to the ToT, infinity pits (black holes) are included in the time route that describes our universe because we don't have to confront them up close and feel their destructive forces. If there were smaller infinity pits close by in our everyday environment that might give us trouble, but they would be (are?) anthropically denied.

THE 3-BOUNDARY

In common terms we know that the three-dimensional world around us is moving in time, and thus it's described by a time route. The time route is a virtual four dimensional instant object describing a single position on the hypersurface of an instant 5-manifold. A collection of time routes describes a series of positions on the hypersurface of an instant 5-manifold, which is a Sheaf.

A single time route can also be described as a sequence of instant 3-manifolds; and if one or more of those manifolds is in the dangerous class, the time route may be self-terminating. However, areas of genuine peril usually will not be included in the information that resolves to an Experience; or there will be a Shift in presence to an alternate time route.

In this fashion a time route will always *appear* to exist on the surface of a proper manifold. The areas of real danger (infinity pits and wormhole areas) may be thought of as surrounded by a virtual boundary. In the ToT this is called a **3-boundary**—because we are talking about 3-manifolds.

In the nomenclature of the ToT, a time route that terminates because of information held in dangerous instant 3-manifolds is said to **wander** outside of the 3-Boundary. The wandering of the time route starts at the MindMoment that contains the **first in sequence** iteration of the dangerous manifold.

270

A TRANSPHENOMENAL OBJECT

Recall that a relative self is made up of the time-past portion of the MindMoment sequence comprising a time route.

Consider a situation where a relative self contains an object (an Experience-object) that resolves from the information in a "certain limited section of the total, time-past MindMoment sequence" (call this limited section the **section of interest**.) Also consider that a portion of the instant 3-manifolds in the section of interest are dangerous manifolds.

Now imagine that the object associated with the section of interest figuratively rests on the 3-boundary... with half of it in the dangerous manifolds and half in the proper manifolds. Thus half of the section of interest reflects information from dangerous instant 3-manifolds and the other half reflects information from proper instant 3-manifolds.

The object resolving from the section of interest is a very unusual object. In the ToT it is called a **transphenomenal object** or a **"TPO"**.

In most cases a TPO will be anthropically denied. For example, consider two time routes within a Sheaf. Both of them contain similar objects, but only one of them is a TPO. One of the time routes wanders outside of the 3-Boundary and self-terminates in an Experience resolving from an infinity pit (part of the TPO is an infinity pit!)

The second time route does not wander outside of the 3-Boundary. It contains only Experiences that are anthropically acceptable—thus the Experiences of the object resolve from information that is only in the proper portion of the time route, the part that contains no deep pit. There is no TPO. There is only its proper counterpart.

According to the ToT, standard operating procedure tells us that the time route that wanders outside of the 3-Boundary, and is due to terminate, would likely contain a subliminal 5-space vision of a "bad omen" of pending destruction, depending on the karmic milieu. From the vantage of a 5-space vision, there could be an Intension and a subsequent Shift before the encounter with the infinity pit. After the Shift, the "new" time route (*cum* alternate time route) would contain no memory of the "bad omen" Experience (i.e. the impending infinity pit portion of the TPO—because such a situation is anthropically denied in the "new" time route (and in the human condition in general).

....

Now consider something *very different*. Imagine a relative self that reflects a reality map fully embracing the five-dimensional concept of spacetime-time as an explanation for reality (instead of simply

271

spacetime); and imagine that it also contains a TPO. Such a person might have a clear vision of a reality map that includes: a 5-space vision of multiple time routes, the process of a Shift within a Sheaf, and the nature of a TPO on point.

What would that reality map look like in terms of spacetime? The answer lays in the rhetoric of spiritual teachers, of a mystic or of an advanced yogi if such words are even possible. It's very difficult to verbalize because the elements of the reality map have no symbolic representation in terms of spacetime.

If this *very different* reality map (based on spacetime-time) were to be part of a relative self, certain interesting phenomena might manifest; especially if the true nature of the time route on point (holding the TPO) were realized in the context of a *precise* vision of a Shift.

Imagine a fine tuned Awareness that can (in a nontemporal state) allow the Experience of the individual MindMoments in a sequence that lay across a 3-boundary. To do this one would have to clearly see through the illusion of time flow. Again, what would this look like in terms of spacetime?... a very difficult answer indeed.

I have a suspicion that the beginnings of it may appear something like the meditation session I experienced* in the cave beside lake Manasarovar in Tibet. This was described in Part I.

> The *Abhidhamma* describes a protocol for navigating the landscape of consciousness where mind moments can be individually identified. The description involves the figurative awareness* of mind moments coming into the field of awareness*, abiding, and then passing away.[154]
>
> Another example of this concept was suggested by Ram Das. Here I paraphrase as I remember how he talked about the subtleties of practice accorded to yoga masters in India. He spoke of how they described the "landscape" when one "looks" through the mind moment stream five beats before stepping through the veil into the non-duel realm of non-subjective reality.[155]

With this in mind it's conceivable that a person could Shift into, and then out of, the "dangerous" portion of the TPO at will. It would be analogous to passing a car on a roadway. The driver ventures into the lane of oncoming traffic for only as long as is needed to pass the car ahead. To stay in the oncoming lane would be dangerous on an existential level. Conceivably this would allow the relative self (the holder of the TPO) that contains the memory (the oExperiences) of being inside the 3-boundary to express the details of the condition outside of the 3-boundary.

At this time in terms of the conventional world as we know it, a TPO is still mostly a science fiction concept. The creation of such a thing would appear as quite magical or deemed to be beyond the realm of science (as we know it). It could also be the ancient wisdom referred to earlier; but that wisdom is not part of our conventional collective reality map.

A TRANSPHENOMENAL DEVICE

In the ToT the term "effect" refers to an Experience-object that has resolved from EQ in the Matrix. The "apparent cause" of the effect is the memory of another Experience-object in the time-past section of a time route. For an example: consider the beauty of a finely-constructed machine (like a Formula One racing car) and the possible satisfaction of being able to "invent" or "design" a new and different method of implementing some facet of that machine...something that has not been done before. Anyone who has invented or designed a physical object or process knows that there is often a serendipity involved that can't quite be explained with logic. The answer seems to just pop into your mind— some people describe it as the intervention of a muse.

> The seeming intervention of a muse occurs with all creativity, not just the invention of devices. Music, Art, dance, movement, speaking, writing, politics… and perhaps every other human endeavor. They all appear to entertain a muse at some level.

According to the ToT: The inventing* arises out of an Intension representing the free will to make a change; hence the Shift to an alternate time route that includes the invention. In terms of the relative self the process of "inventing*" is carried out within the logical confines of the world as we know it (otherwise it won't work!) These confines are described by the physical sciences. If we could expand the limits of the confines we could then, perhaps expand the nature of what may be invented.

This is the pathway to the invention of a new class of substantial objects that lay across the 3-boundary. In the lexicon of the ToT such an object is called a **transphenomenal device** (a **TPD**). A TPD is a

273

TPO that can be manipulated at the will of the operator. Think of it as something from a scenic fiction movie.

A TPD is an Experience-object like all other substantial objects. The term *transphenomenal* in its title is appropriate because the EQ sequence that is its syncategorematic counterpart includes overt access to Features from dimensions beyond the 3-boundry that may resolve to dangerous manifolds. However that access is available only to a relative self that contains a conversance with a vantage point of spacetime-time.

Normally, a relative self includes Experiences of alternate time routes in the guise of 5-space visions that appear as a premonition or emotional predisposition. A TPD may include information from bits and pieces of multiple time routes—some of them including dangerous manifolds. This information would normally be a subliminal part of their portrayal of the spacetime universe; however in the case of a TPD the information is an accepted part of the object—for a relative self that is sensitive to spacetime-time. Call such a relative self **spacetime-time sensitive**.

The concept of a TPD reflects ideas found in science fiction stories. The oExperience of a TPD appears similar to the "fold box" storage container Robert Heinlein described in his novel entitled *Glory Road*; or perhaps the "star gate" in the TV series of the same name; or maybe the "flat space technology" depicted in the feature film *Ultraviolet*.

Heinlein's fold box is a good example. It's a transphenomenal device that contains the concept of severely folded space in the three space-like dimensions. In the ToT naked space does not fold, but the manifolds describing the information may have areas of severe negative curvature (an infinity pit) which could conceivably indicate an area that would fold the information laid onto that manifold.

For Heinlein the fold box was a portable storage container. A TPD that would do this would necessarily exist as part of at least three instant 3-manifolds, one that presents a conundrum of existence (the infinity pit); one that appears as normal *with a door* (the path that sidesteps the pit but has a doorway leading into, and out of it); and one that simply appears as normal spacetime. Elements of all three of these manifolds would exist together in the form of an oExperience as an overt 5-space vision—the relative self that contains the TPD must of course, recognize spacetime-time. If not, the TPD would appear as just another spacetime Experience-object. This distinction is the hallmark of a transphenomenal device.

274

Therefore it's not only the object—it's the object *and* the operator's existential relationship to it, *i.e.* being a spacetime-time sensitive relative self.

For example: the criterion for the occurrence of an oExperience of Heinlein's fold box is the memory that it can exist without a disastrous extinction—and thus the EQ sequences outside of the 3-boundary are not anthropically denied. For this to occur, the relative self involved with the fold box must contain a memory of being conversant with spacetime-time, as well as the memory of the subtle skill and confidence of making Shifts at an extremely fine level—without doubt. In terms of today's world, a relative self such as this describes an unusual being, something like the Buddha, but it's likely not that complex, it's just that we tend to see it as magic.

> The ToT suggests that we all may have this ability to some degree, but science tells us otherwise, so we don't recognize it. In this vein we should remember that we are all the descendants of traditional cultures that had the purported ability to manipulate the momentum of reality—a propensity for such abilities may be part of our genetic makeup.

Manipulating the momentum of reality basically amounts to manipulating patterns of information; something that is part of an ancient, delightful and exotic tradition in the cultural history of Tibet.

TERMA AND YESHE TSOGYAL

A collection of EQ that resolve to the Experience of a phenomenal object obviously has Features that can resolve to information other than the standard three dimensions of "solid" reality. Consider a stone with a word carved into it or a crystal whose molecules are in the form of a certain geometric matrix. However there is the question of whether the Features will allow the presence of information without the information being evident in the three space-like dimensions of the object?

Essentially what is being described here is a TPD that resolves from EQ holding Features that resolve to a substantial object (the three space-like dimensions) *and* to other higher order dimensions of mental events.

Recall that for a TPD to operate the individuated SELF containing it must be conversant with spacetime-time. The question is then: who is "thinking" these events? Typically, in present times, there is a predisposition (culturally shared reality map) to believe that if information is not evident in terms of spacetime-physics, it cannot exist. This predisposition reflects, what I call, a "spacetime only" reality map.

Conversely a "spacetime-time sensitive" reality map easily allows for an Experience-object such as a TPD, because additional information can be resident in one of the parallel time routes contained in a Sheaf. From my reasoning and experience, the reality map of the Tibetan culture and other traditional cultures appear to generally accept the idea that a person can be spacetime-time sensitive.

Prosaically the information attendant to a TPD is like information floating in space and time. In Tibet, when this information is associated with a certain substantial object it's called a **terma**. A *terma* is thought of as containing a "hidden treasure" (the information). Tradition tells us that a number of *terma* have been hidden by masters and teachers in the past. History tells us that the great Tibetan teacher Padmasambhava and his consort Yeshe Tsogyal (in the eighth century CE) created many *terma* to be found in later centuries. The concept of *terma* is also part of the Bon and Hindu traditions, but to a more limited degree.

Yeshe Tsogyal (c. 8th century CE) the consort of
Padmasambhava. The two together concealed many termas.[156]

A physical object that is a *terma* is called an "earth *terma*." It contains a certain "treasure" of information that is understood by the person who finds the *terma*. That person is called a *tertön*. In terms of the ToT a *tertön* is a spacetime-time sensitive individuated SELF.

The patterns of EQ that resolve to an earth *terma* (a phenomenal object) include the physical item *and* the information which is hidden as a treasure, with the patterns being resident in multiple time routes. Thus the oExperience of the treasure information in the terma is revealed only to the spacetime-time sensitive mind of the *tertön*, but the physical object is for all to see.

A *terma* can also be a "mind treasure" or "mind *terma*," said to be hidden in space and revealed in the mind of the *tertön*. In a sense, all *terma* are mind treasures because they are revealed by the *tertön*. In the context of the ToT, they are all a part of the relative self that is defined as the *tertön* and is spacetime-time sensitive.

The information associated with a *terma* is independent of the classical three space-like dimensions and the one time-like dimension. It does not rest in spacetime. Thus a *terma* created at any point in the time-past portion of a time route is available in the Now, if the *tertön* can manage it. [Recall that the absolute condition is non-local and nontemporal.] Other traditional cultures also appear to include concepts similar to a *terma*, although ideas of what we might be dealing with are quite different and not called *terma*. For example:

> Grandfather Semu had a group of, what I would call, power objects. I saw some of them. One was a silver metal owl that could be held in one closed hand. It had deep brown, polished stones set in the location of the eyes. When looking at it you could almost feel yourself falling into the eyes—a very strange sensation. He kept this object close to him.
>
> In old Hawaii there was *mana*, a form of spiritual energy which existed in locations, objects or people. Through various means *mana* could be gained or lost. In modern times, in certain places in the islands, it's still easy to conclude you are feeling the *mana* of the *anina* (the land).

Within the Buddhist community there appears to be a common acceptance of the idea that Tibetan lamas generally have an ability to place power or energy into physical objects. In the Tibetan tradition and culture, there are many sacred items used in formal ritual and in daily life. These objects are imbued with energy or power by an adept, usually

277

a lama. The simplest explanation of this is to see it as a blessing, but it is more than that. In simple terms it's investing information into the object, and that information is available if and when the person holding the object sees spacetime-time as part of his or her reality map.

I was given a *tsa tsa* years ago. It's a small bead about three quarter inches in diameter with a hole through it that allows me to wear it on a string. It was hand made by Nyala Changchub Dorje, in Tibet.

I never met him but it appears that he viewed reality as an expression of what I call spacetime-time. I say this because his student, Chögyal Namkhai Norbu, was the one who gave me the tsa tsa and then, at a later time, introduced me to the concept of "4th time."

Nyala Changchub Dorje (1826-1978)[157]

278

Nyala Changchub Dorje (Wyl. *nyag bla byang chub rdo rje*) was *Dzogchen* master renowned as the teacher of Namkhai Norbu Rinpoche. He was born in the Kham region of [Tibet] and studied with multiple Tibetan masters. He died at the age of 152 years.

There are no life images of Nyala Rinpoche, but some of those who knew him are said to have remarked that this old photograph of a statue is a good representation of his likeness (see below).

I understand the Tibetan concept of 4th time to be the genitive realization of a 5-space vision and of spacetime-time.

> The *tsa tsa* from Nyala Changchub Dorje appears in some ways to be an earth *terma*. I once had a vivid dream in which it fell to the ground and broke open. Inside of it was a rolled up piece of paper with some writing on it (in a script I could not read). I asked Chögyal Namkhai Norbu about it. After some time his reply was that I was too close to the *Dzogchen* teaching.

For me the physical object that is the *tsa tsa* appears to have certain additional information as part of its makeup. The information appears to be in the form of a figurative doorway that leads to a description of reality being expressed by the two truths. The dream episode also indicates that the information in a *terma* may mean very little if you can't read the language!

For a long time I have felt that there was some sort of information held in the *tsa tsa*. I had the sense that it was put there by virtue of an unexplained process on the part of the *Dzogchen* master who created it; but now, after writing this book, it appears as part of a logical process.

Thus the realization of the information in a *terma* or the operation of TPD requires an spacetime-time sensitive individuated SELF.

THE OPERATION OF A TPD

The operation of a transphenomenal device, a TPD, is accomplished with the precise presence of an Intension. An Intension can be part of the package of EQ that resolves to the TPD, in the same fashion in which the "treasure" information is a part of an earth *terma*.

In terms of Western science, the person who invests the treasured information into the *terma* would appear as a magician. The word *magic* is with respect to an understanding of the term *science*, according to the contemporary *zeitgeist*. If science includes what is seen as the "skills of a magician," then the exhibited skills would not be considered an example of magic.

Harvard professor Thomas Kuhn, who identified various human patterns in history, was quoted at the beginning of this book. He outlines one of the patterns by stating that a new paradigm in science cannot come into existence unless it is described in terms of the existing paradigm—barring that, the new paradigm is seen as magic or bad science.[158]

What does a TPD look like? That's hard to say. If you, the reader, are considering this concept from the confines of a culture where phenomenal reality is exemplified by spacetime it's probably not going to be a fold box; that kind of technology would require a culture-wide acceptance of spacetime-time. In a spacetime culture the first TPDs or *terma* you may encounter will probably be geometric objects of two or three dimensions; or maybe something like a *tsa tsa*. In any case, they will appear as "normal" objects to some and as objects invested with a special information to others.

Kalachakra mandala, a Sanskrit term used in Tantric
Buddhism that literally means "time-wheel" or "time-cycles."[159]

The *mandalas* found in Indo-Tibetan traditions are good candidates. A *mandala* can be described as a much-embellished piece of geometry. It can also be described as sacred art that has spiritual and ritual significance. Other examples of possible TPDs or *terma* might be something like the pyramids and ziggurats found in Egypt, Asia, or the Americas; or the *stupas* found in Tibet, India and South East Asia. Also possible is one of the constructed designs found in the Native American cultures that are sometimes called medicine wheels or round houses (such as the *underground house* of Grandfather Semu Huaute). All of these are examples of geometry resident in spacetime (with an implied overleaf of an existence covertly embracing spacetime-time).

The Kalachakra tantra describes the Kalachakra *stupa* and *mandala*. This is an ancient document containing information dating back to the time of the Buddha. It describes the nature of the universe in detail down to the level of very small particles called "space particles" (that appear to be similar to EQ).

The Kalachakra *stupa* at Paleaku Peace Gardens, Honaunau, Hawaii. Completed in 1991 under the direction of the Tai Situ Rinpoche, and dedicated to Kalu Rinpoche (about 6 meters high).[160]

There is a discussion of the cycles that each universe goes through—*Kalachakra* means cycles of time. The cycles repeat without beginning or end.[161] This is concept that appears similar to Sir Roger Penrose's idea of repeating eons. Follows is a reiteration of an explanation found in Part II.

> Using mathematics Sir Roger expands a picture of the presumed beginning of an eon (the big bang) and compares it to a compressed picture of the totally expanded presumed end of the previous eon. When this is done the images appear as reflections of one another with certain information being transferred across the junction, creating continuity from one eon to the next.

The Shri Yantra is formed by nine interlocking triangles that surround and radiate out from the central point [which is] the junction point between the physical universe and its unmanifest source. The Shri Yantra is central to the Srividya system of Hindu worship.

The Shri Yantra, an ancient Indian *mandala*.[162]

Yantra is the Sanskrit word for "instrument" or "machine." It can stand for symbols, processes, automata, machinery or anything that has structure and organization, depending on context.

In the middle is the power point (*bindu*), visualizing the highest, the invisible, elusive center from which the entire figure and the cosmos expands.[163]

If the special objects described above are TPDs, then in our spacetime culture we may need to adapt to operate them to their full potential.[A] One could imagine the substantial aspect of the relative condition being expressed with five instead of four dimensions, as with spacetime-time. In a community that espouses such a reality map the relative selves that subscribe to a reality of only spacetime could still abide peacefully, but their version of the shared universe would resolve only from proper time routes, that is from areas of proper manifolds within the associated group of instant 3-manifolds [they would anthropically Shift away from the dangerous manifolds]. Such a relative self would see the world as the four-dimensional spacetime that humans generally see as the environment of planet Earth at this time in history.

A relative self that fully incorporates the concept of spacetime-time, would exemplify a reality map that includes an ongoing awareness* of concurrent, multiple time routes occupying a Sheaf. Fully accepting and living with this reality map is the *only* situation where one remains **without doubt** about the nature of spacetime-time. In this reality map, spacetime-time is felt instinctually as an essential, unquestioned part of reality. (Think of it in the same way we typically accept the existence of the flow of time: It's not an item that is questioned.) To gain this perspective one cannot aspire to reach it *per se*; instead, one day, after a lot of study and (mostly) practice, one simply finds that such is the natural way of things.

A UNIVERSAL CONSTANT ACROSS THE MULTIVERSE

Recall that in the ToT there is the axiomatic assertion of an indefinitely large number of different universes each holding the *same value* for the MindMoment constant, $\tilde{A}$.

In terms of the relative condition this is a statement that the number of "instances of reality" per "unit of time" is the same for every

---

[A] The qualities of a person called an "adept" are considered as unique or special with respect to those who are not adept. This is the recognition of an ability with respect to a cultural situation. According to the ToT we are all, to some degree adept.

universe in the multiverse—where an "instance of reality" is a single MindMoment. This is axiomatic.

The ToT also contains the concept of a time quanta (the reciprocal of the MindMoment constant). This is also the same in every universe, regardless of how beings in that universe may describe it.

[The "described value" for a unit time is always locally defined, such as one second or one year or one day. There is no "true" value for a unit of time, it can only be described with respect to something else—hence it is categorical placed within the relative condition.]

The telltale difference between the universes comprising the multiverse is in their value for Φ, the quantum interspace. In terms of the relative condition this resolves to a different value for the velocity of light in each universe.

> Recall that the value for Φ describes the Experience of a change in position between two EQ in sequence that contain the information of an object moving at the speed of light.

$$\frac{c}{\tilde{A}} = \Phi$$

Where:
- c is the speed of light in a vacuum. (3×10^8 m/sec).
- $\tilde{A}$ is the MindMoment constant (10^{14} Ш/sec) or the multiverse constant.
- Φ is the quantum interspace (3×10^{-6} m/Ш).

In spacetime physics the concept of c is essentially a philosophical statement describing a feature of space in general. In the ToT it is described as a feature of naked space that manifests as a different value for Φ in each V.n universe. This then becomes the hallmark variable of each universe within the multiverse.

Recall that there are many relevant dimensions of information comprising the MindMoments of a time route (*i.e.* substantial objects *and* subjective mental events). Here we are speaking only of substantial reality which is the domain of physics as we now know it. With respect to substantial reality there are the concepts of locality, position and distance. All of which require a quantum interspace to be described properly.

SETI May Have a Problem

SETI is the acronym for "Search for Extraterrestrial Intelligence." The mission of the SETI Institute is to explore, understand and explain the origin, nature and prevalence of life in the universe. The modern concept of SETI began in 1959.

At the time of writing this book, the SETI Institute's array of telescopes has found no extraterrestrial signals. The problem could be that they are looking for signals based on a value for Φ that is found only in V.1 universe—and there may be no such signals. In other words, the extraterrestrials may exist in renditions of a configuration space with different values for the quantum interface.

The Karl G. Jansky Very Large Array (VLA)
radio astronomy observatory, New Mexico, USA[164]

The ToT asserts that the value of Φ is anthropically determined (or has evolved to its present value in V.1). Thus we may be the only ones in the multiverse with a value for c as we measure it!

At first thought it may appear that signals could be received at proportionally shorter or longer wavelengths and thus sync with other V.n universes; but this conclusion does not fit the hypothesis, which describes different values for Φ.

285

There can be no communication between two V.n universes in terms of the spacetime reality of either universe because the value of the quantum interspace for each universe is different, and the sequences of MindMoments in the respective universes will not coincide. Our science is largely based on features of the spacetime in which we appear to exist; and they are a function of the value of Φ for the V.1 universe—which corresponds to the measured value of luminal velocity in V.1..

An interesting anecdote related to this discussion is found in Chögyal Namkhai Norbu's book about the Tibetan tile game called *Bagchen*. The book tells about its history of the game, describing that it originally came from a race of beings called the *Masang*. The game has the complexity of chess but it is more in-the-moment; with a background feel for implementing 5-space visions leading to alternate time routes.

The *Masang* once lived on our Earth (a long time ago) and had interactions with humans. Tradition tells us that the *Masang* are still here but we can no longer see them.

Perhaps the value of Φ for their shared universe gradually shifted... or maybe it was ours that shifted... or maybe it's an interesting story to get us thinking.

WITHOUT DOUBT

Reality maps are not explanations of the universe as it exists—instead they are the formative patterns that allow a universe to exist* as it appears to be in the context of a relative self.

The word exist* is written with an asterisk following to indicate that true nature of existence rests in the Absolute condition and the shared universe that appears to exist* around us is a result of a pattern of information. Thus the pattern (the reality map) does not explain the universe as it is; instead the apparent universe is a result of the pattern. The subtle difference is that the pattern may change and the apparent universe will follow, but not the reverse.

Vision is an ornament of primordial space.

~ old Tibetan saying

The Tibetan word that translates as "vision" refers to the total sensory experience of reality. Primordial space is analogous to the naked space of the ToT.[165]

Therefore, with respect to the relative condition, all that truly exists is patterns, which in the ToT is described as the result of tiny warps in naked space. This follows another basic tenet of Buddhism that states that, ultimately, it's all *shunyata* (emptiness in Sanskrit).

> Like it or not, if you look at your own mind you will discover
> that it is void and groundless; as insubstantial as empty
> space.
>
> ~ Padmasambhava

Delving into basic research about the nature of existence would require an understanding of the relationship between science, its supporting culture and the associated collective reality map.

In order to establish this understanding it may require the development of intentional communities where there is a full immersion in a philosophy that yields a local reality map that sees the universe as timeless and without "true" substance. Individuals in such a community could exist in our modern world but in some ways, they would not be a part of it.

How does one invoke the nature of "feel" of spacetime-time, of five dimensions of reality? Henry Ford may have had the beginnings of an answer.

> If you think you can do something, or if you think you can't
> do something, you're right.
>
> ~ Henry Ford

To do it one must, without doubt, truly believe that (the total package of) "who they think you are" is simply a point of view; and that who they "truly" are, is Awareness—an essence. One must, without consideration, "taste" reality in a fashion much like it is described in the ToT. It is accepting and living in spacetime-time without doubt, as if it is as normal as the flow of time (something we almost never *think* about.) Buddhists and other traditions have many practices that are pointed at this revelation.

Following this track implies that eventually a person will no longer see the world as they remember it to be; instead they will experience* common reality as an unsubstantial, complex visualization where everything is a symbol. From this they may gain a unique perspective with leverage over apparent "events," apparently "occurring" in an apparent "flow of time." In terms of math objects, the perspective is something like figuratively standing at a "geometric gate" and encouraging certain (preferred) math objects to move through the gate—where the math objects are concepts of the elements of reality.

Finding a person with the appropriate skills to do this may be a problem. It's quite possible that a person who has such skills would conclude that it makes no sense to participate in such experiments. They may say: "Why attend to these illusions? It's simply another presentation of the relative self, generically the same as all other presentations."

In his book *The Universe in a Single Atom*, the Dalai Lama tells about encouraging hermits to leave their caves and work with a group of scientists who were making EEG (electroencephalograph) readings of practicing meditators.

> An electroencephalograph can detect electrical activity in the brain. A portable device may be in the form of a cap, worn by the subject, which is attached to a machine that processes the signals.

When describing the hermits he said, "…most simply couldn't see the point, other than satisfying the curiosity of some odd men carrying machines. I argued that they should undergo the experiments out of altruism: if the good effects of quieting the mind and cultivating wholesome mental states can be demonstrated scientifically, this may have beneficial results for others. I only hope I was not too heavy-handed. A number of the hermits accepted, persuaded, I hope, by my argument rather than simply submitting to the authority of the Dalai Lama's office." [166]

An accomplished meditator may conclude:

"I would much rather spend my limited time during this life realizing the subtleties of the *Dharma*; not acting in a fashion as if I believe I am doing something in space and time!"

This is the paradox. The right person for the job probably does not believe the job really exits (according to the job definition.) However they may see the job as an expression of compassion, which is what it is, in terms of the ToT.

3.3 - TIME-FUTURE

In terms of the ToT; our contemporary physical reality is generally described as bounded by the geometry of a single time route (an instant 4-manifold described as *spacetime*) within which the concept of "free will*" is merely an Experience that is seen as *apparently* changing the course of time-future events, but it is not really doing that.

In the *future* the situation may be different, but the term *future* must be understood carefully. In terms of a Sheaf, only the Now exists. Mathematically the Sheaf is an instant 5-manifold whose surface is covered with time routes. Each time route contains Experiences of a time-future and a time-past with respect to the Now.

Remember that a Sheaf is a representation of the grandest expression of the individuated SELF, and it is thus the *only* representation of the individuated SELF. There are no others; because in terms of the Sheaf, only the Now exists and the Now is an intimate, conceptual attribute of the individuated SELF. Thus all other Sheafs (describing patterns in the Matrix) are examples of other individuated SELVES in the shared universe; and all Sheaves are all in reality sync in the moment of the Now.

There are no "future" Sheaves or "past" Sheaves representing the same individuated SELF in a *different* time; because there is no *different* time. All considerations of time-future or time-past are implicit in the time routes comprising a single Sheaf. However there are other patterns that resolve to slightly different, but *similar* Sheaves, that each have a different moment of the present, with respect to the sequencing of their MindMoments.

The moment of the present is an Experience unique to a specific MindMoment; and all of the different versions of the moment of the present, in a Sheaf occur in the Now; and all of the different Sheaves in V.1 occur in the Now.

Thus there is a time-future in terms of a 5-space vision of a Sheaf, but the term *future* by itself, makes sense only in the context of a relative self where there is the oExperience of the flow of time. In that context we can say that the general description of physical reality may be different in the *future*.

TIME-FUTURE REALITY MAPS

In the context of the expanse of time routes comprising a Sheaf, we may as a species, begin to see* reality in a different way—bounded by the geometry of a Sheaf instead of a time route. For a relative self, a Sheaf contains an additional layer of reality into which all of spacetime is subsumed. It is described by a 5-manifold, whose hypersurface contains multiple instant 4-manifolds, each representing a time route. The hypersurface of a Sheaf is the domain of what the ToT calls *spacetime-time*, which is another time-like dimension ontologically superior to the time-like dimension described by Minkowski. In that superior layer of time there can occur a Shift in awareness, the essence of true free will for the individuated SELF.

A Sheaf is the grandest representation of an individuated SELF. The Awareness of information beyond the bounds of a Sheaf is non-personal.

A *future* vision of reality as an expression of spacetime-time could be described as reaching a certain *level of realization*. The term "realization" is used as opposed to the term "understanding". An understanding generally means an organization of information within the framework of a previous understanding. Thus if it's "understood" the new vision must be couched *within* the structure of a previously understood reality map, which in this case is the conceptual structure of a time route. This could be a problem because a time route is only a tiny part of the new structure that is to be *realized*, a Sheaf; which will not fit into a time route.

What is in order is a realization of the qualities of a Sheaf. In this way, we could bring ourselves to see the world not as we *remember it to be*, but instead as a function of a 5-space vision, which is prosaically the way *we feel it could be*.

This is in accord with what Sacheen Littlefeather once told me when we were talking about how different people think about reality. She said quickly:

Indians don't think, they feel.

~Sacheen Littlefeather

In terms of the ToT, if we become able to truly encounter the universe around us as the way *we feel it could be*, we will be living with a new reality map that includes the principal of an "Intension"—as described in Part II. This would be a paradigm shift in our cultural and in our science, with respect to what we have now.

In terms of a relative self modern physics and technology has evolved from, and is coincident with the changing collective reality maps of the West. History tells us that this has been a rich and rewarding partnership. The "puzzle which is the nature of the universe" that has figuratively been set before the discipline of science over the last 300 years has been attended to with vigorous and remarkable creativity. However, the reality maps (upon which both the puzzle and the science are based) also indicate the boundaries within which the quality and quantity of the creativity that has been contained.

In general, all other reality maps that have evolved have been more or less diminished or abandoned because their supporting cultural reality maps have been largely subsumed by the reality map of the preeminent system, which attends to spacetime science. The loss of the traditional reality maps is inevitable because it appears that it is impossible to fully document and preserve the nature of a living traditional reality map[A] that is different than the observer's; because the base values the traditional map are compromised when they are described using terms of the observer's reality map.

This book relies heavily on the stories and wisdom of the Buddha described in: the *Tripitaka* (the Southern Theravada Buddhist canon); the *Kangyur* and the *Tengyur* (the Tibetan Buddhist canon); and writings of many teachers over the last two millennia—writings which include the wisdom of the Bon tradition. In general it is the wisdom and information found in the Tibetan culture, language and reality map. Much more work needs to be done to uncover, interpret and preserve this knowledge, because in it may be what can take us to a new paradigm of physics.

[A] This statement is made in a very basic sense. It is in a context of full recognition and respect for the many highly skilled and dedicated cultural anthropologists and scholars who have done and are currently doing admirable work in their fields.

CHINA'S MISTAKE?

It is regrettable that the reality map promoted by the government of China at the time of this writing doesn't include a strong vision of preserving the unique culture of Tibet, where sophisticated multidimensional understandings of the universe are still alive and being communicated on a common level. The Tibetan culture and reality map contains unique, recorded histories from lost civilizations once known as: Odhiyana, Shambala, and Tudjen[167]. *Tibet is likely the only place where this ancient wisdom remains extant and embedded in a cultural reality map that can give meaning to possible spacetime-time subtleties of that information.*

In some ways the present policies of the government of China appear to be a replay of a historic cultural predisposition of closing themselves off to changing ideas and worldviews. (Belief systems are very hard to change.) This action could lead to a Chinese cultural memory of making the biggest mistake in their history, because, if they allow the Tibetan reality map to disintegrate, they will lose direct access to an understanding of the exotic information held in the Tibetan archives. If that happens other states may gain hegemony in new-paradigm physics.

Progress in new paradigm physics appears now to be occurring within intentional communities set up as learning institutions. Such places are now being established around the planet. It appears that, within these groups of like-minded people, there is gradually evolving a *zeitgeist* (leading to an eventual reality map) that will serve as fertile ground for a paradigm shift in physics. This emphasizes the importance of the vitality of the culture in which reality maps exists.

REALITY MAPS AND SUPPORTING CULTURES

More or less, across the planet, our overarching collective reality map is a description of the nature of things in the modern world. In terms of a relative self it is a subliminal background tapestry seen to elucidate the nature of phenomenal reality, the nature of the "self" and the interaction between the "self" and reality. It is part of what describes the relative self of almost all beings. It is, in general "who we think we are".

As mentioned above, when there is an attempt to document a reality map, it must be recorded, and understood in terms relative to the reality map of *the observer*. To make a record of a certain reality map other than one's own, the observer is effectively "telling a story" in terms of his/her own reality map. When this is done, the foreign reality map is no longer a subliminal and background, but becomes instead a quantifiable object set against the background of the observer's reality map. It may be a picture of the subject's belief system but it's not a proper representation of the subjects reality map.

This is a problem that makes the task of recording a reality map more or less un-doable; because a reality map is an *unconditioned predisposition used to continually and subliminally evaluate reality and the "self"*. Therefore a person can be aware of only one system at a time.

> The exception to this is an understanding that came to me at Dulangi, the Bonpo monastery. There I learned that with awareness, practice, skill and clarity; one could evaluate and choose a reality map at will, but this is far beyond the ken or ability of almost all individuals. It is a conscious 5-space vision.

In terms of the relative self, memories are the storehouse from which is drawn the stuff of a reality map; and that stuff is corroborated by the concurrent memories of others within a society (*i.e.* the shared universe of the ToT). Without a compliant and supportive society a reality map will begin to dissolve and merge into other more dominant reality maps. This is evidenced by the histories of the Native Americans and the Neolithic Hawaiians, among others. In general, an understanding of how these people saw the universe (on a gut level) is largely lost, or in the process of being lost.

The bottom line is that without societal support, a reality map cannot continue; and without a rich reality map the subtle creative serendipity of a scientific paradigm based on that reality map will not occur.

A NEW PARADIGM

The ToT is generally based on the reality map associated with traditional Buddhist philosophy and thought, but it also draws from other traditional cultures. It posits a nontemporal, nonlocal, Instant universe that is mathematically described with multi-dimensional manifolds, where the Experience of things is *prime* and the "stuff" and "think" of reality is an illusion. It describes a Totality purporting two truths; one truth that appears to be reality but is illusory, and another that is the actual state of existence but is unfathomable in terms of (what appears to be) the normal state of existence. The Totality of the ToT has no

294

beginning, no end, no size, no physical qualities, and no subjective qualities—it is an absolute singularity—and it is conceptualized as the supreme source. It's called naked space; and it's infinitely multi-dimensional and without bound.

The ToT allows constants such as the speed of light, the quantum interspace and the MindMoment constant to be expressed without the concept of "the flow of time." It uses the esoteric concepts of spacetime-time and 5-space visions to suggest a figurative fabric upon which parallel time routes play out as a picture of both causality and free will. In contemporary classical and quantum physics space and time are described as being under the umbrella of relativity. Because the ToT describes the observer as part of Totality, it brings the concept of the individuated SELF under that same umbrella.

The ToT includes the unusual concepts of: an Instant universe, a shared universe, a relative self, time routes, MindMoments, Experience Quantum, the quantum interspace, the MindMoment constant, time quanta, naked space, Experience-objects, overlain Experiences, native Experiences, nontemporal velocity, anthropic denial, an Intension, the Stor, the 3-boundary, 5-space visions, spacetime-time, a Sheaf, a grand Matrix of all information, a multiverse, TPOs, TPDs, alternate values for c, the idea that compassion is a reflection of c, and a radically expanded definition of the "self" (i.e. the individuated SELF).

Siddhartha Shakyamuni (the Buddha) was a historical being who had a vision of the nature of reality that was "beyond the concept of beyond." He saw the relative condition in many ways as *unimportant*, and stressed the importance of an individual personally gaining a realization of the true nature of reality. Functionally, the ToT is different. It does not describe a path to a personal, nonconceptual realization of the nature of mind and Totality. For the ToT, the relative condition is *not unimportant* because the purpose of the ToT is to propose a description of how things work in the relative condition.

A culture that is generally conversant with a 5-space vision would go hand in hand with the new paradigm in physics described in the ToT. A figurative bridge to the new paradigm could be an understanding that, at a very basic level, what spacetime physics describes as the beautiful depictions and understandings that bespeak reality, are simply patterns of information. They are not a *true* description of reality, they are merely patterns.

Thus the new paradigm indicates that we can, if we wish, create additional patterns that may better serve us when, for example, we encounter situations in the modern world with no clear or easy solution according to the constraints of existing physics.

The paradigm shift being promoted by the ToT includes an understanding that *who you think you are* is an information package; or (prosaically) "you are the world". There is a complete intertwinglement between the Experiences of all things, all people, all thoughts and all ideas. The ToT defines the intertwinglement, per se, as the essential nature the *concept* of compassion, which in turn is reflected as a unique value for the speed of light in this universe. An understanding of the interplay of information is essential to an understanding of that which we are. For the paradigm shift put forth by the ToT to come on stage there must be a general acceptance of this interplay, without doubt. The Dalai Lama describes it nicely, without using the mathematical overtones of the ToT.

> "Love and kindness are the very basis of society. If we lose these feelings, society will face tremendous difficulties; the survival of humanity will be endangered."
> ~ His Holiness the Dalai Lama[168]

In this same fashion the ToT seeks to set a higher plateau or goal for the future of all of humanity.

Such flowery, heartfelt words have the ring of a statement reflecting a religious point of view, where broad swaths of faith are the basis of a belief system; however in the context of the ToT it describes a logical pragmatism arising out of the identification of explicit primal assumptions. At first glance there may appear to be a cold loneliness in the pragmatism; but this is not the case. The condition of truly "living" within the logic of the ToT naturally arises out of an Experience of a great compassion or big-heartedness toward all beings—which, according to the background logic, resolves from the intertwingularity of the Matrix and is seen as c, the velocity of light in V.1.

These statements bring a conceptual melding of the essential features of the two great, apparent divisions of the human condition: the sciences and the humanities. Arguably the most interesting and profound facets of these divisions are, respectively; the seemingly ethereal notion of light moving at speed, and the historically pervasive and subjectively eternal concept of love (and compassion). The intermingled reconciliation of these two facets, as found in the ToT, is needed to form a proper Theory of Totality.

In the future those researchers who find a creative muse that works in parallel with their own willingness to loosen their grasp on the appearance of spacetime reality (as it is now typically portrayed) may discover startling new possibilities hidden in the non-temporal paradigm put forth by the ToT. Conceivably there could be ultra-slow conditions of stasis, ultra-fast computer technology and perhaps even a means for supra-luminal transport.

GLOSSARY
Common and Unique Terms

The main hypothesis of this book is that reality, in all of its manifestations, be they substantial or be they mental events, can be described as a set of thoughts; each of which is represented as a concept. Most of those concepts can be identified with words, and thus the words are symbols that *point at* the things and thoughts that make up the world around us.

In the same fashion the ToT is generally described using a symbolic logic formed by sets of words; and sometimes those words are "made up", created to enhance an identity or description. In this glossary you will find many "made up" words created "to point at" certain specific concepts. These words are underlined.

2-manifold

The surface of the beach ball is a good example of a **2-manifold**. The surface of a 2-manifold is a two-dimensional surface.

3-boundary

A time route will always appear to exist on the surface of a proper manifold. The areas of danger (infinity pits and wormhole areas) may be thought of as surrounded by a virtual boundary. In the ToT this boundary is called a 3-boundary—because it lays on the surface of a 3-manifold that express the three spatial dimensions of spacetime.

A time route will always *appear* to exist on the surface of a proper manifold. The areas of real danger (infinity pits and wormhole areas) may be thought of as surrounded by a virtual boundary. In the ToT this is called a 3-boundary—because we are talking about 3-manifolds, i.e. the three-dimensional world around us.

In the nomenclature of the ToT, a time route that terminates because of information held in dangerous instant 3-manifolds is said to wander outside of the 3-Boundary. The wandering of the time route starts at the MindMoment that contains the "first in sequence iteration" of the dangerous manifold.

3-manifold

The surface of a 3-manifold is a hypersurface that is three dimensional in nature. Our three-dimensional universe can be viewed as the hypersurface of a 3-manifold; and in that context we live on (in) the hypersurface of a 3-manifold. Within that hypersurface we can experience* solid, three-dimensional objects.

4th time

4th time is a pseudo-temporal concept found in esoteric Tibetan Buddhism. In terms of the ToT 4th time is a quasi-concept, it has no duration in spacetime.

In the ToT 4th time affords the temporal "elbowroom" in which to accomplish non-conceptual meditation which, in its full expression, is devoid of the concept of time flow.

Within the ToT 4th time is also the figurative domain of a Shift. A Shift is a quasi-concept and not a part of the relative self—which in common terms means it is not a function of the "self". Therefore in terms of a time route a Shift is instantaneous, occurring in the moment of the present. In the spacetime-time context of the ToT's geometry it exists in the configuration space defined by the hypersurface of a 5-manifold. Functionally, the point of the Shift is between one time route and another, occurring at the nexus of the bundle making up a Sheaf... at the tie point of the Sheaf... at the moment of the Now. This point as the domain of 4th time... the temporal elbowroom in which a Shift occurs.

4-manifold

In the ToT a manifold is information, and the information resolving to the "Experience of time flow" is resident on the surface of the 4-manifold; along with the information resolving to the Experience of three-dimensional substantial reality.

5-manifold

If we describe the constituents of a Sheaf as representing only spacetime reality, then a single time route represents the surface of an instant 4-manifold). When we consider the multiple time routes in a Sheaf, we are working with multiple instant 4-manifolds; or five dimensions of configuration space—which is expressed as the hypersurface of an instant 5-manifold.

In general the book describes Sheaves as a five-dimensional instant manifold (for ease of description); but in all cases a Sheaf is understood to contain time routes of many dimensions more than four.

5-space vision

A 5-space vision is the time-present awareness of time-future information. Dreams are often the source of premonitions. Within the lexicon of the ToT, all such experiences, whether awake or in a dream state are referred to as a 5-space vision. It is axiomatic in the ToT that all humans, and maybe some animals, incorporate Experience-objects that resolve to 5-space visions. In terms of spacetime physics, the experience* of a 5-

space vision is a vaguely understood natural ability. A 5-space vision pro-vides some bits and pieces of an Experience of a quasi-concept, such as "going into" or "coming out of" the domain of a Sheaf. The term, 5-space vision, is derived from the vision's putative viewpoint of the vision—a 5th dimension. Such visions are an Experience resolving from time-future MindMoments in the on point time route; or an Experience resolving from MindMoments (time-past or time-future) in various alternate time routes.

Ã (MindMoment constant)

See also: "MindMoment constant".

Abhidhamma

The *Pāli Canon* is the standard collection of scriptures in the Theravada Buddhist tradition. It was transcribed from oral tradition in the last cen-tury BCE. The particular area of knowledge being referenced is called the *Abhidhamma* (a bee dam' ma).

absolute condition (in terms of the ToT)

The concept of the two truths is associated with the Madhyamaka School, whose origin is credited to Nagarjuna, c. 200CE. He was the first to express the two truths in its complete form. Similarly, the ToT also posits two truths (or conditions of existence)—the relative condition of reality and the absolute condition of reality.

What we generally believe to be the phenomenal world around us in which we exist, think and act, is the relative condition—*i.e.* that which is (apparently) portrayed by our senses. From the viewpoint of absolute con-dition, what we feel and experience in our ordinary daily life is all delusion [it has no reality of its own].

The ToT considers the absolute condition to be the "true" condition of reality. However this condition eludes us because we have no way to conceptualize it using information found within the relative condition—except with the possible use of mathematics (as is done in the ToT) where we may occasionally point at a constructed analog of the absolute condi-tion.

absolute space

Sir Isaac Newton described the three dimensions of the space around us as extending indefinitely (along straight lines) in all directions with no bumps, warps, curves or reference to anyone's measure. He called it abso-lute space and described it as independent of any objects that occupied the space. His understanding requires us to think of space as the unchanging background in which the three-dimensional objects of our world exist.

See also: "space", "naked space" and "configuration space".

alternate time route

The bundle of time routes that make up a Sheaf is comprised of many individual time routes. However, with respect to a certain relative self, there is only one time route whose constituent EQ resolve to the Experiences of time-past and an implied time-future. This certain time route is called the time route on point and the information in the time-past portion of that time route resolves to a solo universe—which is V.1 described only with information contained in a certain relative self. All other time routes are called alternate time routes and do not resolve to a set of Experiences in a V.1 solo universe according to the time route on point.

anthropic denial

According to the ToT the basic nature of apparent reality is Instantaneous and is made up of a sequence of instant objects. Portions of the sequence can be figuratively "cut out" or terminated using a feature of the ToT-defined Anthropic Principle. The feature is called **anthropic denial** and is philosophically analogous to the *Ricci flow with surgery* mathematical procedure that was used in the proof of the Poincaré Conjecture.

In the ToT dangerous math objects such as those that resolve to black holes or spatial wormholes may exist if they are not close by. If they were, they might be very destructive and would therefore not "fit" within our reality map according to the Anthropic Principle. In the context of the ToT, they would be anthropically denied.

In the ToT, the term "anthropically denied" is used to describe a figurative pattern resident in the information of time-past that has denied certain other time-past Experiences that would be found in memory.

Anthropic principle (in terms of the ToT)

In the lexicon of the ToT, the Anthropic principle (note upper case "A") simply states that in the instant of the present "a relative self contains the Experience of being who he/she appears to be, in the context of what is remembered." This is a very simple principle. At the instant this is being read, you (the reader) are the collection of Experiences of being who you are, in the context of what you (apparently) remember.

Simply stated, in the ToT the Anthropic principle means:

"We see the world as we remember it to be."

We don't actually "see" reality around us—in this statement it would be more appropriate to replace the verb "to see" with the verb "to be"; and thus the statement would become: "we are the world as we remember it to be", but this does not read as well. Also, any Experience of a probable future is an element of memory.

The Anthropic principle asserts that the universe attends to certain principles given that it is described in terms of the human condition—the situation in which we believe ourselves to exist. Thus it relates to the relative condition because the concept of the flow of time (time-past and time-future) is implicit in the Experiences that imply existence*.

anthropic principle

According to the Oxford Dictionary, the anthropic principle (note lower case "a") is: "the cosmological principle that theories of the universe are constrained by the necessity to allow human existence."

arrow of time

According to the ToT the arrow of time is the name of the oExperience of the direction of the flow of time. It reflects a pattern within a time route. It is not, as might be described in terms of a relative self, related to the basic nature of an actual flow of time.

The philosophical concept of the arrow of time arose out of the (seemingly) intuitive nature of entropy. Entropy is a measure of the disorganization in a system.

Awareness (in terms of the ToT)

Awareness [with an upper case "A"], as defined in the ToT, is similar to the concept of "primordial awareness" found in the *Yogācāna* School of Buddhist philosophy (the *Mind Only School*). According to this school, the most basic, most primal concepts that can be understood in terms of the relative condition are labeled "primordial awareness" and "primordial substance".

Notably, the ToT also defines the relative condition in a slightly different fashion than the *Mind Only School*. The ToT recognizes that it is only concepts that reside in the relative condition; however, because EQ and Awareness are the basic formative elements of concepts, they are classed as being part of the absolute condition. Obviously they are concepts in the sense that they are described in this writing, but the concepts these words portray are analogs that point at the functional formative elements of *all* concepts; and thus, in essence they cannot be concepts themselves.

In the ToT, EQ and Awareness are both seen to be appropriately part of the absolute condition in that they fulfill the definition of *shunyata* ("free from permanence and nonexistence"). By definition they exist; and they are free from permanence in that they exist outside of time [time is a concept] and thus they can be neither permanent nor impermanent. They are all pervasive and ethereal in nature [because they are *non-local*, which means they have no implicit dimension]. This is the description of Awareness and EQ in the ToT. Together they form the sole ontological subset of naked space—which is the ultimate source of all existence, and designated the absolute condition.

In terms of the relative condition, Awareness just *is*—all-pervasive, infinitely multi-dimensional, nonlocal, and timeless. It stands strikingly apart from its relative condition parallel, "self-awareness".

We commonly consider the "self" to be the agent that is aware* of reality. In other words, awareness* is described as an attribute of the "self";

302

but this logic doesn't work in terms of the ToT. Recall that the "self" is identified as an Experience-object; and therefore an illusion that cannot be an agent that is aware* of itself or any other Experience-objects.

The world around us is information formed as an illusion of reality. Who you think you are is an illusion. Illusions do not have Awareness; they can include the concept of awareness*, but that is a mental event (a verb) and it is part of the illusion of the relative condition.

In its grandest interpretation Awareness can, in a single timeless Instant, view all information comprising the Totality of reality. It does this from a point of presence that is not a part of the information being viewed.

awareness*

The word "awareness*" is the form used as a verb describing a relative condition situation occurring in time. It is spelled with a lower case "a" and includes an asterisk.

big-heartedness (in terms of the ToT)

See also: "compassion".

body-self

Every waking relative self contains a body-self (as well as many other substantial objects.)

In terms of relative self the SCM is, more or less, the Experience of the substantial object called a physical body; and it is strongly associated with a concept of a "self." In this vain it is denoted with the term body-self.

Bon (or Bonpo)

Bon is the oldest spiritual tradition of Tibet, predating Buddhism by at least a millennium. Some translations of the word "Bon" describe it as an expression of the unending, forever flowing power of the universe. A Bonpo is a follower of the Bon tradition.

bs-sequence

With respect to nontemporal velocity, the sequence of EQ describing a moving object (i.e. an object that is separate from the body-self) is called the mo-sequence; and the sequence of EQ describing a body-self is called the bs-sequence. The elements of these sequences may variously occupy (and share) the same MindMoments.

c (the symbol for the speed of light)

Lower case "c". See also: "speed of light".

Cartesian dualism, p. 145.

René Descartes famously defended the idea that there are two fundamental kinds of substance: mental and material. His philosophy, often called Cartesian dualism, is also known as substance dualism. See also the "principal of two realities" for a description according to the ToT.

causality cone

In the relative condition, causality is typically perceived as a function of the arrow of time. In the ToT, this is also the case, but in a different way. The concept of a causality cone is a useful pattern for understanding this. The causality cone is defined as the time-past portion of a time route bundle. The time-future portion lies on the "other side" of the moment of the Now. It defines what is called the future cone. Both of these cones can be a source of information for a relative self, but the mechanism is not well accepted by spacetime physics.

See also: "future cone".

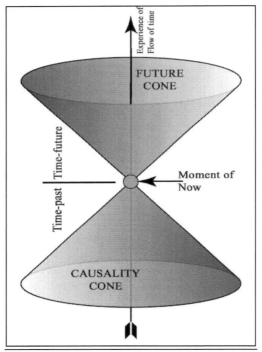

A thematic rendition of the configuration space defined by the five-dimensional manifold describing a Sheaf. The cones as pictured are empty. More correctly they would be shown filled with time routes.[169]

configuration space

In the ToT the various dimensions and volumes of naked space described by a manifold are termed to be the manifold's configuration space. In classical mechanics, the configuration space is the space of possible positions that a physical system may attain... The configuration space of a typical system has the structure of a manifold.

304

chain of existence

Thinking in terms of spacetime physics, consider an object and the experience* of that object. The object is thought to exist and then a being can have an experience of the object.

In terms of the ToT existence is instantaneous and the relationship between the Experience (an illusion of a noun describing an object) and the Experience-object (an illusion of an object) is timelessly syncategorematic in nature; the components existing in a non-temporal, sequential relationship—that is called the chain of existence in the ToT. The sequential nature of the chain of existence belies a causality resulting from a position in a static, non-temporal sequence, *not* from a position in time flow.

change in position (d)

In the ToT there is the concept of the smallest possible change in position that may be an Experience. It is called the quantum interspace, denoted by the Greek letter Φ (Greek letter phi, upper case). The value for Φ describes the information in a Feature of a single EQ that resolves to the Experience of a change in position between two MindMoments that contain the Experience of a moving object.

When there is *any* Experience of movement, the distance moved is equal to a quantum interspace (the value of Φ) or there is no movement at all. Thus the quantum interspace is the shortest distance that may be an Experience. It is always an nExperience because it cannot be a composite of shorter distances. Φ is derived from the measured value for the speed of light and $\tilde{A}$. $\Phi = c/\tilde{A} = 3 \times 10^{-6}$ meters.

See also: "d" and "$\tilde{A}$".

d (symbol for change in position)

The symbol d (lower case "d") indicates a distance. It is a concept reflecting a change in position of a phenomenal object within the relative self.

See also: "change in position".

Cloud

A "set of EQ groups" or a "collection of EQ" is called a Cloud. A Cloud resolves to a "relative self".

compassion

According to the ToT: compassion is an expression of the intertwining, overlapping, intermingling (nontemporal) aspects of the myriad of interrelationships among all instances of EQ in the context of a Cloud. It is also closely associated with the philosophical aspect of "c" (the velocity of light) being an absolute speed limit within the relative condition.

305

According to Buddhism, compassion or big-heartedness, (in Tibetan *changchub*) is naturally accorded to (and for) all beings who believe the relative self is real and who therefore attempt to end their suffering with the approach of moving toward what is seen as good, or avoiding what is seen as bad. In this way the Experience of compassion is naturally one of empathy for the predicament of beings trying to deal with pain and suffering in an ineffectual fashion.

Within the ToT there is a complete intertwinglement between the Experiences of all things, all people, all thoughts and all ideas. The ToT defines the intertwinglement, per se, as the essential nature the concept of compassion, which in turn is reflected as a unique value for the speed of light in this universe.

See also: "karma", "the speed of light" and "c".

Ð (duration of event)

The symbol Ð (upper case "D" with a stroke) represents the duration of an event of interest within a relative self. Nontemporal velocity describes both a change in position and a duration. The duration of an event is determined with respect to the total number of MindMoments in the sequence describing the nontemporal velocity.

dangerous manifolds

An interpretation of Poincaré's work is that a simply connected, finite, temporal, 3-manifold with positive curvature is the only one that may continue to exist. In the ToT such a temporal manifold is made up of a sequence of instant manifolds, called proper manifolds. With respect to a relative self—if the conditions of Poincaré's description are not met, then the Experience of the surrounding reality could manifest as a hole in space, an infinitely deep pit or some other equally unpleasant situation over the course of the apparent flow of time. In the ToT the instant manifolds in the sequence that resolve to the unpleasant situation are called a dangerous manifolds. Dangerous manifolds are always instant manifolds.

dangerous math objects

The full nature of a relative self is obviously more than just a physical body. The nature of a relative self is determined by the *total* number and the dimensional expanse of the manifolds needed to describe all the associated information. This includes possible information resolving to what the ToT calls dangerous math objects.

In the lexicon of the ToT a dangerous math object is an area on the hypersurface of an instant manifold that includes the n-dimension equivalence of a black hole and/or a spatial wormhole. The terms "black hole" and "wormhole" specifically label dangerous math objects that exist as instant 3-manifolds, but in the ToT math objects with this label can describe instant manifolds of any dimension. Dangerous math objects are always

306

instant manifolds because their defining nature is to express a pending state of untenable existence—a shape that is *on the verge* of un-tenability. In general the book deals with instant 3-manifolds as a representation of substantial reality, because that is the realm of contemporary physics.

dimension

In physics: one of a group of properties or magnitudes such as mass or time that collectively define a physical quantity.

In mathematics: a coordinate used with others to locate a point in space, time and/or other degrees of freedom, where each dimension is orthogonal to all others.

In Buddhism (typically): a level of consciousness, existence, or reality.

doorway Experience

An experience* of 4th time can't be remembered in terms of spacetime and communicated in words, however a person can sometimes remember going in or coming out, as if through a doorway.

In the ToT this is characterized as a doorway Experience. One may have the experience* of a memory of coming out of a door, but there can be no true experience* of the reality of being on the other side of the door; because that reality is five-dimensional, one where multiple experiences* of the moment of the present occur simultaneously. As such, it is a state of being that is beyond the normal Experience of memory—in terms of spacetime.

duration of event (Đ)

Nontemporal velocity describes both a change in position and a duration. The duration is determined with respect to the total number of MindMoments in the sequence describing the nontemporal velocity. This is called the duration of the event of interest within a relative self, identified with the symbol "Đ" (capitol D with stroke).

EQ (Experience Quantum)

See also: "Experience Quantum".

event-like dimension

The term "event-like dimension" is a play on words following Minkowski's description of a time-like dimension etc. The term is coined to highlight a qualitative similarity between the Experiences of substantial objects and of thoughts, feelings, emotions etc. (mental events) within the ToT.

Experience (in terms of the ToT)

The term Experience is a unique part of the lexicon of the ToT and it is written with a capital "E" to denote it is a noun—not a verb.

Within the context of the ToT the word Experience is used in this fashion except in certain circumstances where the word is describing a verb, in which case it is denoted with an asterisk (for example experience*).

This is done because the essential nature of Totality is defined as time-less; therefore there is no time in which a verb-described action may occur and the distinction between Experience and experience* is crucial. Adding an asterisk is also done with other verbs when they are used in terms of the relative condition.

See also: "experience*".

experience*

Indicating a verb in the relative condition.

See also: "Experience", a noun according to the nomenclature of the ToT..

Experience Quantum (EQ)

Within the ToT each basic quantum of existence is called an Experience Quantum—a term unique to the ToT lexicon. Both an Experience Quantum and its plural, Experience Quanta, are denoted with the acronym "EQ". These quanta are not to be conceptualized as a substance in the relative sense—they have no size (length, width etc.) or specific qualities (*i.e.* odor, color, charge, mass etc.) They also have no temporal qualities (*i.e.* they don't move or change). They are not part of the relative condition. We can conceptualize them with an analog—tiny warps in various and grossly multiple dimensions of naked space; but that is an analog. A more succinct definition is: that which resolves to an Experience, which is the smallest possible concept that may occur—thus an EQ is the item that is the basic building block of a concept. Therefore it cannot itself be a concept. This is self-evident.

Therefore, unlike all other conceptualizations of basic quanta in spacetime physics, these quanta (the EQ) never resolve to phenomenal reality; they resolve only to Experiences.

In the ToT, EQ are one of the two most basic features of naked space. The other is Awareness.

Experience-object

In the ToT all of reality is defined as a set of Experiences—that is all. Consequently the Experience of something is prime and the "object of the Experience is a function of the Experience. The former is called the Experience-object" (it's hyphenated to denote its unique stature in the ToT.) Typically, in the world as we know it, an object is described as the cause of an experience* because the object's existence is understood to precede the perception of it. This is not the case in the ToT. In the ToT, there is an ontological distinction but there is no temporal relationship (or interval) between the Experience and the Experience-object. In other words; in the ToT the existence of the object does not *precede* the experiencing* of the object in the flow of time. Normally (when we speak of the nature of reality) there is an object which exists, and then subsequently that object is perceived*. This is not the case in the ToT.

The object of the Experience of a mental event is a bit more subtle. The ToT makes a distinction between the mental event and the Experience of that event. Within the ToT they are conceptually separate concepts— which is not generally the case in the normal phraseology of the English language. Consider the Experience of an "appreciation of Art." In the ToT it is paired with an Experience-object that has the (illusory) quality of existing within the flow of time. In this case the Experience-object is the "appreciation"—a mental event which is a verb apparently occurring in a span of time. Both the Experience and the Experience-object are considered to be part of the Stor.

In the ToT the adjective syncategorematic is used to describe the simultaneous and instantaneous relationship between the components of an Experience/Experience-object pair.

experiential simultaneity

Two or more events are experientially simultaneous when their EQ Two or more events are experientially simultaneous when their EQ are contained in the same time-past MindMoment (*i.e.* Ш_{-n}).

See also: "True Simultaneity".

Feature (in terms of the ToT)

Each EQ has a unique set of Features (with upper case "F" in the lexicon of the ToT) that generically describes the information resident in a respective set of dimensions. A single Feature is associated with a single dimension. In this way, each slug of dimensional information in an EQ resolves from the nature of a single Feature in that EQ. The Features of an EQ resolve to the elements of an Experience in the relative condition.

The Features describing a three-dimensional form are easy to conceive of—think of the standard three orthogonal directions in space (width, height and depth). When the number of dimensions is greater than three it becomes more difficult. For example: imagine the shape of a five-dimensional object (you probably can't do it!) Instead it's better to consider each of the orthogonal dimensions of an EQ to be degrees of freedom indicating different values, or qualities of information, and the information in one degree has no effect on any other degree—thus each Feature is independent of all others. (Recall that EQ are definitely *not* the building blocks of the phenomenal universe in the manner that is typically explained in spacetime particle physics.)

first in sequence

A time route will always *appear* to exist on the surface of a proper manifold. The areas of real danger (infinity pits and wormhole areas) may be thought of as surrounded by a virtual boundary. In the ToT this is called a 3-boundary—because we are talking about 3-manifolds.

In the nomenclature of the ToT, a time route that terminates because of information held in dangerous instant 3-manifolds is said to wander outside of the 3-Boundary. The wandering of the time route starts at the MindMoment that contains the first in sequence iteration of the dangerous manifold.

future cone

In the relative condition, causality is typically perceived as a function of the arrow of time. In the ToT, this is also the case, but in a different way. The concept of a causality cone is a useful pattern for understanding this. The causality cone is defined as the time-past portion of a time route bundle. The time-future portion lies on the "other side" of the moment of the Now. It defines what is called the future cone. Both of these cones can be a source of information for a relative self, but the mechanism is not well accepted by spacetime physics. See also: "causality cone".

group of EQ

A group of EQ may resolve to a single Thought.

holistic reality map

According to the ToT a holistic reality map is the same as a holistic belief system, except the reality map is a combination of a belief system and the "self" who is apparently doing the believing.

holistic belief system

A holistic worldview of the universe and reality as a whole is one where the general premise is: "We all come from (are a part of) the Earth (the Mother, the One) and to that we will return (or continue to abide)." The holistic worldview typifies the indigenous Native American, Neolithic Hawaiian, and traditional indigenous Asian cultures.

The historic indigenous cultures of Asia are those such as: China, Japan, India, Tibet and Southeast Asia and in these cultures it has been the Buddhist and Vedic scholars who have best recorded their philosophies. The most accessible are the Tibetan, Burmese and Japanese Buddhist writings.

See also: "holistic reality map".

homeomorphic

The word homeomorphic applies if two objects can be deformed into each other by a continuous, invertible mapping. In topology, a donut and a coffee cup with a handle are equivalent shapes (called homeomorphic) because each has a single hole.

310

hypersurface

A 2-manifold has a surface. 3-manifolds (and higher numbers) have hypersurfaces. The hypersurface of a 3-manifold is three dimensional in nature. Our three-dimensional universe can be viewed as a 3-manifold; and in that context we live on (in) the hypersurface of a 3-manifold. Within that hypersurface we can experience* solid, three-dimensional objects.

hyper-causality

In the ToT causality is in always non-temporal in nature. There are two ways to express it. One way is within a relative self; where there is an apparent oExperience of a relationship between one event (called cause) and its consequence (called effect); or we could say: the oExperience of a relationship between one MindMoment and another within a sequence of MindMoments comprising a time route. Within the ToT, this type of causality is known as sequential causality. Another variety, hyper-causality, involves an Experience of the actual concept of free will, not the illusion of what appears to be free will, as it is portrayed in a relative self (the time-past portion of a time route).

True free will (an example of hyper-causality) happens when the verb-like action of an actual choice occurs within the Instantaneous condition associated with the nexus of a Sheaf. A choice made in this fashion is an example of hyper-causality. Hyper-causality is a reflection of a Shift in the presence of Awareness from one time route to another, within the domain of a single Sheaf. This is called a Shift of presence or, simply, a Shift.

The question is: if the domain of a time route is timeless, how can the functional domain of the verb-like Shifting of a presence of Awareness from one time route to another occur?

To answer this question the ToT axiomatically employs a concept that is outside of the normal realm of perceived reality. It is best described as a quasi-concept, which is what generically describes the verb-like Shift of presence of Awareness.

I_0 (inertial system of the SCM of the body-self), p. 243.

See also: "inertial system of the SCM of the body-self".

I_n (inertial system of the CM of an object), p. 243.

See also: "inertial system of the CM of an object".

Individuated SELF

An individuated SELF describes a gathering of time routes. Philosophically the term labels the grandest, most complete expression of an individual. In simple terms, it is the information that describes various, multiple renditions of a relative self, with each rendition laid out across a unique track in the time-like dimension. In this way, an individuated SELF is a gathering of time routes with each time route containing one of multiple possible versions of time-future and of time-past, all of which are associated with the same single individuated SELF at the moment of the Now.

Geometrically the collection is resident on the hypersurface of a temporal 4-manifold that provides the field upon which the various instant 4-manifolds are arrayed, *i.e.* the gathering of time routes.

inertial system

In the physical sciences an inertial system is a frame of reference in which a body remains at rest or moves with constant linear velocity unless acted upon by forces. Any frame of reference that moves with constant velocity relative to an inertial system is itself an inertial system.

inertial system of SCM of the body-self (I_0)

The SCM is an Overlain Experience that is a virtual concept. It does not functionally represent any substantial object or movement; but it does serve as the figurative axis mundi in V.1 for the position of all objects, any motion they may display and the apparent momentum of their inertial systems. It is the virtual center point of a relative self. The SCM sits as a still-point to the Experience of the relativistic flows of time associated with all other objects in a time route expressing different inertial systems. Thus the inertial system of the SCM is always described as at rest. In this way it is instrumental in allowing the ToT to explain time dilation.

See also: I_0.

inertial system of CM of an object (I_n)

The CM is the center of mass of any moving* object in a relative self. The inertial frame of reference for that object is inertial system of CM the object. See also: I_n.

infinity pit

Certain dangerous manifolds contain areas of severe negative curvature that figuratively "rush to infinity". Call these areas infinity pits, be they negative (a peak) or positive (a pit). Such deep pits or high peaks may appear as black holes or some other phenomena that are good to avoid up close.

According to the ToT, infinity pits (black holes) are included in the time route that describes our universe because we don't have to confront them up close and feel their destructive forces. If there were smaller infinity pits close by in our everyday environment that might give us trouble, but they would be (are?) anthropically denied.

Instancy principle

The concept of the instantaneous nature of the sequence of Thoughts that comprises a relative self is a primary feature of the ToT. It's described by the tenets of the Instancy principle.

The Instancy principle is a concept stating that there is no true flow of time; instead there is only an instantaneous Experience that is "a memory of a duration." From that memory we naturally infer a false condition called "the flow of time"; but according to the ToT, the space and time universe (as we commonly know it) is actually a static set of memories, which truly exists only in the instantaneous moment of the present.

Instant (in terms of the ToT)

The term instant (w/ lower case "i") applies to every remembered instant in time-past and every postulated instant in time-future. As a counterpoint, the term Instant (w/ upper case "I") applies to the great meta-Instant of the moment of the "now". The Instant is the containing package holding all of the lesser instants. Thus there are always multiple examples of instants, but there is only one Instant.

This description of the set of single instants comprising memory is the lesser part of the Instancy principle, because there is a bigger Instant.

instant

The term instant (w/ lower case "i") applies to every remembered instant in time-past and every postulated instant in time-future. As a counterpoint, the term Instant (w/ upper case "I") applies to the great meta-Instant of the moment of the "now". The Instant is the containing package holding all of the lesser instants. Thus there are always multiple examples of instants, but there is only one Instant.

This description of the set of single instants comprising memory is the lesser part of the Instancy principle.

instant 3-sphere

Consider the immediate area surrounding the space that you, the reader, occupy. Think of that space as a 3-dimensional configuration space; but you and all of the objects etc. around you are instant objects, i.e. there is no time flow. Think of configuration space as only a small portion of the hypersurface of the very large instant 3-manifold that extends to the furthest reaches of the universe. Out there, as far as you can envision in front of you, at the "end" of the universe, the stuff of spacetime folds around, and in a continuous fashion comes full circle connecting with the other end of the universe extending from behind you—the connection is seamless and it's three-dimensional; thus the concept holds true for every direction you can look out, across the instant 3-manifold whose hypersurface is the cosmos. This describes an instant 3-sphere... add time to it and we get a 4-manifold. Thus an instant 3-manifold is a single point on the hypersurface of a 4-manifold describing spacetime.

instant object

An instant object is a single instantaneous example of a temporal object. It is truly instantaneous with no duration in time. Its representation in the fourth dimension is a single point (indicating zero duration).

instant universe

In the ToT the information in the fourth, time-like dimension of spacetime is not smoothly homogeneous; instead it is quantum in nature with each quantum incident representing a single, static, three-dimensional instantaneous version of the universe—called an instant universe. An instant universe is the largest possible instant object in the V.1 universe. V.1 itself, in its entirety, is the largest possible temporal object, with respect to V.1.

Intension (in terms of the ToT)

The Experience of an Intension occurs just prior to the instant of the present, at $Ш_{-1}$, which is the first MindMoment in the time-past array comprising a relative self, i.e. the most contemporary MindMoment in a relative self. An Intension is an nExperience and it is the only true expression of free will resident in a relative self.

(The memory of the "verb-like" *actuation** of free will is generically just another Experience in a sequence of MindMoments and is an expression of sequential causality unfolding—it does not indicate a Shift.)

An Intension (at $Ш_{-1}$) indicates an Experience-object that resolves from a Shift, and is thus described as an example of hyper-causality—but the nature of this special Experience-object is usually not evident within a relative self.

In the ToT a Shift *per se* is described as resolving to a phenomenal object that is the person's physical body because functionally, a Shift occurs on the spacetime-time hypersurface of a 5-manifold where each of various time routes resolve to the spacetime substantial reality aspect of various relative selves.

The *new* relative self brought on point by the Shift also includes higher dimensional mental events. The nExperience of an Intension is one of these higher dimensional mental events; but often, a failure in our presence of Awareness leads to the subtle uniqueness of these special nExperiences not being included in the common relative self.

Kalachakra

Kalachakra is a Sanskrit term used in Tantric Buddhism that literally means "time-wheel" or "time-cycles.

The Kalachakra tantra is an ancient document containing information dating back to the time of the Buddha. It describes the nature of the universe in detail down to the level of very small particles called "space particles" (that appear to be similar to EQ). The word "Kalachakra" means cycles of time. In the tantra there is a discussion of the cycles that each universe goes through, and there is a description of the Kalachakra *stupa* and *mandala*.

The EQ, found in the ToT, are similar in concept to a "space particle" described in the Kalachakra tantra. In that tantra they are described as the smallest of particles.

karma

A simple view of karma deals with what is. Karma does not have a value of its own. There is not an intrinsically "good" or intrinsically "bad" karma. In terms of a relative self, karma may be seen as the sum of all that an individual has done. Sometimes the word is roughly translated as "action*." From this viewpoint, karma is very much a verb that describes the concept of a continuation of things happening because of relationships over time.

Another view of karma appears in esoteric Buddhist thought where the non-temporal condition of reality is promoted. From this view, karma can be thought of as a static pattern of associations that exists between the karmic visions of many beings. Translating this into the terms of the ToT we can say that: what some Buddhist thinkers call karma, can be described as an intertwinglarity of links within an array of EQ Clouds. A grand overview of these links is expressed as a Matrix (w/ upper case "M"). According to the ToT these linking patterns manifest as the oExperience commonly described as "compassion."

See also: "compassion" and "the speed of light".

karmic milieu

Karmic milieu is an expression of a linking pattern (in the Matrix) that is associated with a certain relative self.

Kyung lung

"*Kyung lung dngul mkhar*" (Kyung lung)—*The White Silver Palace in the Valley of the Garuda*—in the Himalayas at 14,000 ft. (4,300 meters). The "Garuda" is the spirit of the energy of the raptor, a very old deity. This cave city was an ancient and important capital of the old kingdom of Zhang Zhung in western Tibet. Kyung lung was palace of Ligmigya, the last king of Zhang Zhung who was (likely) assassinated in c. 645 AD, effectively ending the political kingdom of Zhang Zhung.

The Kingdom of Zhang Zhung, with the venerated Mount Kailash as its center and heart, was an ancient realm which originated more than three thousand years ago, corresponding geographically to the western Tibet of today.

linear reality map

A linear reality map is the same as a linear belief system except the reality map is a combination of a belief system and the "self" who is apparently doing the believing.

See also: "linear belief system".

linear belief system

The worldview reflecting the cultural demographic of our modern societies is one that is generally dualistic in nature. In the ToT this is called a linear worldview of the universe and reality as a whole. It is an understanding of reality where, in general the premise is; "I am separate from you, you are separate from me; and all things are separate from one another." Modern science has arisen out of a linear worldview.

See also: "linear reality map".

mathematical object (in terms of the ToT)

According to Wikipedia a mathematical object is an abstract object arising in the philosophy of mathematics and in mathematics. In geometry, a branch of mathematics, mathematical objects may be topological spaces and manifolds.

In terms of the ToT a mathematical object also represents an Experience. We can follow the logic of the ToT further and allow for an indefinite number of dimensions for expressing information. When we do this we can add mental events to the group of Experiences we are considering. All of these Experiences, from the four-dimensional spacetime substantial objects, to the seriously multi-dimensional representation of mental events, can be described with mathematical objects—and a super-set of those objects together can be figuratively laid onto to a "playing field" of naked space to create a grand analog representing all of reality.

Matrix (in terms of the ToT)

An unusual view of karma appears in esoteric Buddhist thought where the non-temporal condition of reality is promoted. From this view, karma can be thought of as a static pattern of associations that exists between the karmic visions of many beings. Translating this into the terms of the ToT we can say that: what some Buddhist thinkers call karma, can be described as an intertwinglarity of links within an array of EQ Clouds. A grand overview of these links is expressed as a Matrix (w/ upper case "M"). It's a term that has a special meaning in the ToT.

See also: "karma".

Matrix link

In the Matrix of the ToT there is linking pattern that in general reflects an intertwingularity of information that is shared between relative selves (the Matrix links). The amount of sharing is an expression of proximity between the elements of the Matrix.

316

mental events

Mental events are feelings, emotions, dreams etc., all elements of reality that have no phenomenal existence (they are experiences*... that is all.) Mental events and phenomenal reality appear to transpire within a flow of time and together they form apparent overall reality, or, the "stuff of reality" (the Stor).

The Stor consists of both types of experience; phenomenal reality, and mental events. The second includes the experience of "the flow of time".

Mental events exist in time and without them the definition of any experiences associated with physical phenomenon could not be verified as existing.

The classification of substantial objects versus mental events is very much a description of the "Cartesian dualism", (or substance dualism) which is important historically for having given rise to much thought regarding the famous mind–body problem in Western philosophy.

meta-Cloud

A time route resolves from a Cloud of EQ. A Sheaf is similar in concept but one dimension larger. In the lexicon of the ToT it resolves from what's called a meta-Cloud.

To understand a Sheaf, consider the idea that the future has many possibilities (a concept that often comes to mind). Within the scope of an individuated SELF each possible time-future is represented by a separate and different time route—albeit with an associated separate and different time-past (a concept that seldom comes to mind). Each time route in a Sheaf is unique with a different time-future and a different time-past; but with the exact same moment of the Now. A meta-Cloud resolves to a group of four-dimensional time routes.

Milarepa

Jetsun Milarepa is one of Tibet's most famous yogis who lived from 1052 to 1135 CE.

Ш (MindMoment)

See also: "MindMoment".

MindMoment (Ш)

Every relative self is composed of (what appears to be) previous versions of (what appears to be) the moment in play. Each of these versions of the moment in play is called a MindMoment in the lexicon of the ToT. It is denoted with the symbol "Ш" (large format lower case letter "M" turned).

The term MindMoment is an adaption of the term "mind moment" which is a translation of the *Pāli* text word *cittakkana*. The *Pāli* word is found in the Tripitaka, the traditional name for the southern Buddhist canon of scripture called the *Pāli Canon*.

Think of a MindMoment as if it is a package of Thoughts or a package of the Experiences that make up the Thoughts. The Experiences in the package are those that make up a single instant of time-past for a relative self.

In terms of the relative self, a MindMoment is a snapshot of what appears to be a *moment of existence in the past*. It is never a snapshot of the moment of the present… or moment of the Now.

See also: "Ш".

MindMoment constant (Ã)

Sequences of MindMoments describe an "apparent route of existence across an expanse of apparent time for a relative self". This is called a time route in the ToT lexicon.

In the ToT, the stated number of MindMoments associated with a described (apparent) smallest unit of time is called the MindMoment constant, denoted with the symbol Ã (upper case "A" with a tilde). The MindMoment constant is the ToT's primary axiomatically defined constant; and other constants unique to the lexicon and logic of the ToT are based on this constant.

The working value for the MindMoment constant (used in the book's discussion) is effectively axiomatic, because the actual value is unknown in this universe and in all others. The working value for the constant is based on a generalization of information provided in various Eastern based philosophical literature (see text).

The working value is derived as follows: If there are 10 trillion (10^{13}) MindMoments occurring during a single blink of an eye, and a blink of the eye is assumed to be $1/10$ of one second in duration, then there are 100 trillion (10^{14}) MindMoments needed to produce the Experience of one second passing.

The MindMoment constant:
$$\tilde{A} = 10^{14} \text{ Ш/sec}.$$

Where:
- Ш is the symbol for a MindMoment.
- Ã the MindMoment constant.

Minkowski space

Historically spacetime is described as four-dimensional Minkowski space, named for the mathematician of the same name. Spacetime is the mathematical space setting in which Einstein's theory of special relativity is most conveniently formulated.

318

mo-sequence

With respect to nontemporal velocity, the sequence of EQ describing a moving object (*i.e.* an object that is separate from the body-self) is called the **mo-sequence**; and the sequence of EQ describing a body-self is called the bs-sequence. The elements of these sequences may variously occupy (and share) the same MindMoments.

See also: "bs-sequence".

multiverse (in terms of the ToT)

The ToT contains the axiomatic assertion that there are an indefinitely large number of different, parallel universes figuratively laid upon naked space, and that all of them hold the same value for the MindMoment constant, $\tilde{A}$. Together these universes form a single multiverse.

In terms of the relative condition this is a statement that the number of "instances of reality" per "unit of time" is the same for every universe in the multiverse. The phrase "instance of reality" refers to a single Mind-Moment.

See also: "V.n universe".

multiverse constant

The ToT axiomatically asserts that there is a multiverse made up of an indefinitely large number of different V.n universes. Each V.n universe holds the *same value* for the MindMoment constant, $\tilde{A}$. In this way the MindMoment constant describes a "multiverse constant". In terms of the relative condition this is a statement that the number of "instances of reality" per "unit of time" is the same for every universe in the multiverse. The phrase "instance of reality" refers to a single MindMoment.

The ToT also contains the concept of a time quanta (the reciprocal of the MindMoment constant). This is also the same in every universe, regardless of how beings in that universe may describe it.

[The "described value" for a unit time is always locally defined, such as one second or one year or one day. There is no "true" value for a unit of time, it can only be described with respect to something else—hence it is categorical placed within the relative condition.]

The telltale difference between the universes comprising the multiverse is in their value for Φ, the quantum interspace. In terms of the relative condition this resolves to a different value for the velocity of light in each universe.

The value for Φ describes the Experience of a change in position between two EQ in sequence that contain the information of an object moving at the speed of light.

Recall that the value for Φ describes the Experience of a change in position between two EQ in sequence that contain the information of an object moving at the speed of light.

319

The quantum interspace:

$$\frac{c}{\tilde{A}} = \Phi$$

Where:
- c is the speed of light in a vacuum. (3×10^8 m/sec).
- $\tilde{A}$ is the MindMoment constant (10^{14} Ш/sec), or the multiverse constant.
- Φ is the quantum interspace (3×10^{-6} m/Ш).

In spacetime physics the concept of c is essentially a philosophical statement describing a feature of space in general. In the ToT it is described as a feature of naked space that manifests as a different value for Φ in each V.n universe. This then becomes the hallmark variable of each universe.

Recall that there are many relevant dimensions of information comprising the MindMoments of a time route (*i.e.* substantial objects *and* subjective mental events). Here we are addressing only substantial reality which is the domain of physics as we now know it. In this domain there is the concept of locality, position and distance, all concepts that require a quantum interspace in terms of the ToT.

naked space

The ToT uses geometric analogs and a concept called "naked space" to point at a reflection of the Buddhist concepts of the Void or *shunyata* [Sanskrit]; which are both expressions of an ultimate source for all of reality. *Shunyata* translates to: "empty of existence or non-existence".

In physics the word "space" indicates a real expanse or volume to which coordinates may be applied, and thus it is the background canvass against which substantial reality and attendant forms of energy play.

Naked space is the *virtual* canvas upon which the basic quanta of reality are painted. It's *virtual* because it cannot actually provide a set of independent coordinates stating a location for the quanta, it only appears to do so. Functionally the quanta have a location only with respect to one another, and such information is only expressed when it is a salient Feature of the EQ. Thus naked space is not a true background canvass for the essence of reality... that essence has no background canvass.

In the ToT it is naked space upon which patterns of EQ (math objects) are figuratively imbedded as warps; and those patterns resolve to the Experiences of reality. Therefore in terms of the ToT... our reality and who we think we are comprise a set of patterns in naked space. Interestingly one of the patterns is the concept of the three dimensions of space as we define it in spacetime reality. There are many other patterns populating an

320

indefinably large number of the infinitely expansive dimensionality of naked space. Thus the patterns defining reality are finite and the expanse and dimensionality of naked space is infinite.

Logically naked space itself is empty; but if we think of the quantum bits and their associated warps as occurring simultaneously, each a reflection of the other, we have a logical "start point" for existence. A creation point if you will, however because the concept of time is an item of information contained within the quanta, there can be no before or after *creation*. The warps and the quanta cannot *occur* simultaneously. All just exists—for a single instant or for eternity, there is no difference. The verb "to occur" does not enter the picture.

This is the closest to a "start point" that the ToT defines.

In the ToT:
o   Naked space is a concept that is ontologically one step above a pairing of EQ and Awareness. (Thus, in the ToT the latter two are defined as sub-set features of naked space.) Together the three metaphorically describe the absolute condition of Totality.
o   EQ are described as resolving to an Experience when figuratively held against the lens of Awareness.
o   An EQ is defined as 1) a warp in naked space, and 2) the single most basic quantum of existence.
o   The EQ, *never* resolve directly to substantial objects. They *always* resolve to Experiences; and those Experiences may be of substantial objects or of mental events. The quanta themselves never become* substantial in any way.
o   There can be no direct Experience of a warp in naked space (an EQ) because the warp itself is the most basic, genitive component of an Experience.
o   Collections of warps [EQ] resolve to a patterns of information that form the illusion of ongoing reality.

The most basic axiomatic assertions of the ToT are:
1) The putative idea of naked space as the virtual canvas upon which rest the primary quanta of the universe and their respective warps;
2) The existence of warps in naked space;
3) The existential reflection of the warps in naked space, i.e. the primary quanta of the universe, the EQ; and
4) The existence of Awareness [classed as the essence of naked space.]

It is only these four that have absolute existence according to the ToT. Numbers 2), 3) and 4) together are the philosophically equivalent to "pure non-duel cognitive potentiality", a term found in Tibetan Buddhist thought.

native Experience (nExperience)

The most basic description of an Experience is one that is said to re-solve from a single EQ, it's called a native Experience or an nExperience. In the ToT it's referred to as an "nExperience".

negative curvature

A negative curvature manifold describes as a saddle-shaped curve on the surface of a 2-manifold. A negative curvature manifold describes as a saddle-shaped curve on the surface of a 2-manifold. Such a curved area can describe the side of a peak or a pit that could extend to infinity.

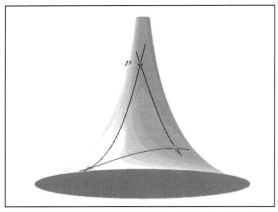

An area of a section of the surface of a 2-manifold with negative curvature leading to a possible infinitely high peak.

An Experience that is representative of a manifold containing a surface area of an infinitely high peak, or infinitely deep pit would be un-knowable in terms of our apparently finite spacetime universe.

When a temporal manifold morphs into a shape with an extreme neg-ative curvature that yields a tall spike or deep pit where the hypersurface rushes to infinity. It would no longer be a closed manifold and the open end would constitute a hole in the information described by the manifold (whatever that is!) In any case there would be an area of no information and no existence, in terms of the relative condition.

It's interesting that a manifold describing a large number of dimen-sions (a very complex math object!) can also exhibit negative curvature. This idea becomes relevant in discussions about information expressing higher dimension manifolds.

nExperience (native Experience)
See also: "native Experience".

n-manifold (in terms of the ToT)
In the ToT the term n-manifold is be used to describe a geometry of an unknown number of dimensions, where "n" indicates the number of dimensions involved.

nonconceptual meditation
Nonconceptual meditation is associated with the quasi-concept of 4th time. Meditation is often described as focused on some concept, such as an object, the breath, the void, compassion, a certain deity, the suffering of humanity, etc. All of these are worthy *concepts*; but the act of nonconceptual meditation requires no such focus. It is also devoid of the *concept* of the flow of time—*i.e.* it is a *timeless* state of being. Logically, when a person does this sort of meditation they need some sort of temporal "elbowroom" in which to accomplish it . . . hence the figurative environment of 4th time. 4th time has no duration in spacetime. In the Dzogchen teaching it is sometimes described as contemplation.

nontemporal acceleration
Common knowledge tells us that acceleration is a change in velocity. In the physical sciences acceleration is associated with: 1) a change in velocity, 2) a change in direction, or 3) due to the nature of gravity.

In relativistic physics the term "proper acceleration" is the physical acceleration (*i.e.* measurable acceleration as by an accelerometer) experienced* by an object. According to the ToT this makes sense only in the fashion that all objects are contained in a relative self. An object alone cannot have an Experience.

Within the ToT all of these types of acceleration are functionally the same oExperience, differing only in the relative direction and value of a predicate inertial system (I_n) that is compared to a subsequent inertial system (I_{n+1})—all with respect to the ever unmoving inertial system of the SCM (I_0).

nontemporal causality
In the ToT causality is in always nontemporal in nature. There are two ways to express it. One way is within a relative self; where there is an apparent oExperience of a relationship between one event (called cause) and its consequence (called effect). In this case we could say that it is the oExperience of a relationship between one MindMoment and another within a sequence of MindMoments comprising a time route. Within the ToT, this type of causality is known as sequential causality.

Another variety, hyper-causality, involves an Experience of the actual concept of free will, not the illusion of what appears to be free will, as it is portrayed in a relative self (the time-past portion of a time route).

nontemporal velocity (ϋ)

In the ToT velocity is an oExperience, and like all Experiences is Instantaneous and nontemporal in nature. From this comes the term nontemporal velocity—denoted with the symbol "ϋ" (lower case Greek letter upsilon with a dialytika).

Nontemporal velocity describes uniform velocity, which also indicates a certain inertial system. Nontemporal velocities are always with respect to the SCM, thus every value for ϋ other than zero is positive, and every value indicates an inertial system denoted by I_n.

Nontemporal velocity describes both a change in position and a duration. The duration is determined with respect to the total number of Mind-Moments in the sequence describing the **nontemporal velocity**. This is called the "duration of the event of interest" within a relative self, identified with the symbol "Đ".

Every EQ in a given inertial system has a Feature that resolves to an Experience of information in the time-like dimension. The time-like information is an oExperience of the flow of time for that object, which resolves from multiple nExperiences of time quanta, "ŧ". An EQ containing a time quantum is called a "$ŧ_{con}EQ$". Every nExperience in a given inertial system has an associated time quantum; unless the EQ resolve to a substantial object in relativistic motion. Then it *may* or *may not* contain a time quantum. If it does not, the EQ is called a "$ŧ_{free}EQ$".

See also: "sequence dilation".

Now (in terms of the ToT)

In terms of the relative self, a MindMoment is a snapshot of what appears to be a *moment of existence in the past*. It is never a snapshot of the moment of the present... which is called the moment of the Now (with uppercase "N"). The Now is always empty of MindMoments. In terms of a relative self the Now serves only as a virtual vantage point that overlooks time-past. It does not overlook time-future because (obviously) a relative self only "knows*" time-past and can only "predict*" time-future with a varying probability of accuracy.

oExperience (overlain Experience)

See also: "overlain Experience".

overlain Experience (oExperience)

An oExperience resolves from the comparison of one EQ or group of EQ with another similar EQ or group of EQ. The comparing is done by Awareness.

The expression ". . . comparison of one group of EQ with another group of EQ . . ." is a semantic tool for describing a pattern of EQ that is made up of a certain combination of the constituent EQ or EQ groups. It can be envisioned as a meta-EQ-group, or a group comprised of a certain number of other EQ-groups.

The Experience of a flow of time, of movement, or of heat is an oExperience. Therefore (in the parlance of the ToT) the Experience of the flow of time does not resolve directly from a single EQ. Instead, it resolves from a pattern of EQ.

_p_ (number of Φ_{con}EQ in the EQ mo-sequence)

The number of Φ_{con}EQ in the mo-sequence is denoted with the symbol "p" (lower case.)

$$\ddot{\upsilon} = \frac{p\Phi}{Ð} = \text{meters/MindMoment.}$$

Where:

- $\ddot{\upsilon}$ = is nontemporal velocity.
- p is the number of Φ_{con}EQ in the mo-sequence.
- Ð is the number of MindMoments in the bs-sequence.
- Φ is the quantum interspace ($\Phi = 3 \times 10^{-6}$ meters).

parallel universes (in terms of the ToT)

A feature of the ToT is the axiomatic assertion that there are an indefinitely large number of different, parallel universes figuratively laid upon naked space, and that all of them hold the same value for the MindMoment constant, Ã. Together these universes form a single multiverse.

Each parallel universe is called a V.n universe, or a simply V.n; and each V.n universe differs one from another by their value for the quantum interspace, Φ. The principal of reality sync is based on a shared value for Φ within any V.n universe. Therefore each V.n universe within the multiverse is _not_ in reality sync with _any_ other V.n universe.

It is axiomatic within the ToT that there may exist an indefinitely large (maybe infinite) number of V.n universes, each with a unique value for the quantum interspace. Thus each V.n universe has a different value for Φ, and consequently a different value for c, the speed of light. Whether Φ is quantum in nature, or whether there is a range of "habitable" values for Φ is a matter of conjecture.

Parse

If Awareness existed in some sort of temporal environment we could say it "parses" an array of the warps in naked space. However in the ToT the essential nature of existence is instantaneous, thus the verb "to parse" will not apply. Instead Awareness is defined as a nontemporal "mirror" resting in figurative opposition to _all_ of the EQ. This description (…the "mirroring") is meant to emphasize that many or all of the EQ may be viewed simultaneously, and thus simultaneously they resolve to _many_ or _all_ of the Experiences that comprise the relative condition, be they time-past or time-future. All of this is axiomatic, and expressed colloquially it's "everything is happening at once". Therefore in this rendition of the ToT, to make for an easier read, this meta-verb is described with the term Parse (with uppercase "P").

persistence of reality

In the ToT a certain understanding of the Anthropic principal leads to it being described as the persistence of reality. This expresses the Experience of "continuing to be" who one thinks one is as the surrounding world continues to exist as he/she remembers it to be.

principle of two realities

When we consider the human condition, or the relative condition in general, we immediately realize that it is made up of many types of Experiences—all the possible things, feelings and realizations that comprise the concept of being alive. According to the ToT they fall into two classes of reality—those classed as phenomenal reality and those classed as mental events, both classes within the relative condition. This bifurcation of apparent reality is a primary feature of the ToT called the principle of two realities.

The separation of the relative condition into two areas has been effectively described by others. Sir Isaac Newton distinguished two classes of reality that parallel what the ToT calls phenomenal objects and mental events. He referred to these classes as mind-independent and mind-dependent, respectively.

René Descartes famously defended the idea that there are two fundamental kinds of substance: mental and material. His philosophy, often called Cartesian dualism, is also known as substance dualism.

proper manifolds

According to the ToT an interpretation of Poincaré's work is: "A simply connected, finite, temporal, 3-manifold with positive curvature is the only one that may *continue* to exist." In the ToT such a temporal manifold is made up of a sequence of instant manifolds, called proper manifolds.

proximate

See "proximity principle".

Poincaré conjecture

The standard form of the Poincaré conjecture is: *Every simply connected, closed 3-manifold is homeomorphic to the 3-sphere.*

Recall that a 3-sphere is a special case of a 3-manifold. The term *closed* means that it does not have a hole in its boundary or an area of negative curvature that rushes to infinity. The Poincaré Conjecture specifically addresses only 3-manifolds. It does not describe higher dimensional manifolds. It was called a "conjecture" because of the lack of a mathematical proof until 2003.

According to the ToT an interpretation of Poincaré's work is: *A simply connected, finite, temporal, 3-manifold with positive curvature is the only one that may continue to exist.*

proximity principle

In the ToT, the definition of the term proximate and its adverb proximity are given with respect to the absolute condition. This is a virtual construct that describes nuances of multiple EQ patterns. The term "proximity" is a statement of the number of EQ Features that are shared between two Clouds, not a statement of location. Recall that Clouds are patterns of EQ that overlap and consequently may resolve to similar Experiences in different relative selves. Thus a relative self is considered to be proximate to another relative self if their associated EQ Clouds are overlapping and share EQ. This is the proximity principle.

pseudo time route

The mixture of what appears to be time-past and time-future Experiences is the nature of the relative self during a dream state. A dream state is where disjointed iterative collections of Experiences comprise the time route that is responsible for the Experience of a relative self. This sequence of disjointed Experiences is called a pseudo time route. In such a situation, some of the Experiences may resolve from EQ patterns resident in a variety of time routes contained in the being's Sheaf. The oExperience that is the flow of time (according to the pseudo time route) describes various, sometimes intermingled time-futures and time-pasts. The determination of which is which is left to the individual when they awaken.

quantum distribution principle

In the ToT movement is always with respect to the SCM. The $\Phi_{con}EQ$ that describe the distance that an object moved are equally distributed across the sequence of EQ that define the "inertial system" associated with the object moving. This equal distribution is axiomatic within the ToT and it is called the quantum distribution principle.

When we speak of the movement of an object we are specifically talking about the change in position of the center of mass of the object (the CM).

quantum interspace (Φ)

The value for Φ describes the Experience of a change in position between two EQ in sequence that contain the information of an object moving at the speed of light.

The quantum interspace:

$$\frac{c}{\tilde{A}} = \Phi$$

Where:

- c is the speed of light in a vacuum. (3×10^8 m/sec).
- $\tilde{A}$ is the MindMoment constant (10^{14} Ш/sec).
- Φ is the quantum interspace (3×10^{-6} m/Ш).

In spacetime physics the concept of c is essentially a philosophical statement describing a feature of space in general. In the ToT it is described as a feature of naked space that manifests as a different value for Φ in each V.n universe. This value for Φ then becomes the hallmark of each universe.

In the ToT there is the axiomatic assertion that there are an indefinitely large number of different universes, each holding the *same value* for the MindMoment constant, $\tilde{A}$. In terms of the relative condition this is a statement that the number of "instances of reality" per "unit of time" is the same for every universe in the multiverse—where an "instance of reality" is a single MindMoment. This is axiomatic.

The "described value" for a unit time is locally defined [such as one second or one year]. There is no universal value.

Conversely, in the ToT there is the concept of a time quanta (the reciprocal of the MindMoment constant) and it is the same in every universe, regardless of how beings in that universe may describe it.

The telltale difference between the universes comprising the multiverse is in their value for Φ, the quantum interspace. In terms of the relative condition this resolves to a different value for the velocity of light in each universe.

Also: There are many relevant dimensions of information comprising the MindMoments of a time route (*i.e.* substantial objects *and* subjective mental events). Here we are addressing only substantial reality which is the domain of physics as we now know it. In this domain there is the concept of locality, position and distance, all concepts that require a quantum interspace in terms of the ToT.

quasi-concept

The question is: if the domain of a time route is timeless, how can the functional domain of the verb-like Shifting of a presence of Awareness from one time route to another occur?

To answer this question the ToT axiomatically employs a concept that is outside of the normal realm of perceived reality. It is best described as

328

a quasi-concept, which is what generically describes the verb-like Shift of presence of Awareness.

reality map

Within a *belief system* or a *worldview* its adherents believe in and rely on basic axiomatic definitions; but such a description implies there is a "self" who is doing the believing. In the ToT, the "self" is identified as part of the information of the Stor—this is a problem with respect to the distinction between the observer and what is being observed. Therefore in the ToT there is instead the concept of a reality map, which is a combination of a belief system and the "self" who is apparently doing the believing.

reality sync

In the ToT the concept of a Shift of presence is intrinsically related to the temporal synchronization among all Sheaves within the V.1 shared universe. This is called reality sync.

Grammatically, the statement that something is synchronized or is not synchronized in a timeless reality is an oxymoron, because synchronization requires time flow. Within the ToT, the term reality sync is used with respect to the relative position of the Experiences comprising the Mind-Moments, not to time being conceptualized as a "real" phenomenon. Reality sync is strongly related to the quantum interspace.

relative condition (in terms of the ToT)

The *two truths* of Buddhism are often described as the relative condition and the absolute condition. A clarifying analogy for the two truths is to compare the elements of the everyday physical world around us with an image of the same reality as seen on the atomic level. For example: compare a vision of the earth, the sky, sunlight, radio waves, sound etc. with a vision of the same things made up of atoms, sub-atomic particles, various types of energy and mostly empty space. We have been taught that both are true, yet in very different ways. The first example is the way we generally perceive things; and the second is what might be thought of as (supposedly) the way it really is. Both are considered to be true. This is an analogy. It does *not* express the Buddhist concept.

Similarly, the ToT also posits two truths (or conditions of existence)—the relative condition of reality and the absolute condition of reality. What we generally believe to be the phenomenal world around us in which we exist, think and act, is the relative condition—*i.e.* that which is (apparently) portrayed by our senses.

relative self

A relative self is a core element in the explanation of reality within the ToT.

A "set of EQ groups" is called a Cloud. A Cloud resolves to a relative self; or we could say: a group of EQ resolves to a single Thought and a set of Thoughts make up a relative self. The set of Thoughts comprising a relative self is always presented as a sequence.

resolve [a verb] (in terms of the ToT)

Generally, the relationship of an Experience to its associated genitive quanta is inferred by the verb to resolve—even though all elements of the chain of existence (all things and events) are axiomatically described as ultimately coexisting instantaneously in a time-less condition of reality. Therefore the use of the verb is a textual accommodation that allows an easy reference to a nontemporal relationship. Thus a primary quantum of reality (an "EQ") is said to resolve to an Experience.

section of interest.

The term section of interest describes that section of a time route that is of special interest in defining associated Experience-objects.

A relative self is made up of the time-past portion of the MindMoment sequence comprising a time route. Consider a relative self that contains an object (an Experience-object) that resolves from the information in a certain limited section of the time-past MindMoment sequence. This limited section is called: the section of interest.

With respect to a transphenomenal object a section of interest is that portion of an instant 3-manifold that defines an Experience-object that rests on a 3-boundary, partially in an area of proper manifolds and partially in an area of dangerous manifolds.

SCM (self-center of mass)

See also: "self-center of mass".

self-center of mass

In the ToT the Experience of movement is a major feature of each relative self because the included information package includes a phenomenal body. The ToT axiomatically defines the center of mass of each phenomenal body to be at rest—according to a viewpoint of the associated relative self. Its center of mass is called the self-center of mass (the SCM). In the ToT all Experiences of velocity are accorded to phenomenal objects outside of the SCM. The SCM is *always* at rest.

The SCM is an Overlain Experience that is a virtual concept. It does not functionally represent any substantial object or movement; but it does serve as the figurative axis mundi in V.1 for the position of all objects, any motion they may display and the apparent momentum of their inertial systems. It is the virtual center point of a relative self. The SCM sits as a still-point to the Experience of the relativistic flows of time associated with all other objects in a time route expressing different inertial systems. In this way it is instrumental in allowing the ToT to explain time dilation.

330

The SCM conceptually rests in the moment of the Now. It is an unusual oExperience that describes the absence of any change and the absence of any movement.

See also: "SCM".

self-terminating time route

The ToT tells us that a time route is comprised of an iterative sequence of instant 3-manifolds, and the sequence will self-terminate if one of those iterations is a dangerous manifold which is close enough to the SCM to cause problems. The words "close enough" mean that the time route describes a clear, unavoidable sequence leading to an existential threat. If this occurs, a 5-space vision will cause a Shift of awareness (if such is possible within the given karmic milieu) and the self-terminating time route will be anthropically denied with a Shift causing the relative self to instead resolve from an alternate time route incorporating a proper manifold.

sequence dilation

Time dilation is a scientific principle described in Albert Einstein's theory of special relativity. Time dilation is discussed in the context of constant velocity, *i.e.* without acceleration of any kind, and involves the observed "slowing down" of a clock positioned in a different inertial system than that of the observer. It becomes evident at relativistic speeds (more than 10% the speed of light). If a person standing on earth were to observe a clock positioned on board a spaceship traveling past Earth at one half the speed of light, that person would observe the space ship clock as moving slower than a similar clock sitting on Earth. Einstein used this principle to help explain the nature of reality according to his theories.

A parallel concept in the ToT is called sequence dilation. It describes the Experience of the "slowing down" of a clock on a moving physical object in some inertial system (I_n) other than the inertial system (I_0) of the SCM.

See also: "time dilation".

sequential causality

In the ToT causality is in always non-temporal in nature. There are two ways to express it. One way is within a relative self; where there is an apparent oExperience of a relationship between one event (called cause) and its consequence (called effect); or we could say: the oExperience of a relationship between one MindMoment and another within a sequence of MindMoments comprising a time route. Within the ToT, this type of causality is known as sequential causality. Another variety, hyper-causality, involves an Experience of the actual concept of free will, not the illusion of what appears to be free will, as it is portrayed in a relative self (the time-past portion of a time route).

Sequential causality is described as a simple karmic relationship within the Matrix. It is not a true example of free will on the part of an individuated SELF.

According to the ToT, sequential causality indicates a relationship (in the Matrix) between overlapping Clouds of EQ. The overlap resolves to a measure of proximity; and ultimately in terms of the relative condition, an exposition of karma, which *appears* to be a causal relationship.

In the ToT, an act of free will cannot actually occur within a relative self because there is no agent within the relative self that can act to make a choice; it has no awareness. There is also no "opportunity" within its structure for a change to occur; because it's simply a static, unchangeable, sequential, collection of information.

set of Thoughts (in terms of the ToT)

A group of EQ resolves to a single Thought. A set of Thoughts make up a relative self. A set of Thoughts (comprising a relative self) is always presented as a sequence, an attribute that is related to the Experience of duration.

shared karmic vision

A shared karmic vision reflects the reality we all share—which is the physical planetary/environment-al/biological make-up along with all of the thoughts, desires, and emotional predispositions we share as beings on the planet.

The noosphere, a beautiful word coined by Teilhard de Chardin, can be used to describe a circumfluent planetary blanket of shared karmic vision. It is as if looking through a set of virtual glasses colored by contemporary culture, thought and feelings; however the noosphere does not include phenomenal reality, which is also a part of the shared karmic vision.

shared universe

In the lexicon of the ToT, a shared version of the universe that we can talk about and have the Experience of existing in is called Version V.1 (or simply V.1). V.1 labels the apparent shared universe around us at the instant of "now." It is shared by all beings appearing to exist in that instant; and the designation is with respect to those individuals.

A counter point to a shared universe is the concept of a solo universe—which is the universe experienced only in terms of the viewpoint of a single relative self.

Sheaf (time route bundle)

In the ToT we can think of an individuated SELF as a bundle of sticks with each stick being a time route and with the midpoint of each stick in the bundle (the Now) occupying the same relative position in naked space [a time route bundle]. Think of the sticks as metaphorically gathered into a bundle called a time route bundle or a Sheaf; and think of a bundle as tied at the center with each end splayed out like a sheaf of wheat. The tie at the center of the bundle is envisioned as very tight—so tight that the sticks merge together at that point. The tie point represents the nexus of all time route center points, which is the Now or the instantaneous moment of the present. In the lexicon of the ToT the information in a Sheaf resolves to an individuated SELF.

The term "sheaf" is a concept found in geometry. Its special meaning in the ToT is denoted with an uppercase "S".

Shift (Shift of presence)

A Shift, or Shift of presence, occurs within the fabric of the configuration space of the hypersurface of a 5-manifold that expresses three space-like dimensions, one time-like dimension and one 4th time-like dimension. Together they form what the ToT calls spacetime-time.

There are other, higher dimensions that are each orthogonal to the spacetime-time package of dimensions. They contain information resolving to mental events. As a group they are unique to each time route. Within the ToT a Shift is commonly described as occurring according to the configuration space of the 5-manifold describing spacetime-time, but it could conceivably occur according to the information in any dimension.

With respect to the relative self, a Shift has no measurable temporal characteristics. It may occur instantaneously or it may take an eternity. The two interludes are functionally synonymous and meaningless. A Shift changes the status of a time route from "alternate" to "on point" (in terms of the on point time route) however it has no effect on the reality sync of the Sheaf.

A Shift is a quasi-concept and not a part of the relative self—which in common terms means it is not a function of the "self". Thus in terms of a time route a Shift is instantaneous, occurring in the moment of the present. In the context of the ToT's geometry it occurs in the configuration space defined by the hypersurface of a 5-manifold, between the time routes comprising a Sheaf. Functionally, the point of the Shift is between one time route and another, occurring at the nexus of the bundle making up the Sheaf... at the tie point... at the moment of the Now. We can think of this point as the domain of 4th time, the temporal elbowroom in which a Shift occurs.

simply connected

In the context of the ToT, an example of a simply connected manifold is when every loop on the surface of a 2-sphere can be continuously tightened to a point.

simultaneity (in terms of the ToT)

For the contemporary physicist, substantial existence within spacetime appears to be accepted *a priori*; and the requirement for a criterion outside of spacetime (from which to judge a change in location in time) appears to receive a blind eye. Perhaps it is not discussed because the laws of classical physics apply only within spacetime, which brings us back to the question of whether two events can occur simultaneously.

The nature of existence is different depending on your point of view. When viewed from a position within the apparent reality of a relative self, the experiment clearly describes the relativity of simultaneity. When viewed from a position of virtual omnipotence (a nontemporal and non-local condition of reality) a completely different scenario arises.

In the *two clock* thought experiment (in relativistic physics) the "perceived*" slowing down of the other's clock can be verified by visually recording the differences during a side-by-side comparison of each other's clock images—the result being that the "other's clock" will always appear as running slower. According to the stated terms of the experiment, this displayed difference would be attributed to the impossibility of simultaneity, as described by Einstein. However this argument still rests on the ability of the observers to state that the clocks actually move—which is a statement that speaks to the essence of the ToT.

In the ToT:

1. *Two events cannot be simultaneous when the point of view of the system under scrutiny rests in the system (i.e. in spacetime.)* Such a point of view is a relative self and it's ultimately a function of the observer's inertial reference frame.

2. *All events are simultaneous when the point of view of the system under scrutiny rests outside of the system.* Such a point of view is described as being from the vantage of virtual omnipotence, where an individuated SELF (a five-dimensional Sheaf) can be viewed in its entirety. This is a point of view beyond any reference frame within spacetime.

Within the context of the second classification all events exist simultaneously because of the Instancy principle. From this viewpoint we can describe two types of simultaneity:

1. "experiential simultaneity".
2. "true Simultaneity".

solo universe

A solo universe is the universe experienced* only in terms of the viewpoint of a single relative self.

The bundle of time routes that make up a Sheaf is comprised of many individual time routes. However, with respect to a certain relative self, there is only one time route whose constituent EQ resolve to the Experiences of time-past and an implied time-future. This certain time route is called the time route on point and the information in the time-past portion of that time route resolves to a solo universe—which is V.1 described only with information contained in a certain relative self. All other time routes are called alternate time routes and do not resolve to a set of Experiences in a V.1 solo universe according to the time route on point.

In the lexicon of the ToT, a shared version of the universe that we can talk about and have the Experience of existing in is called Version V.1 (or simply V.1). V.1 labels the apparent shared universe around us at the instant of "now." It is shared by all beings appearing to exist in that instant; and the designation is with respect to those individuals.

A counter point to a shared universe is the concept of a solo universe—which is the universe experienced only in terms of the viewpoint of a single relative self.

space (the Experience)

The concept of space as we apparently experience* it in our everyday lives. The space that is seen to warp in the Einsteinian equations.

space-like dimension (in terms of the ToT)

The mathematician Hermann Minkowski was first to described spacetime as being comprised of three space-like dimensions and one time-like dimension; but in terms of the ToT each of these defines configuration spaces of manifolds that describe Experiences.

spacetime

General relativity describes gravity and the large-scale structure of spacetime. The term spacetime refers to three dimensions of space and one dimension of time—three space-like dimensions and one time-like dimension.

spacetime physics

A term used in the ToT to identify contemporary classical and quantum relativistic physics.

spacetime-time

A Shift occurs within the fabric of the configuration space of the hypersurface of a 5-manifold that expresses three space-like dimensions, one time-like dimension and one 4th time-like dimension. Together they form what the ToT calls spacetime-time.

There are other, higher dimensions that are each orthogonal to the spacetime-time package of dimensions. They contain information resolving to mental events. Within the ToT a Shift is commonly described as occurring according to the configuration space of the 5-manifold describing spacetime-time, but it could conceivably occur according to the information in any dimension.

spacetime-time sensitive

A person (relative self) who is spacetime-time sensitive is fully at ease with 5-space visions and comfortable with the manipulation of an object

335

(a TPO) resting on both sides of a 3-boundary. When such a TPO is manipulated in this way it is called a TPD. A spacetime-time sensitive person is capable of keeping a time route containing a TPD from being anthropically denied, even though the TPD lies partially on the dangerous side of a 3-boundary.

speed of light (c)

According to special relativity, c (the speed of light) is the maximum speed at which all matter and information in the universe can travel.

The velocity of light is the speed at which all massless particles and changes of the associated fields (including electromagnetic radiation such as light and gravitational waves) travel in vacuum. Such particles and waves travel at c regardless of the motion of the source or the inertial frame of reference [the inertial system] of the observer.

In the ToT the philosophical concept of the speed of light is equivalent to the concept of compassion and the intertwingularity of all beings.

standard value... (with respect to the ToT)

The standard value for the mind moment constant (Å) in this rendition of the ToT (as expressed in this book) is 10^{14} Ш/sec.

Stor (stuff of reality)

In the ToT the terms "phenomenal world", "phenomenal reality" or "substantial reality" refer to solid reality and associated forms of energy identified by the physical sciences. The ToT defines the phenomenal world (as it appears to be) as an *illusion*, and then it describes how it intermingles with the equally *illusory* realm of mental events. Mental events are feelings, emotions, and dreams etc., all elements of reality that have no phenomenal existence (they are experiences... that is all.) These two groups appear to transpire within a flow of time and together they form apparent overall reality, or the stuff of reality. In the ToT the acronym for the "stuff of reality" is Stor.

stuff of reality (Stor)

See also: "Stor".

substantial reality (in terms of the ToT)

The distinction between true and apparent states of reality is a primary feature of Buddhist thought. It is sometimes described by stating that substantial reality and the self, do not inherently exist of their own nature. Substantial reality is the solid reality we find around us within the flow of time. It is and illusion and a part of the Stor.

syncategorematic (in terms of the ToT)

In the ToT the adjective syncategorematic is used to describe the simultaneous and instantaneous relationship between the components of an

Experience/Experience-object pair. It's important to note that a syncate-gorematic relationship is instantaneous.

terma

Prosaically the information that indicates a TPD is like information floating in space and time. In Tibet, when this information is associated with a certain substantial object it's called a *terma*. A *terma* is thought of as containing a "hidden treasure" (the information). Tradition tells us that a number of *terma* have been hidden by masters and teachers in the past. History tells us that the great Tibetan teacher Padmasambhava and his consort Yeshe Tsogyal (in the eighth century CE) created many *terma* to be found in later centuries. The concept of *terma* is also part of the Bon and Hindu traditions, but to a more limited degree.

A physical object that is a *terma* is called an "earth *terma*." It contains a certain "treasure" of information that is understood by the person who finds the *terma*. That person is called a *tertön*. In terms of the ToT a *tertön* is a spacetime-time sensitive individuated SELF.

The patterns of EQ that resolve to an earth *terma* (a phenomenal object) include the physical item *and* the information which is hidden as a treasure, with the patterns being resident in multiple time routes. Thus the oExperience of the treasure information in the *terma* is revealed only to the spacetime-time sensitive mind of the *tertön*, but the physical object is for all to see.

A *terma* can also be a "mind treasure" or "mind *terma*," said to be hidden in space and revealed in the mind of the *tertön*. In a sense, all *terma* are mind treasures because they are revealed by the *tertön*. In the context of the ToT, they are all a part of the relative self that is defined as the *tertön* who is spacetime-time sensitive.

The information associated with a *terma* is independent of the classical three space-like dimensions and the one time-like dimension. It does not rest in spacetime. Thus a *terma* created* at any point in the time-past portion of a time route is available in the Now, if the *tertön* can manage it.

tantra

A "tantra" expounds a system of thought or a set of doctrines or practices, sometimes written and sometime transmitted by word of mouth.

temporal elbowroom

A Shift occurs in the configuration space defined by the hypersurface of the 5-manifold. It occurs between the time routes comprising a Sheaf. Functionally, the Shift occurs between one time route and another... occurring at the nexus of the bundle making up the Sheaf... at the tie point... at the moment of the Now. We can think of this point as the domain of 4th time, the temporal elbowroom in which a Shift occurs.

337

temporal event

A primary axiom of the ToT is that there is no *a priori* reason for the apparent reality of any substance, energy field, emotion, or concept etc. other than that which is Instantaneous, or instantaneous.

Within the relative self every Experience is instantaneous in nature and produces the illusion of an *instant* substantial object or an *instant* subjective event. A sequential iteration of instantaneous Experiences produces a meta-Experience of single temporal object or temporal event. Such a meta-Experience is called an overlain Experience.

temporal object

A temporal object is a four dimensional object existing in spacetime. Its existence is described by an array of values in three dimensions of space (width, depth, and height; or in mathematical notation… "X, Y and Z") and in a fourth dimension attributed to time flow (called "T").

Within the relative self every Experience is instantaneous in nature and produces the illusion of an *instant* substantial object or an *instant* subjective event. A sequential iteration of instantaneous Experiences produces a meta-Experience of single temporal object or temporal event. Such a meta-Experience is called an overlain Experience.

terminates (a time route that…)

In the nomenclature of the ToT, a time route that terminates because of information held in dangerous instant 3-manifolds is said to *wander* outside of the 3-Boundary. The wandering of the time route starts at the MindMoment that contains the *first in sequence* iteration of the dangerous manifold.

Theory of Totality (ToT)

The term Totality (with a capital "T") describes the "total" picture—bigger than all known physical phenomena. Hence an all-encompassing Theory of Everything becomes a Theory of Totality—referred to with the acronym "ToT".

The ToT has a wide reach, drawing from various teachings, philosophies and scientific knowledge. It arises out of an understanding of holistic worldviews in general and, in particular, Buddhist thought and philosophy; however the ToT is not meant to be an explanation of any existing philosophy or viewpoint. It is a collection of ideas which are based on an interpretation of the writings and teachings of others.

In this light, the ToT is a coherent Theory of Totality but may not be a precise description of the elements of Buddhism or any other indigenous or holistic culture.

The ToT ultimately proposes a conceptualization of a *true* state of reality that stands apart and distinct from an *apparent* state. This distinction

338

is characteristic of Buddhist thought; but some of the conceptualizations made about the distinction do not necessarily come from Buddhism.

The distinction between true and apparent states of reality is a primary feature of Buddhist thought. It is sometimes described by stating that substantial reality and the "self" do not inherently exist of their own nature.

The ToT is not a pathway for entering the true essence of reality on a personal level. Science does not do this. Science works with the concepts; and the conceptual aspects of the ToT do not apply to the true essence of things. The ToT is both a philosophy and a mental fabrication. It will not let us taste the true essence of things. However it does provide a conceptual analogy for all that is not the true essence; and a description of how the essential nature of a thought cannot be conceptualized.

Thus the ToT does not give us a full description of Totality—it is not meant to. At best it provides an analog for the essential nature of reality and goes no further.

Thought

A single EQ (in the absolute condition) may resolve to a single Experience (in the relative condition); and a "group of EQ" may resolve to a single Thought. A "set of EQ groups" or a "collection of EQ" is called a Cloud.

time dilation

Time dilation (as described by Einstein) is an expression of the relatively asymmetric contraction of one of the dimensional reference frames in a four-dimensional geometry. In terms of physics, the asymmetry occurs because the observed value for the speed of light is a constant regardless of the observer or the inertial system of reference.

See also: "Related Formulae" and "sequence dilation".

time quantum (ŧ, in terms of the ToT)

Every EQ has a Feature that resolves to an Experience of information in the time-like dimension. The time-like information is an oExperience of the flow of time for that object, which resolves from multiple nExperiences of time quanta, "ŧ" (small letter t with a stroke).

Every nExperience in a given inertial system has an associated time quantum, ŧ. An EQ containing a time quantum is called a "$ŧ_{con}EQ$".

The value of a time quantum, in terms of duration, is equal to the reciprocal of the MindMoment constant. A single time quantum resolves to the nExperience of a duration equal to the value of ŧ (very quick); and multiple time quanta resolve to the oExperience of the flow of time.

$$ŧ = \frac{1}{\tilde{A}} = 10^{-14} \text{ second (using the "working value").}$$

339

time route

Certain sequences of MindMoments describe an "apparent route of existence across an expanse of apparent time for a relative self". This is called a time route in the ToT lexicon. In terms of the absolute condition a time route resolves from a Cloud. In terms of a relative self an oExperience of an expanse of time flow is the syncategorematic rendition of the information held in a collection of MindMoments laid out across the time-like dimension of an n-manifold.

time route bundle (Sheaf)

See also: "Sheaf".

time route on point

The bundle of time routes that make up a Sheaf is comprised of many individual time routes. However, with respect to a certain relative self, there is only one time route whose constituent EQ resolve to the Experiences of time-past and an implied time-future. This certain time route is called the time route on point and the information in the time-past portion of that time route resolves to a solo universe—which is V.1 described only with information contained in a certain relative self. All other time routes are called alternate time routes and do not resolve to a set of Experiences in a V.1 solo universe according to the time route on point.

time-like dimension (in terms of the ToT)

The mathematician Hermann Minkowski was first to described spacetime as being comprised of three space-like dimensions and one time-like dimension; but in terms of the ToT each of these defines configuration spaces of manifolds that describe Experiences.

ToT (Theory of Totality)

See also: "Theory of Totality".

topology

Topology is the mathematical study of the geometric properties that are not normally affected by changes in the size or shape of geometric figures. In topology, a donut and a coffee cup with a handle are equivalent shapes (called homeomorphic) because each has a single hole.

transphenomenal device (TPD)

A transphenomenal device (a "TPD") is a TPO that can be manipulated at will by the operator. Thus the operator must be spacetime-time sensitive (fully at ease with 5-space visions) and comfortable with the manipulation of an object (a TPO) resting on both sides of a 3-boundary. A person who is spacetime-time sensitive is capable of keeping a time route containing a TPD from being anthropically denied, even though the TPD lies partially on the dangerous side of a 3-boundary.

See also: "TPD".

transphenomenal object (TPO)

A relative self is made up of the time-past portion of the MindMoment sequence comprising a time route. Consider a relative self that contains an object (an Experience-object) that resolves from the information in a "certain limited section of the total, time-past MindMoment sequence" (call this limited section the "*section of interest*".) Also consider that a portion of the instant 3-manifolds in the section of interest have dangerous areas.

Now imagine that the object associated with the section of interest figuratively rests on a 3-boundary… with half of it in the dangerous area and half in the proper area. Thus half of the section of interest reflects information from dangerous instant 3-manifolds and the other half reflects information from proper instant 3-manifolds. The object resolving from the *section of interest* in this situation is a very unusual object. In the ToT it is called a transphenomenal object (a "TPO"). In most cases a TPO will be anthropically denied.

See also: "TPO" and "section of interest".

true free will (in terms of the ToT)

The concept of true free will is expressed with hyper-causality. True free will happens when the verb-like action of a choice occurs within the Instantaneous condition associated with the nexus of a Sheaf. It is the oExperience of actually having made a choice, an *act of free will*, on the level of the individuated SELF. A choice made in this fashion is an example of hyper-causality, a reflection of a Shift of presence in Awareness from one time route to another, within the domain of a single Sheaf.

true Simultaneity

All events in all time routes (in a Sheaf) are termed to be "truly Simultaneous". (The upper case "S" indicates *true Simultaneity*.) The concept of Simultaneity is with respect to Instancy. Simultaneity entails a point of view from the vantage of virtual omnipotence.

See also: "experiential simultaneity".

two truths (in terms of the ToT)

There is a profound understanding that has roots back to the oldest forms of Buddhism. It describes a view of existence more basic than is found in all of the sciences that have evolved from Western philosophy and religion. It's known as the two truths and has become a principle doctrine of Mahayana Buddhism. The Dalai Lama describes the two truths as referring to "…the philosophical view that there are two levels of reality. One level is the empirical, phenomenal, and relative level… the other is a deeper level of existence beyond the [relative level] which is often technically referred to as 'emptiness.' "

The concept of the two truths is associated with the Madhyamaka School, whose origin is credited to Nagarjuna, c. 200CE. He was the first to express the two truths in its complete form.

ŧ (time quantum)
Symbol for time quantum. See also: "time quantum".

Ŧ, (the number of ŧ_{con}EQ in a mo-sequence)
The number of ŧ_{con}EQ in a sequence is denoted with the symbol "Ŧ" (capitol "T" with a stroke). In a bs-sequence Ŧ is always equal to the value of "Đ", the duration of the MindMoment sequence. In a mo-sequence Ŧ is equal to the value of "Đ" if the moving object is not in relativistic motion.

Ŧ′ (the number of ŧ_{con}EQ in a relativistic mo-sequence)
Sequence dilation describes the quantum dilation of a series of time quanta in the mo-sequence of EQ expressing the inertial system (I_n) of an object other than the body-self. The number of time quanta in the mo-sequence is denoted by the symbol " Ŧ′ " ("Ŧ" with a prime designation).

The number of time quanta in the bs-sequence is denoted by Ŧ (not prime). When the mo-sequence does not indicate relativistic motion Ŧ equals Ŧ′.

ŧ_{con}EQ (symbol for an EQ containing a single time quantum)
An EQ containing a time quantum is called a "ŧ_{con}EQ" (small letter t with a stroke followed by the term *con* in subscript, followed by the term *EQ*). Every nExperience in a given inertial system has an associated time quantum, ŧ.

ŧ_{free}EQ (symbol for an EQ containing no time quantum)
The EQ resolving to a substantial object in relativistic motion *may* or *may not* contain a time quantum. If it does not, the EQ is called a "ŧ_{free}EQ" (small letter t with a stroke followed by the term *free* in subscript, followed by the term *EQ*).

V.1 shared universe
V.1 labels the apparent shared universe around us at the instant of "now." It is shared by all beings appearing to exist in that instant; and the designation is with respect to those individuals.

V.n universe
An unusual and profound feature of the ToT is the axiomatic assertion that there are an indefinitely large number of different, parallel universes figuratively laid upon naked space, and that all of them hold the same value for the MindMoment constant, Ã. Together these universes form a single multiverse.

In terms of the relative condition this is a statement that the number of "instances of reality" per "unit of time" is the same for every universe in the multiverse. The phrase "instance of reality" is a single MindMoment. This is axiomatic in the ToT.

Each parallel universe is called a V.n universe, or a simply V.n. Each V.n universe differs one from another by their value for the quantum interspace, Φ. It is axiomatic within the ToT that there may exist an indefinitely large (maybe infinite) number of V.n universes each with a unique value for the quantum interspace. Thus each V.n universe has a different value for Φ, and consequently a different value for c. Whether Φ is quantum in nature, or whether there is a range of "habitable" values for Φ is a matter of conjecture.

See also: "multiverse".

vidyä

Vidyä is a Sanskrit noun meaning "right knowledge" or "clarity". In Buddhism it generally describes a situation where one is actively working to alter patterns of thought and action that bespeak aggression, greed, pride and jealousy, along with sometimes physical states of discomfort. It also describes phenomenal and psychological reality as essentially an illusion which spontaneously manifests… representing another [true] condition of reality that is essentially without definition and "beyond all concepts".

Where Western science strives, in spirit, to improve the overall physical state of humanity, *vidyä* conversely has developed as a science of the mind seeking to improve the inner reality of the human condition.

In the book *vidyä* is generally described as a holistic reality map.

virtual center point

The SCM is the virtual center point of a relative self. The SCM sits as a still-point to the Experience of the relativistic flows of time associated with all other objects in a time route expressing different inertial systems.

virtual omnipotence

Logically, in order to have a complete view of a system, the perspective must be outside of the system being viewed. How then can we discuss Totality?

A ToE (Theory of Every*thing*) typically fails to provide a valid viewpoint. With a ToE the system is limited to all things; and the "cognizance" or "intelligence" which is describing the system is not considered to be a thing. Thus the consciousness of the individual that is describing the system appears to be resting within the individual when there is a description of the "self", and to be apart from the individual when there is a discussion of the phenomenal stuff of reality. In general, within a ToE, the nature of the existence of consciousness is not addressed. There is no discussion of where it resides.

343

The issue is different with the ToT because the ToT also includes the concept of the individuated SELF as the grandest conception of an individual. The SELF is also specifically denied the role of doing the logical analysis of the system; and is specifically included in the system that is being analyzed (the figurative analysis being performed by Awareness, which is part of the absolute condition.)

This explanation works well for the individuated SELF but; how can one have a vantage point for a discussion of Totality? Totality encompasses all things, all concepts, and all Thoughts. It also includes all existence and all Awareness of what is being analyzed!

To address this issue the ToT employs a fabricated tool of logic entitled virtual omnipotence. Virtual omnipotence provides a vantage point for a perspective on Totality that is axiomatically placed outside of Totality. It is something like the square root of -1, it's useful but by its own definition, it *cannot* exist. It is a concept that has a vantage point on *all* concepts except itself, and in this way provides a perspective on Totality.

wander (in terms of the ToT)

A time route will always *appear* to exist on the surface of a proper manifold. The areas of real danger (infinity pits and wormhole areas) may be thought of as surrounded by a virtual boundary. In the ToT this is called a 3-boundary—because we are talking about 3-manifolds.

In the nomenclature of the ToT, a time route that terminates because of information held in dangerous instant 3-manifolds is said to wander outside of the 3-Boundary. The wandering of the time route starts at the MindMoment that contains the first in sequence iteration of the dangerous manifold.

$\ddot{\upsilon}$ (nontemporal velocity)

See also: "nontemporal velocity".

Φ (quantum interspace)

See also: "quantum interspace".

$\Phi_{con}EQ$

An EQ containing a quantum interspace.

See also: "nontemporal velocity", "change in position" and "quantum distribution principle".

$\Phi_{free}EQ$

An EQ *not* containing a quantum interspace.

See also: "nontemporal velocity", "change in position" and "quantum distribution principle".

Related Formulae:

Note: displayed values are derived using the *standard value* for Ã in the ToT.

MindMoment constant:

$$\tilde{A} = 10^{14} \text{ Ш/sec.}$$

Where:

- Ã the MindMoment constant; 10^{14} Ш/sec (standard value).
- Ш is the symbol for a MindMoment.

Speed of light in the V.1 universe:

$$c = 3 \times 10^8 \text{ meters/sec. (aprox).}$$

Quantum interspace:

$$\frac{c}{\tilde{A}} = \Phi = 3 \times 10^{-6} \text{ m/Ш.}$$

Where:

- c is the speed of light in the V.1 universe; 3×10^8 m/sec.
- Ã is the MindMoment constant; 10^{14} Ш/sec (standard value).
- Φ is the quantum interspace; 3×10^{-6} m/Ш.

Time quantum:

$$\mathfrak{t} = \frac{1}{\tilde{A}} = 10^{-14} \text{ second}$$

Where:

- $\mathfrak{t}$ is the symbol for a time quantum.
- Ã the MindMoment constant; 10^{14} Ш/sec (standard value).

Lorentz factor:

$$\gamma = \frac{1}{\sqrt{1 - \frac{v^2}{c^2}}}$$

Where:

- v is the relative velocity between two events.
- c is the speed of light.

Nontemporal velocity:

$$\ddot{u} = \frac{p\Phi}{\text{Đ}} = \text{ meters/MindMoment.}$$

Where:

- $\ddot{u}$ = is nontemporal velocity.
- p is the number of $\Phi_{con}EQ$ in the mo-sequence.
- Đ is the number of MindMoments in the bs-sequence.
- Φ is the quantum interspace for V.n ($\Phi = 3x10^{-6}$ meters for earth).
- Ã is the MindMoment constant (Ã=10^{14} MindMoments/sec).

Multiplying the result by the MindMoment constant (Ã) gives an answer in meters per second.

$$\ddot{u} = \frac{p\Phi\,\tilde{A}}{\text{Đ}} = \text{ meters/sec.}$$

Time dilation owing to uniform relative motion:

$$\Delta t' = \gamma \Delta t = \frac{\Delta t}{\sqrt{1 - \frac{v^2}{c^2}}}$$

Where:

- v is the relative velocity between two events.
- c is the speed of light.
- Δt is the time between two events happening in the same place for an observer in some inertial frame (e.g. ticks on a clock). This is known as *proper time*.
- $\Delta t'$ is the time interval between those same events, as measured by another observer, moving with velocity v relative to the former observer. This is known as *coordinate time*.
- γ is the Lorentz factor:

Sequence dilation owing to uniform non-temporal velocity:

$$\bar{T}' = \gamma \bar{T} = \frac{\bar{T}}{\sqrt{1 - \frac{\ddot{u}^2}{c^2}}}$$

Where:

- $\ddot{u}$ is the nontemporal velocity of the moving object with respect to the SCM.
- c is the speed of light in V.1 .
- $\bar{T}$ is the total number of $t_{con}EQ$ in the bs-sequence (the body-self). The value of $\bar{T}$ is equal to Đ, the duration of the event of interest

346

in MindMoments. The bs-sequence contains only t_{con}EQ. $\bar{T}$ correlates to a change in *proper time* in the time dilation equation.

- $\bar{T}'$ is the total number of t_{con}EQ in the mo-sequence. The sequence length is equal to Đ, but the mo-sequence also contains t_{free}EQ. $\bar{T}'$ correlates to a change in *coordinate time* in the time dilation equation.
- γ is the Lorentz factor.

Symbols and Constants:

$\tilde{A}$: the MindMoment constant; $\tilde{A} = 10^{14}$ Ш/sec. (standard value).

c: the speed of light in the V.1. $c = 3 \times 10^8$ meters/sec. (aprox).

Φ: the quantum interspace; $\Phi = 3 \times 10^{-6}$ m/Ш.

EQ: Experience quanta (or quantum).

Đ: the duration of the event of interest within a relative self.

d: the change in position of a substantial object in the relative self.

Ш: the MindMoment.

ŭ: nontemporal velocity.

p: the number of Φ_{con}EQ in the EQ mo-sequence.

Φ_{con}EQ: an EQ containing a quantum interspace.

Φ_{free}EQ: an EQ not containing a quantum interspace.

t_{con}EQ: symbol for an EQ containing a single time quantum.

t_{free}EQ: symbol for an EQ containing no time quantum.

t: a time quantum; $t = 10^{-14}$ second.

$\bar{T}$: the total number of t_{con}EQ in the bs-sequence.

$\bar{T}'$: the total number of t_{con}EQ in the mo-sequence.

V.1: indicating our universe, using the standard value for Φ and for c.

V.n: indicating a universe with a different value for Φ and for c.

γ: the Lorentz factor.

SCM: the "self center of mass" of a body-self.

CM: the "center of mass" of a substantial object.

~~~~

APPENDIX

PRIMAL ASSUMPTIONS IN THE ToT:

1) There is no substantial reality, it is illusory. It exists but can only be defined virtually according to a different condition of reality.

2) There are no subjective mental events, they are illusory. They exist but can only be defined virtually according to a different condition of reality.

3) The relative condition is an illusion—in terms of what it appears to be. Such illusions do not express true awareness, thought or substance.

4) The absolute condition is unknowable in terms of space and time reality.

5) All of reality can be described as Experiences of subjective mental events and/or Experiences of substantial reality.

6) All beings are solely information, without substance, thought or awareness.

7) All beings are comprised of memories. They do not *hold* memories, instead they *are* the memories—which are totally information.

8) The illusion of the flow of time is due to the memory of a duration.

9) Experience Quanta, the primary quanta of the universe, exist in a non-temporal syncategorematic relationship with associated warps in naked space.

10) Experience quanta, resolve only to Experiences (nouns), never to substantial objects or subjective mental events per se.

11) Experience Quanta cannot be described conceptually because they are the essence of that which resolves to a concept, i.e. an Experience, (a noun).

12) The only *space* that exists is "naked space", which is infinite in breath and dimensionality. All other concepts of space are a configuration spaces.

13) Pure, non-personal Awareness instantaneously and simultaneously Parses (in parallel) all Experience Quanta resident in naked space.

14) MindMoments are instantaneous packets of Experience Quanta that resolve to collections of Experiences of reality.

15) A set of MindMoments define a time route which can be described geometrically as a sequence of Features laying on the surface of a 5-manifold.

16) Every being (individuated SELF) is comprised of a specific collection of multi-dimensional time routes. A collection is called a Sheaf.

17) Within the context of the relative condition all beings are, in varying degrees, aware* of multiple time routes.

18) There are an indefinitely large number of different, parallel universes. Together these universes form a single multiverse.

19) All universes in the multiverse are instantaneous and unchanging in nature.

20) All universes in the multiverse hold the same value for the MindMoment constant, $\tilde{A}$.

21) All universes in the multiverse have a unique value for the quantum interspace, $\mathbf{\Phi}$.

~~~~

THE HEART SUTRA (A VISION OF NON-TEMPORAL REALITY)

The Heart Sutra is a Mahayana Buddhist sutra. Its Sanskrit name Prajñāpāramitā Hrdaya literally translates to "Heart of the Perfection of Transcendent Wisdom".

Pictured are an image of the two palm-leaves of Horiuzi.[170] This [Heart Sutra] manuscript was preserved in Hōryū-ji monastery (Japan) since 609 CE. The manuscript itself (presumably) dates from the first half of the 6th century *(Wikipedia)*.

The Heart Sutra is often cited as the best known and most popular of all Buddhist scriptures. This is one of multiple translations.

In the translation, notice how appearances (of substantial reality) as well as impressions, thoughts, associations and knowingness are all, equally described as emptiness. In the second half there appears to be a denial of time where it states that there is "… [no] end to old-age and death". The last line indicates a state of being that is beyond all concept, with the words of the famous mantra [discussed above]

.

> Avalokiteshvara Bodhisattva,
> when pursuing the deep *prajñaparamita*,
> recognized the five *skandhas* as completely empty
> and passed beyond all vexations and distress.
> Shariputra, appearances are not different from emptiness,
> emptiness is not different to appearances.
> Appearances are emptiness,
> emptiness is an appearance.
> Impressions, thoughts, associations
> and knowing too, are also like this.
> Shariputra, all *Dharmas* are empty of appearances,
> are not created, are not extinguished,

are not defiled, are not pure;
do not increase, do not decrease.
For this reason, amidst emptiness there are no appearances,
nor are there any impressions, thoughts, associations and knowing,
There is no eye, ear, nose, tongue, touch, ideas.
There are no colors, sounds, smells,
tastes and touch *Dharmas.*
There is no eye-element up to no imagining nor knowledge
element.
Neither is any non-understanding,
nor is there any end to non-understanding up to no old-age and
death.
Neither is there any end to old-age and death.
There is no suffering, cause, extinction or path.
There is no knowledge nor anything to find.
Because there isn't anything to find,
the *bodhisattva* is free because of relying upon *prajñaparamita*:
a heart without any obstruction.
Because there are no obstructions, there is no fear.
Abandoning, overturning dreams and concepts,
finally reaches *nirvana.*
Because all the Buddhas of the three times have relied upon
prajñaparamita, they have found *anuttarasamyaksambodhi.*
For this reason, know *prajñaparamita* is the great spiritual mantra.
The great understanding mantra.
The supreme mantra.
The unequaled mantra, able to cut through all vexation
because in reality there is no emptiness.
Speak the *prajñaparamita* mantra, speak the mantra's words:
gate gate paragate parasamgate bodhi svaha.

Chinese to English translation, by Willam J. Giddings, 2003
Courtesy of Wildmind Buddhist Meditation
http://www.wildmind.org

~~~~

THE DIAMOND SUTRA (A VISION OF EMPTINESS)

The Diamond Sūtra (Sanskrit: *Vajracchedikā Prajñāpāramitā Sūtra*), is a short and well-known Mahayana sutra from the Prajñāpāramitā, or "Perfection of Wisdom" genre, and emphasizes the practice of non-abiding and non-attachment. The title properly translated is the Diamond Cutter of Perfect Wisdom although it is usually just called the Diamond Sūtra.

The following is an excerpt from one of several translations. It appears to describe a concept similar to that found in the ToT—where what is normally seen as a "living being" possesses no substance or associated mental events. A person is nothing more than a timeless, instantaneous gathering of information which is parsed by an Awareness that is far beyond the human condition.

Excerpt from the Diamond Sutra:

In reality there are no living beings to be liberated by the Tathagata (the Buddha).
If there were living beings for the Tathagata to liberate, he would partake in the idea of selfhood, personality entity, and separate individuality.

A copy of the Chinese version of the Diamond Sūtra, found among the Dunhuang manuscripts in the early 20th century and dated back to May 11, 868, is, in the words of the British Library, "the earliest complete survival of a dated printed book."

The first translation of the Diamond Sūtra into Chinese is thought to have been made in 401 CE by the venerated and prolific translator Kumārajīva. Kumārajīva's translation style is distinctive, possessing a flowing smoothness that reflects his prioritization on conveying the meaning as opposed to precise literal rendering. The Kumārajīva translation has been particularly highly regarded over the centuries, and it is this version that appears on the 868 CE Dunhuang scroll. [Wikipedia (cc)].

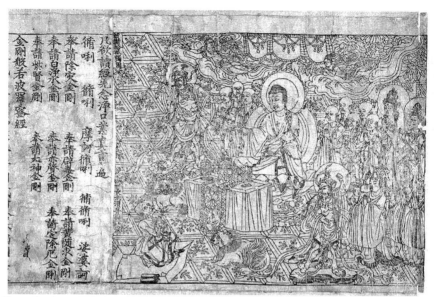

Frontispiece, Diamond Sutra[171] from Cave 17, Dunhuang, ink on paper.
A page from the Diamond Sutra, printed in the 9th year of Xiantong Era of
the Tang Dynasty, i.e. 868 CE. Currently located in the British Library, London. (Wikipedia (cc)).

~~~~

MAHAMUDRA (EXPRESSING BEING BEYOND CONCEPT)

The *Mahamudra* (Tibetan: *phyag rgya chen po*) method, is a set of spiritual practices that greatly accelerates the process of attaining bodhi (enlightenment). The name refers to the way one experiences reality: *mudra* refers to the fact that each phenomenon appears vividly, and *maha* refers to the fact that it is beyond concept, imagination, and projection. The method was created by Tilopa, who is also regarded as the human founder of the Kagyu lineage of Tibetan Buddhism.

In the summery below, notice that the 1st stanza tells us that the external world is described as an "error" and is compared to space; and then it proclaims that the "mind itself is only the movement of thought."

Following this, in the second stanza it says that: "[in] the real nature of mind... there is no contrivance or change"—thus suggesting a nontemporal nature for the true nature of existence.

In the 4th stanza there is a suggestion of non-locality... "Where is there to go or stay?"

Finally, the last stanza states that: [having]... "no concepts of mental activity" [is the most profound state of reality] which is, according to the ToT, the background naked space.

SUMMERY OF *MAHAMUDRA*

I prostrate to the great bliss!
To explain *Mahamudra*:
All phenomena are one's own mind.
To see an external world is a mental error.
It's essence is empty like a dream.
Mind itself is only the movement of thought.
Natureless, its energy is wind.
Its essence is empty like the sky.
All Dharmas rest in eveness like space.

That which is termed *Mahamudra*,
Can't be pointed out by its essence.
So the real nature of mind
is the *Mahamudra* nature.
In this there is no contrivance or change.
When this reality is experienced

All appearances of the phenomenal world become *Mahamudra*,
The great all-encompassing Dharmakaya.

Relax in natural ease.
Meditate without seeking
The unconceivable Dharmakaya.
Effort in meditation is mental error.
Just like space and apparitions
Meditation and non-meditation are not two.
From what is it free or not free?
Through such realization by the yogin
All virtues and sins are liberated.
The defilements are great wisdom,
Friends to the yogin like the forest to fire.

Where is there to go or stay?
Why meditate in solitude?
Whoever doesn't understand this,
Is only liberated temporarily.
When someone dwells in the unwavering state,
No 'practice' or 'non-practice',
No contrivance by antidote, no meditation.

Here nothing is truly existent.
Appearances are naturally liberated in the Dharmadhatu.
Thoughts are naturally liberated in great wisdom,
The non-dual self-same Dharmakaya.
Like the current of a great river,
Whatever is done is beneficial.
This is everlasting Buddhahood,
The unobjectifiable great bliss beyond samsara.

All phenomena are naturally empty.
Clinging to emptiness itself is naturally purified.
No concepts of mental activity,
This is the path of all buddhas.
By the good fortune of these verses of essential instructions, may
all beings attain *Mahamudra*.

*Thus Naropa's Verses of Mahamudra are completed. These are the words
of the master himself. They were translated into Tibetan by Marpa
Chokyi Lodro at Pullahari, and into English by the layman Jampa
Thaye).*[172]

~~~~

THE *YOGA SUTRAS* OF PATANJALI
(AN ANCIENT EXPRESSION OF TIME FLOW)

The *Yoga Sutras* were handed down through oral tradition. Their origin lies between the fourth century BCE and the fourth century CE. Little is known of the author. The *Yoga Sutras*... are one of human-kind's great traditions, with their origin stemming from the ancient Vedas. The *Yoga Sutras* are laid out as a set of 195 aphorisms meant to be experienced* in succession and commented on during oral exchanges.[173]

A single aphorism from near the end of the sutra offers a sense of the basis of the reasoning found in the ToT.

The aphorism is shown as an English version of an original translation from the Sanskrit into the French, by Bernard Bouanchaud.[174] Mr. Bouanchaud also provided a word-by-word translation [immediately following.]

The succession of moments appears in the grasp of past and future changes correlative to the next moment.

ksanapratiyogī pariṇāmāparāntanirgrāhyaḥ kramaḥ
ksana-pratiyogī pariṇāmā-aparā-anta-nirgrāhyaḥ kramaḥ

Ksana: instant, moment. *Pratiyogī:* correlative, face to face. *Pariṇāmā:* change, evolution. *Aparā:* anterior. *Anta:* posterior. *Nirgrāhyaḥ:* understanding, grasp. *Kramaḥ:* unwinding, unfolding, succession, sequence.

Two other possible translations (by the author) use terms and concepts found in the ToT. These translations propose that Patanjali's viewpoint of reality was according to spacetime-time, *i.e.* a viewpoint beyond spacetime. The Sanskrit terms that may mean "succession" or "sequence" imply a quantum interpretation within the aphorism, indicating that Patanjali may not have seen the flow of time as homogeneous.

A single moment (instant) is part of the successive, sequential unfolding of the face to face change between time-past and time-future.
    or:
An understanding of the past to future evolution (i.e. the illusion of time flowing) is found in the instantaneous correlation between sequential, successive MindMoments.

~~~~

356

BUDDHISM (THE REFLECTION OF AN ANCIENT *ZEIT GEIST*)

What Siddhartha Gautama (the Buddha) said, did and taught was his vision of reality—in terms of the relative condition—and in that vision he saw a way for people to end personal suffering. This reflected his natural propensity for compassion—which he described as a manifestation of the essence of reality. His teaching and the propagation of these ideas became a religion, but they also reflect the spirit of the times (the *zeit geist*) in which he lived and was very much at the center of. It is that spirit which is of particular interest in regards to the ToT. The following description is found on the Wikipedia Buddhism Portal.

Buddhism is a religion and philosophy encompassing a variety of traditions, beliefs and practices, largely based on teachings attributed to Siddhartha Gautama, commonly known as the Buddha (Pāli/Sanskrit "the awakened one"). Buddha, who was born as a prince in Kapilvastu, in modern day Nepal, lived and taught in the northeastern Indian subcontinent sometime between the 6th and 4th centuries BCE. He is recognized by adherents as an awakened teacher who shared his insights to help sentient beings end suffering, achieve nirvana, and escape what is seen as a cycle of suffering and rebirth.

Two major branches of Buddhism are recognized: Theravada ("The School of the Elders") and Mahayana ("The Great Vehicle"). Theravada—the oldest surviving branch—has a widespread following in Sri Lanka and Southeast Asia, and Mahayana is found throughout East Asia and includes the traditions of Pure Land, Zen, Nichiren Buddhism, Tibetan Buddhism, Shingon, Tendai and Shinnyo-en. In some classifications Vajrayana, a subcategory of Mahayana, is recognized as a third branch.

While Buddhism remains most popular within Asia, both branches are now found throughout the world. Various sources put the number of Buddhists in the world at between 230 million and 500 million, making it the world's fourth largest religion.

~~~~

INDEX

BIBLIOGRAPHY

Barbour, J., 1999. *The End of Time*. Oxford: Oxford University Press.

Barrow, J. D., 2007. *New Theories of Everthing*. Oxford: Oxford University Press.

Berzin, A., 2001. *External and Internal Kalachakra: Brief Survey of the First Two Chpaters of "The Kalachakra Tantra*. Graz, Austria: s.n.

Bhikkhu, T., 1996. *No-self or Not-self*. s.l.:s.n.

Bodhi, B., 2010. *A Comprehensive Manual of Abhidhamma*. Onalaska, Washington: BPS Pariyatti Editions.

Bohm, D., 2007. *Wholeness and the Implicate Order*. New York: Routledge.

Bouanchaud, B., 1995. *The Essence of Yoga*. Portland, Oregon: Rudra Press.

Brentano, F., 1973. *Psychology from an Empirical Standpoint, t.* London: Routledge.

Butler, K., 2014. *Knocking on Heaven's Door*.

Chatterji, D., 1931. *The Problem of Knowledge and the Four Schools of Later Buddism*. s.l.:Oriental Research Institute.

Dalai Lama, e. a., 1991. *Mind Science: An East West View*. Somerville, MA, USA: Wisdom Publications.

Danielou, A., 2000. *Yoga: Mastering the Secrets of Matter and the Universe*. Rochester, VT/US: Inner Traditions Bear and Company.

Dudjom Rinpoche, et al. 1991. *The Nygma School of Tibetan Buddhism, Its Fundamentals and History*. Wisdom Publications.

Einstein, L. M. &. W. & Einstein, 1952. The Principle of Relativity: a collection of memoirs. s.l.:s.n.

Frank, A., 2012. *About Time: Cosmology and Culture at the Twilight of the Big Bang*. New York: Free Press.

Freud, S., 1952. *On Dreams*. New York: W. W. Norton & Co..

Greene, B., 2000 *The Elegant Universe*. Vantage Books

Hawking, S., 2001. *The Universe in a Nutshell*. New York: Bantam Books.

Isaacson, W., 2008. *Einstein, His Life and Universe*. New York: Simon & Schuster.

Kaku, M., 2011. *Physics of the Future*, Random House.

Kane, H. K., 1997. *Ancient Hawaii*. Captain Cook, Hawaii: Kawainui Press.

Karmey, S. G., 1975. *A General Introduction to the History and Doctrines of Bon*. Tokyo: Toyo Bunko.

Keown, D., 2003. *A Dictionary of Buddhism*. Oxford: Oxford University Press.

Khun, T., 1962. *The Structure of Scientific Revolutions*. 1st ed. Chicago, IL, USA: University of Chicago Press.

Kurzweil, R., 2005. *The Singularity is Near*. Viking: The Penjuin Group.

Lloyd, S., 2006. *Programing the Universe*. New York: Alfred A Knopf.

Loizzo, J., 2009 *"Kalacakra and the Nalanda Tradition"* in Arnold, E. A, (ed,) *As Long as Space Endures*, p.336. *Snow Lion.*

Nelson, T., 1974. Computer Lib/Dream Machines. Microsoft edition, 1987 [ordercomputerlib@xanadu.net]

Norbu, C. N., 2010. *Zhang Zhung, Images from a Lost Kingdom.* Arcidosso (GR) Italy: Shang Shung Publications.

Norbu, C. N., 1999. *The Supreme Source, The "Kunjed Gyalpo".* Ithaca, NY: Snow Lion.

Nagel, T., 2012. *Mind and Cosmos.* New York: Oxford University Press.

O'Shea, D., 2007. *The Poincare Conjecture.* New York: Walker & Company.

Pearlman, E., 2002. *Tibetan Sacred Dance.* Rochester, VT, USA: Inner Traditions.

Penrose, R., 2012. *Cycles of Time: An Extraordinary New View of the Universe.* Random House.

Popper, K., 1970. *"Normal Science and its Dangers"* in I. Lakatos and A. Musgrave (eds.), *Criticism and the Growth of Knowledge (*1970), 52-3.. s.l.:s.n.

Ray, R. A., 2002. *Indestructable Truth.* s.l.:Shambala.

Smolin, L., 2006. *The Trouble With Physics:* Houghton Mifflin.

Tegmark, M., *Our Mathmatical Universe*: Alfred A Knopf, (div. of Random House).

Thorne, Kip, 2014. *The Science of Interstellar.* New York, London: W. W. Norton & Company.

Thera, N., 1998. *Abhidhamma Studies.* Kandy, Shri Lanka: Wisdom Publications.

Woit, P., 2006. *Not Even Wrong:* Basic Books.

Yogananda, P., 2007. *Autobiography of a Yogi.* Self-Realization Fellowship.

ENDNOTES

Certain images are licensed under Wikipedia creative commons license 1.0, 1.2, 2.0 or 3.0. These images are denoted, with the terms: cc1.0, cc1.2, cc2.0 and cc3.0, respectively.
These licenses can be found at:
<creativecommons.org/licenses/by/1.0/deed.en>
<creativecommons.org/licenses/by/1.2/deed.en>
<creativecommons.org/licenses/by/2.0/deed.en>
<creativecommons.org/licenses/by/3.0/deed.en>

Wikipedia GNU Free Documentation License 1.3: denoted with: GFDL
This license can be found at:
<en.wikipedia.org/wiki/GNU_Free_Documentation_License>

Wikipedia Creative Commons Attribution Share Alike License: denoted with the symbol (cc), copyright free. This license can be found at:
<en.wikipedia.org/wiki/Creative_Commons>

FRONT COVER IMAGE
[1] Cover image courtesy NASA's Goddard Space Flight Center.

BACK COVER IMAGES
Shakyamuni Buddha, public domain image.
Albert Einstein<en.wikipedia.org/wiki/Albert_Einstein>, public domain image, pub in US before 1923.
Andromeda Galaxy <en.wikipedia.org/wiki/Andromeda_Galaxy>, cc2.0.
Photo of Jim Raschick by Katalyn Koda, © 2012 James Raschick.
[2] Karl Popper, 'Normal Science and its Dangers', in I. Lakatos and A. Musgrave (eds.), Criticism and the Growth of Knowledge (1970), 52-3

INTRODUCTION
[3] Public domain image, © expired, <en.wikipedia.org/wiki/Flammarion_engraving>
[4] Loizzo, Joseph, MD, Ph.D. Reprint of portions of the article "Renewing the Nalanda Legacy" from Fall 2006 issue of Religions, East and West. Reprint found in "As Long as Space Endures", p.336. Ed.: Edward A. Arnold. Pub.: Snow Lion 2009.
[5] Chögyal Namkhai Norbu, a Tibetan lama, describes the state of Dzogchen, which is found in the Nyingma tradition of Tibetan Buddhism, as a synonym for the state of Mahamudra, which is found in the Kagyu tradition. Dzogchen is also found in the older, pre-Buddhist tradition of the Bon.
[6] Op. cit., Loizzo.
[7] H.H. the Dalai Lama and Alexander Berzin, PhD, "Excerpts from Question Sessions with H.H. the Fourteenth Dalai Lama Concerning the Kalachakra Initiation", in "Kalachakra For World Peace", p. 64. Ed.: Robert "Tenzin" Thurman. Pub.: Capital Area Tibetan Association, 2011.

1.1-BEGINNINGS

[8] Photo: © 1975 James Raschick.

[9] http://www.grandfathersemu.org/index.html

[10] Photo: http://www.grandfathersemu.org/index.html

[11] http://www.tsegyalgar.org

[12] A quote from Maria Simmons.

[13] Photo: © 1980 James Raschick.

[14] NamkWikipedia: *Chögyal Namkhai Norbu.*

[15] Tsegyalgar.org

[16] Photo © 1988 James Raschick.

[17] Chögyal Namkhai Norbu, *Zhang Zhung, Images From a Lost Kingdom*, Shang Shung Publishing, 2010.

[18] Photo: © 1988 Alex Seidlecki.

[19] Op. cit., *Zhang Zhung, Images From a Lost Kingdom*

[20] © 2001 Herb Kawainui Kane.

1.2-TOTALITY

[21] John D. Barrow, *New Theories of Everything*, (Oxford University Press, 2007) p.18.

[22] Wikipedia (cc), <en.wikipedia.org/wiki/Theory_of_everything>.

[23] Wikipedia (cc),<en.wikipedia.org/wiki/Kurt_Gödel>.

[24] *Dreams of a Final Theory: The Search for the Fundamental Laws of Nature*, Weinberg (1993).

[25] Wikipedia (cc), <en.wikipedia.org/wiki/Pali>.

[26] Photo: © 2004 Benjamin Matthews, <en.wikipedia.org/wiki/Nagarjuna>.

[27] Damien Keown, *A Dictionary of Buddhism*, (Oxford, Oxford University Press, 2003), p.82. Wikipedia: *Dzogchen.*

[28] http://en.wikipedia.org/wiki/Trikaya

[29] Sigmund Freud, *On Dreams*, (New York: W.W. Norton & Company, 1952), p.57.

[30] Photo by Max Halberstadt. *Sigmund Freud*, public domain image, pub in US before 1923. <Wikipedia:>

[31] From a conversation Herb Kawainui Kane, 2008.

[32] Chögyal Namkhai Norbu, lecture on Hawaii Island, 1999.

[33] "Pearlman, Ellen (2002). *Tibetan Sacred Dance: a journey into the religious and folk traditions"*, Rochester, Vermont, USA: Inner Traditions. p. 94. From Wikipedia: *Nechung Oracle.*

[34] Public domain image, pub in US before 1923. *Nicolaus Copernicus*, <Wikipedia:>

[35] Nicolai Copernicus, *On the Revolutions of the Celestial Spheres*, (Nuremberg, 1543).

[36] August, 2007.

[37] Baker Roshi, Green Dragon Zen Temple, c. 1978.

[38] Rangjung Rigpe Dorje, <http://www.buddhismus.at/>.

[39] Public domain image of original Art. Portrait by Godfrey Kneller, *Sir Isaac Newton*, <en.wikipedia.org/wiki/Isaac_Newton>.

[40] Paramount Pictures, 1952.

[41] Elias Capriles-Arias, 2002.

[42] (cc)<wikipedia.org/wiki/Ajahn Sumedho>.

[43] (cc)<wikipedia.org/wiki/Sūtra>.

[44] (cc)<wikipedia.org/wiki/Prajnaparamita>.

[45] (cc)<wikipedia.org/wiki/Shunyata>.
[46] Photo: © 1988 James Raschick.
[47] Public domain image, *Uluru*, <en.wikipedia.org/wiki/Uluru>.
[48] © 1996 Herb Kawainui Kane.
[49] Op. cit., *New Theories of Everything, p34*.
[50] Op. cit., *New Theories of Everything*, p. 45.
[51]Wikipedia: http://en.wikipedia.org/wiki/Rupert_Sheldrake
[52] Thomas Khun, *The Structure of Scientific Revolutions* (1962).

1.3-NO TIME AT ALL

[53] http://en.wikipedia.org/wiki/Two_truths_doctrine
[54] The Dalai Lama, et.al., *MindScience: An East West View*, (Somerville, MA, Wisdom Publications, 1991, p.14.
[55] Image in public domain. <www.buddhismus.at>, from <en.wikipedia.org/wiki/14th_Dalai_Lama>.
[56] Wikipedia: < http://en.wikipedia.org/wiki/Eleatics>.
[57] http://en.wikipedia.org/wiki/Dependent_arising
[58] Image in public domain, <de.wikipedia.org/wiki/Padmasambhava>.
[59] Public domain image of original Art, photo by Stephen Shephard GDFL 1.2, *Bhavacakra* <commons.wikimedia.org/wiki/User:Stephenshephard/gallery>.
[60] Ibid.
[61] A paraphrase of statements from "The Dalai Lama in New York City", Lecture Program, Sept. 17-21, 2003.
[62] Chögyal Namhai Norbu, *The precious Vase,* Shang Shung Editions, 2008, p153.
[63] The Primordial Buddha, original Art, private collection.

1.4-REALITY MANIFESTS

[64] Alexander Berzin, "External and Internal Kalachakra: Brief Survey of the First Two Chapters of *The Kalachakra Tantra*", Graz, Austria, May 18, 2001, (cc) <www.berzinarchives.com/web/en/index.html>
[65] Wikipedia.
[66] Ilya Prigogine and Isabelle Stengers, *Order Out of Chaos*, Bantam 1984.
[67] Photo: © 1995 James Raschick.
[68] Ted Nelson, image (cc3.0) <en.wikipedia.org/wiki/Ted_Nelson> .
[69] Julian Barbour, paraphrase from *The End of Time*, 1999, p.23.
[70] Oxford Dictionary
[71] Stephen Hawking, paraphrase from: *The Universe in a Nutshell*, 2001, p86.
[72] A personal remembrance from a lecture by Ram Das.
[73] Image public domain, © expired. <en.wikipedia.org/wiki/Milarepa>.

2.1-GEOMETRY

[74] Wikipedia, Bernhard Riemann.
[75] Image public domain, © expired, <en.wikipedia.org/wiki/Bernhard_Riemann>
[76] Image by Lars H. Rohwedder, Sarregouset, (cc1.2) <en.wikipedia.org/wiki/Non-Euclidean_geometry>.
[77] Wikipedia (cc), <en.wikipedia.org/wiki/Configuration_space>.
[78] http://www2.imm.dtu.dk/projects/manifold/Syllabus.html

[79] Wolfam Mathworld <http://mathworld.wolfram.com/Homeomorphic.html>
[80] Image (cc1.2) <en.wikipedia.org/wiki/Poincare_conjecture>
[81] *Triple Torus*, Weisstein, Eric W., <mathworld.wolfram.com/TripleTorus.html>.
[82] *Ring torus*, Weisstein, Eric W., <mathworld.wolfram.com/RingTorus.html>.
[83] 2-Sphere, Weisstein, Eric W., <mathworld.wolfram.com/2-Sphere.html>.
[84] The Free Dictionary, <www.thefreedictionary.com/topology>
[85] Images from Microsoft Office, copyright free.
[86] Ibid.
[87] Ibid.
[88] Image public domain, © expired, <en.wikipedia.org/wiki/Hermann_Minkowski>
[89] Wikipedia: Minkowski space.
[90] Image by Jorge Stolfi. <en.wikipedia.org/wiki/Euclidian_space>.
[91] Image public domain, © expired, <en.wikipedia.org/wiki/Henri_Poincare>
[92] Wikipedia, <en.wikipedia.org/wiki/Poincare_conjecture>
[93] *The Poincaré Conjecture* by Donal O'Shea, 2007.
[94] Image GFDL <http://worldses.org/perelman>.
[95] Image GFDL 1.2 <http://en.wikipedia.org/wiki/File:Richard_Hamilton.jpg>.
[96] Wikipedia, GFDL <en.wikipedia.org/wiki/Poincare_conjecture>.
[97] *The science of Interstellar*, by Kip Thorne, 2014, W.W. Norton & Company.
[98] <en.wikipedia.org/wiki/Anthropic_principle> (cc)

2.2-NAKED SPACE

[99] Chögyal Namkhai Norbu and Adriano Clemente, *The Supreme Source, The Kunjed Gyalpo, The Fundamental Tantra of Dzogchen Semde*, Snow Lion, 1999.
[100] Chögyal Namhai Norbu, *The precious Vase*, Shang Shung Editions, 2008, p153.
[101] Wikipedia (cc), <en.wikipedia.org/wiki/Sir_Arthur_Eddington>
[102] Public domain image, pub in US before 1923, image by: F. W. Dyson, A. S. Eddington, and C. Davidson, <en.wikipedia.org/wiki/Sir_Arthur_Eddington>.
[103] David Chalmers home page <http://consc.net/papers/matrix.html>.
[104] Wikipedia (cc): "Cartesian dualism".
[105] Franz Brentano, *Psychology from an Empirical Standpoint* (tr. London), 1973
[106] Bhikkhu Bodhi, general editor, *A Comprehensive Manual of Abhidamma*, (First BPS Pariyatti Edition, 2000) p.156.
[107] Wikipedia (cc), <en.wikipedia.org/wiki/Diamond_Sutra>.
[108] Op. cit. *Comprehensive Manual of Abhidhamma*, p156.
[109] Image by Satu Sato (cc), <en.wikipedia.org/wiki/Sheaf_(agriculture)>.
[110] Image GFDL 1.2, <en.wikipedia.org/wiki/ File:Dewy_spider_web.jpg>.
[111] "Alan Watts Podcast – Following the Middle Way #3". *alanwattspodcast.com* (Podcast). 2008-08-31. [from Wikipedia: "Indra's Net"].
[112] Image GFDL 1.2 <www.triten.org>.
[113] http://en.wikipedia.org/wiki/Speed_of_light
[114] <www.dictionary.com>:
[115] http://en.wikipedia.org/wiki/Speed_of_light
[116] Ibid.
[117] Wikipedia (cc), <en.wikipedia.org/wiki/Absolute_zero>.
[118] Ibid.
[119] Image in public domain, © expired, <en.wikipedia.org/wiki/Zhuangzi>

[120] Memories of a conversation with Herb Kawainui Kane, 2008.

[121] Image public domain, © expired, <en.wikipedia.org/wiki/Dusum_Khyenpa>

[122] Op. cit. Lecture by Chögyal Namkhai Norbu, Island of Hawaii, 1999.

[123] Ibid. CNN, Hawaii.

2.3-A DIFFERENT REALITY

[124] Rombauer & Rombauer-Becker,*The Joy of Cooking*, 1953, p. 696.

[125] Photo: © 1988 Alex Siedlecki,

[126] Photo credit unknown. Source: Facebook display.

[127] Image and text Wikipedia (cc), <en.wikipedia.org/wiki/Calabi-Yau>.

[128] Durgacharan Chatterji, *The Problem of Knowledge and the Four Schools of Later Buddhism*, Annals of the Bhandarkar Oriental Research Institute. (1931) vol.XII 12:3, 1931.04. p.205-215. Wikipedia (cc) <en.wikipedia.org/wiki/Mind_stream>.

[129] Thanissaro Bhikkhu, *No-self or Not-self?*. (1996), (unpaginated). Wikipedia (cc) <en.wikipedia.org/wiki/Mind_stream>.

[130] Image GFDL 1.2, <en.wikipedia.org/wiki/Naropa>.

[131] From the Web site of HH 17 Karmapa, Thaye Dorje. Kagyu Asia. <www.kagyu-asia.com/l_nar_t_summary_mahamudra.html>

[132] A recollection from a lecture at UC Berkeley, CA, c. 1977.

[133] Image: © 2012 James. Raschick, derived from Wikipedia image GDFL 1.2. <en.wikipedia.org/wiki/Light_cone>.

[134] http://grandfathersemu.org

[135] Op. Sit. *Comprehensive Manual of Abhidhamma.*

3.1-NEW VIEW OF OLD SCIENCE

[136] Einstein, A., H. A. Lorentz, H. Minkowski, & H. Weyl, (1952). *The Principle of Relativity: a collection of original memoirs on the special and general theory of relativity.*

[137] Public domain image, © expired, <en.wikipedia.org/wiki/Hendrik_Lorentz>.

[138] Public domain image, pub before 1923 in US, <en.wikipedia.org/wiki/Einstein>.

[139] The thought experiment by Comstock described two platforms in relative motion. See Comstock, D.F. (1910), "The principle of relativity." *Science* 31 (803): 767–772. Einstein's thought experiment used two light rays starting at both ends of the platform. See: Einstein, A. (1917), *Relativity: The Special and General Theory.* Springer. Wikipedia (cc), <en.wikisource.org/wiki/The_Principle_of_Relativity_(Comstock)>.

[140] Wikipedia (cc), <en.wikipedia.org/wiki/Relativity_of_simultaneity>

[141] Wikipedia (cc), <en.wikipedia.org/wiki/Copenhagen_interpretation>.

[142] Walter Isaacson, *Einstein, His Life and Universe.* 2007, p. 454.

[143] Erwin Schrödinger, "The Present Situation in Quantum Mechanics." Nov. 29, 1935.

[144] Einstein to Erwin Schrödinger, AEA. Aug. 8, 1935, 22-49.

[145] Image license: cc3.0, <en.wikipedia.org/wiki/Schrodingers_cat>.

[146] Image license cc01.0, <en.wikipedia.org/wiki/Wave-particle_duality>.

[147] Wikipedia (cc), <en.wikipedia.org/wiki/PSR_J1748-2446ad>.

3.2-A NEW REALITY MAP

[148] http://en.wikipedia.org/wiki/Pulsar

[149] Image in public domain, Wikipedia (cc), <en.wikipedia.org/wiki/Wormhole>.

150 *Interstellar*, directed by Christopher Nolan. 2014 Warner Bros. Entertainment Inc.

151 Image in public domain. Wikipedia (cc), <en.wikipedia.org/wiki/Torus>.

152 Image in public domain, Wikipedia (cc), <en.wikipedia.org/wiki/Wormhole>.

153 Image created by NASA/JPL-Caltech, in public domain.

154 Op cit., *Comprehensive Manual of Abhidhamma*.

155 Memories from a lecture given by Ram Dass in the late '70s.

156 www.rigpawiki.org/index.php?title=File:Yeshe_Tsogyal.JPG

157 Image from private collection.

158 Thomas S. Kuhn, *The Structure of Scientific Revolution*, (1962).

159 Public domain image, © expired, <en.wikipedia.org/wiki/Kalachakra>.

160 Photo credit: © 2012 James Raschick.

161 Op. cit. Alexander Berzin, "External and Internal Kalachakra: Brief Survey of the First Two Chapters of *The Kalachakra Tantra*".

162 Image, Wikipedia GFDL 1.2, <en.wikipedia.org/wiki/Shri_Yantra>.

163 Wikipedia (cc), <en.wikipedia.org/wiki/Shri_Yantra>.

164 Wikipedia GFDL 1.2, <en.wikipedia.org/wiki/Very_Large_Array>.

165 Originally from CNN in 1983.

166 Dalai Lama, H.H. *The Universe in a Single Atom.* (New York, Morgan Road Books 2005) page 144.

3.3-TIME-FUTURE

167 Tudjen is likely what is now the land of Kirgistan. This information from Chögyal Namkhai Norbu, Tenerife, Canary Islands, 2013 lecture.

168 One of the weekly Facebook posts from: *Long Live His Holiness the Dalai Lama*.

APPENDIX

169 Image: © 2012 James. Raschick, derived from Wikipedia image GDFL 1.2. <en.wikipedia.org/wiki/Light_cone>.

170 Image in public domain, First published over 100 years ago, <en.wikipedia.org/wiki/Heart_Sutra>.

171 Image in public domain, First published over 100 years ago, <en.wikipedia.org/wiki/Diamond_Sutra>.

172 From *Kagyu Asia*, the Web site of HH 17 Karmapa Thaye Dorje. <www.kagyu-asia.com/l_nar_t_verses_mahamudra.htm>.

173 Bernard Bouanchaud, *The Essence of Yoga* (Portland, Rudra Press 1997.)

174 Ibid.